THE AUTHOR AT WORK,
VICTORIA MEMORIAL MUSEUM,
OTTAWA.

Autobiography of

JOHN MACOUN
Canadian Explorer
and Naturalist

1831-1920

*A Second Edition published as
a Centennial Project of the
Ottawa Field-Naturalists' Club*

Additional Contents of the 1979 Edition

**Published by the
Ottawa Field-Naturalists' Club,
Ottawa, 1979**

Special Publication No. 1

ISBN o - 9690251-0-6

AUTOBIOGRAPHY

of

JOHN MACOUN, M.A.

CANADIAN EXPLORER AND NATURALIST

*Assistant Director and Naturalist
to the Geological Survey of Canada*

1831-1920

With Introduction by
ERNEST THOMPSON SETON

A MEMORIAL VOLUME
PUBLISHED BY
THE OTTAWA FIELD-NATURALISTS' CLUB
1922

CONTENTS

CONTENTS—*Continued*

CONTENTS—*Continued*

CONTENTS—*Concluded*

ILLUSTRATIONS

———

ON JOHN MACOUN

The Ottawa Field-Naturalists' Club could hardly have celebrated its centenary better than by republishing the autobiography of this very great Canadian; for Professor John Macoun was great indeed — as a teacher and a scholar in several fields of natural history, as an explorer, a civil servant and a trenchant advocate of Canada's North-West; and he rose to these heights by his own energy, after arriving in this country in 1850 as a nineteen year old immigrant from Northern Ireland and starting life here as a farmer's hired help.

Let us touch first on his achievement as a scholar. It would appear in 1868 he was offered — and accepted — the Professorship of Natural History at Albert College, in Belleville, Ontario, in spite of his possessing no formal qualification for the job. Indeed, his whole education consisted of nothing more than attending an Irish school until he was thirteen, then an Ontario village school for three weeks in 1856 and finally one brief session at the Toronto Normal School from August to December, 1859. This last qualified him for the school teaching he did until his appointment to Albert College. Otherwise he was entirely self-taught, and he seems to have known no other language than English. Yet how one wishes that more of the Ph.D's in our colleges today could offer their students some portion of the talents which Macoun brought to his teaching!

His first great quality was enthusiasm, something a teacher must have if he is to succeed in arousing his pupils' interest. Macoun was in fact so extraordinarily keen on, at first, botany that, in his early days of teaching at a country school, he "usually rose at four in summer and made a large collection before breakfast;"[1] and the energy he devoted to collecting plants was later to astonish his companion on Sandford Fleming's exploring party of 1872, the Reverend Dr. George Grant, from whose account of the expedition, in his book *Ocean to Ocean*, Macoun quotes so much below. It was from this tireless collecting, and reading all the books he could lay hands on (which were few indeed in his early days), that Macoun acquired the vast knowledge which caused the best botanists in the U.S.A. to accept him as an equal and led his British colleagues to make a special request that he be included in Canada's delegation to the Colonial Exhibition in 1886. His reputation as a scholar and explorer also won him the distinction of being invited by the Marquis of Lorne to become a founding fellow of the Royal Society of Canada when the society was created by this Governor General in 1882; and it likewise gained him an honorary degree from Syracuse University in 1899. His fellow Canadians, unfortunately, did not all share this warm admiration of him; but that is another, and less happy, story of quarrels, caused in part by what one obituarist called Macoun's dogmatic egotism, and also, one cannot doubt, by jealousies which his achievements aroused in lesser men.

A second quality, which Macoun brought to his university work and which is as valuable as it is rare in our colleges today, was his practical experience as a school teacher. No one can teach successfully unless he masters the art of getting down to his pupils' level and of explaining their problems in language both simple enough for them to understand and interesting enough to hold their attention; and there is no place where this art can be better learned than at school with pupils too young for formal lectures. Macoun taught school for about a dozen years all told,[2] of which he spent the last eight at "No. 1 School, Belleville"; and, since this job was itself a promotion and in his first year at it he won a "reputation as a teacher who had no trouble with pupils or trustees", his success in this profession is obvious.

Yet another of his outstanding qualities was an unfailing readiness to help others, for which no less a man than Ernest Thompson Seton experssed his gratitude in the introduction he wrote for the first edition of this book; and few can have benefited more from his generous helpfulness than the field naturalists' of Ottawa.

Macoun was fortunate in his employers at Albert College. The fact that they appreciated his ability is evident, not only from the Professorship Emeritus they gave him when he left them in April, 1879, but also from their readiness to allow him time off for collecting while he was still with them. Had they not done this, he could hardly have accepted Sandford Fleming's last minute invitation to join his famous exploring party of 1872; and this expedition was perhaps the most important turning point in his career.

Pure chance led to his getting the job. Fleming was the Canadian Pacific Railway's chief engineer. The purpose of his expedition was to find an all-Canadian route by which that railway could be carried through the mountains to the west coast and thus fulfil one condition on which British Columbia had entered confederation. Fleming's party originally contained no botanist, but on 17 July[3] they happened to sail from Collingwood, Ontario, on the very same ship on which Macoun was also travelling westwards to collect plants for a Mr. David Watt of Montreal. In a casual conversation with him, George Grant, the expedition's secretary, discovered Macoun's profession, and hastened to inform Fleming of it. Fleming then sought out Macoun and invited him to become the exploring party's official botanist; Macoun delightedly accepted the job. It would, as he told Grant shortly afterwards, give him "a lift that will put me at the head of the whole brigade" of botanists;[4] and it was also to launch him on his career as an explorer of the great North-West.

Yet Macoun had, if possible, even fewer of the practical abilities needed by an explorer than of the formal qualifications expected of university teachers. Thus he was a poor horseman, who, when he rode at all, seems to have retained his seat by gripping his saddle almost as much with his hands as with his knees,[5] he had never even "worn snowshoes",[6] he had had no experience with canoes;[7] and, from the way a companion prepared to rescue him, if necessary, from drowning in 1881, it seems that he also could not swim.[8] These failings never stopped Macoun's travels, but they must have helped to cause one of his more important quarrels.

This was with Charles Horetzky, a former Hudson's Bay Company officer, who was the Fleming expedition's official photographer. At Edmonton Fleming sent Horetzky and Macoun to explore "the northern passes through the Rocky Mountains", while he explored the Yellowhead Pass. Horetzky feared that such a novice as Macoun would prove an incumbrance, and tried in an underhand way to shake him off and get through the mountains ahead of him by a different route, the Pine River Pass. But here Macoun's doggedness triumphed; novice though he was, he did get through on his own, by way of the Peace River Pass, while Horetzky, the veteran traveller, was foiled in seeking the route he had preferred, and only succeeded in completing his journey by rejoining Macoun and travelling on from Hudson's Hope in a boat which Macoun had secured. This unpleasantness doubtless helped to inspire Horetzky's later attack on Macoun, in a pamphlet entitled *Some Startling Facts relating to the C.P.R. and the North-West Lands.*

The date of this publication is significant — 1882; so is the date of another hostile work — Professor H.Y. Hind's *Manitoba and the North-West Frauds,* published in 1883; and both were contributions to a great debate then raging on the value of the prairies, a subject on which Macoun had very definite opinions.

By 1882 Macoun had both left Albert College and joined the Geological Survey. He had followed his first western journey of 1872 with a whole series of explorations of the North-West which he describes below. In 1882 he also published his famous book, *Manitoba and the Great North-West,* in which he gave the opinions he had formed of the country from his own observation of the soil, the water and the plants thriving there, in what were evidently favourable years. The book was both a glowing panegyric on the agricultural possibilities of the prairies and a flat contradiction of accepted views of the day, which were drawn from the earlier reports of another Irishman, Captain John Palliser. That enterprising explorer had concluded from his journeys of 1857-59 that much of the Canadian prairie was part of the so-called "Great American Desert", and agriculturally worthless; and it is hardly an accident that his views were supported against Macoun by Professor Hind, for Hind too had travelled over the prairies and seen the country in the same years as Palliser. In retrospect one may perhaps say that both parties were in some degree right. The land has indeed produced the crops Macoun prophesied, but no one who knew southern Saskatchewan in the bitter "dust-bowl" years of the 1930's will blame Palliser for thinking it a desert.

When Macoun left Albert College in 1879, he took a job as an explorer in the Department of the Interior, under Sir John A. Macdonald's newly elected government. It is an interesting commentary on the old "Spoils System", which lasted until Sir Robert Borden created the Civil Service Commission in 1918, that Macoun could not then be given the "tenure", which today public servants take for granted. Sir Charles Tupper, to whom he owed his appointment, could promise him no more than "to make me permanent as long as they (the Conservatives) were in power."⁹ However, no Liberal government ever saw fit to displace him; and in 1881 Sir John promoted him to be Botanist to the Geological and Natural History Survey of Canada (as it was then called), with "a first-class clerkship and $1500 a year."¹⁰ This job was not quite what Macoun wanted, for, as a botanist, he had expected to be employed in "the Agricultural Department." Instead, he found himself working at the infant National Museum of Canada, (which then belonged to the Survey), and it was no bed of roses.

His accommodation at the museum in Ottawa was poor, for the Survey could allot to him only one room in the building to which it had recently moved from Montreal. There were personal frictions too, with his subordinates, who resented his being put over them; with his superior, Dr. A.R.C. Selwyn, Director of the Survey, whom he particularly infuriated in 1887 by seeking, and gaining, directly from the Minister a promotion which Selwyn would gladly have denied him; and, perhaps worst of all, with the paleontologist Dr. Whiteaves, a very busy man, who let moths and dermestid beetles destroy the national collection of bird skins, which included many collected by Dr. Bell on Hudson Bay in 1885, more collected by Dr. G.M. Dawson, the future Director of the Survey, and still more collected by Macoun himself in Ontario. This negligence must go far to explain the poverty of Ottawa's ornithological collection to which Roderic Macfarlane so repeatedly and bitterly called attention in the account of the birds of the North-West which he wrote for his, and Charles Mair's, *Through the Mackenzie Basin* in 1908.

But if the National Museum was sometimes an uncomfortable place for Macoun, his services to it were still splendid. He contributed nearly 100,000 plants to its herbarium. In due course he did much to build up its collections of birds and mammals too, an area of the Museum's activity to which not his least contribution was recruiting and training that able field worker, William Spreadborough. In addition to much other writing, and to public speaking, he produced for the Museum the various bulky and learned catalogues which Mr. W.A. Waiser has listed in his most useful bibliographical essay; he lobbied tirelessly to get the Museum a building of its own, and these efforts were rewarded in 1911 when the Victoria Memorial Museum was opened; and, on top of all these activities, Macoun still found spare time in which to give the Ottawa Field-Naturalists' Club the assistance which this book so suitably commemorates.

In 1912 Macoun was partially disabled by a stroke, and in the next year he was finally superannuated, at the ripe age of 82, but, as an exceptional honour, was allowed to keep his official titles in his retirement. He spent his last seven years at Sidney on Vancouver Island; and there he proved that, even as a disabled octogenarian, John Macoun was incapable of idleness. For, to compensate for his stroke, he now taught himself to write left-handed and did it well; he also continued collecting, and, before he died, he had given the B.C. Provincial Museum of Natural History "a practically complete set of flowering and other plants"[11] which he had gathered on Vancouver Island. Then, on 18 July, 1920, his death at last ended what had been an abundantly varied and useful, as well as a long, life.

RICHARD GLOVER

[1] *Autobiography,* p. 37.

[2] Namely on a permit at an unnamed village from, apparently, some time in 1856 to mid-1859 (Autobiography, pp. 29, 33); at Castleton, Ontario, from January to November, 1860, and then No. 1 School, Belleville (*Ibid,* p. 37).

[3] Grant, *Ocean to Ocean,* p. 15.

[4] *Ocean to Ocean,* p. 35.

[5] Autobiography, p. 68.

[6] *Ibid,* p. 81.

[7] "I was totally ignorant of river navigation," he says of himself as late as 1881. *Ibid,* p. 188.

[8] *Ibid,* p. 188.

[9] *Autobiography,* p. 135.

[10] *Ibid,* p. 219.

[11] *Autobiography,* p. 301.

INTRODUCTION

I T is just thirty-eight years ago since first I came in contact with John Macoun. I was a young man then, riding and farming on the prairies of Western Manitoba, but my thoughts were not on the farm. My eyes were ever turning to the wild life about me—the birds and flowers. I was suffering too, amid the pleasure of it, suffering from the knowledge-hunger—the total absence of books and guides. Botanies were indeed scarce in those days, and I had made a collection of prairie flowers (now in the St. Louis Herbarium) with only the popular names attached; in some cases they were names which I had given them, for lack of better.

Then I met a government official at Winnipeg, who said: "Why don't you write to Professor John Macoun at Ottawa? He is the best naturalist in Canada and is one of those big men who always are ready to help a student."

So, without introduction of any kind, I sent a preliminary collection of plants to Macoun, asking if he would name them for me. His answer is before me now, in his own handwriting:

OTTAWA, August 15th, 1884

My Dear Sir:

"I reached home yesterday, after having been absent about nine weeks and, in going over my correspondence, find yours.

"Any assistance I can give regarding botany you can always have for the asking, so do not be backward in that line.

"The names of your plants are as follows:" (Here follows a long list.)

"Your plants are all common forms on the prairie except No. 23, (*Physalis lanceolata* Michx,) which, as far as I know to the contrary, is rare. I would like to know the exact locality where found, etc.

"Wishing you every success in botany and ornithology, and

agreeing with you, in the deep interest attached to the birds of the West, I am, dear Sir,

Truly yours,

J. MACOUN.

"To E. T. SETON, ESQ."

That letter, written entirely in his own hand, is characteristic of the man and his life. With nine weeks' mail piled on his desk, he, nevertheless, unselfishly paid first attention to the student who sent him specimens and craved his help.

The friendship thus begun continued through life. Many other students of botany and lovers of nature found this same portal to his heart, their common interest in the wild things.

His universal kindness and helpfulness, and his vast erudition in natural science, combined with the fact that he was the pioneer naturalist of Canada, with official recognition as such, have given him a permanent place in our records, as well as in our affections. He will be remembered by posterity as the father of exact natural history in Canada, and I am proud indeed of the chance to stand among his mourners, who yet rejoice that our standard-bearer died in the fullness of life and the fullness of success.

May 8th, 1922.

CHAPTER I

1831-1850

HISTORY OF THE MACOUN FAMILY—EARLY LIFE IN IRELAND—
MANY AMUSING EPISODES AND INCIDENTS OF CHILDHOOD.

IN writing my memoirs I intend to give at the very commencement a sketch of what I know of our family history. I was born on April 17, 1831, in the parish of Maralin, called also Magheralin and, in ancient times, Linn, County Down, Ireland. The parish of Linn was very old as in the Annals of Ireland it is stated that it was assessed, in the reign of Edward the First of England, for a contribution towards one of the crusades. Our parish church was apparently very old and its graveyard, which was elevated somewhat above the surrounding ground, was also very old. I remember that our seat in the church was next to the Earl of Clanwilliam, and the rector, when I was leaving, gave me a paper in which he told me that we were one of the oldest families in Maralin. This paper is still in the possession of one of the members of my family. The graveyard was very interesting on account of the names on the tombstones of those who had died there over two hundred years ago. Amongst others, I noticed that a member of our family, James Macoun, had lived to be 105 years of age and was buried here in Maralin. Later I learned more of his history from my uncle, Joseph Kincaid and James Bell —two old men when I was a boy. The James Macoun, known in our family as the "old man," was born in 1601 and died in 1706. He was, as far as we know, our first progenitor to settle in Ireland. Before this the family was Scotch. This first Irish ancestor evidently fought under Cromwell.

What I am going to refer to now is from information received from the two old men previously mentioned and from Macaulay's History of the reign of William the Third.

In 1641 a rebellion took place in the north of Ireland called the Forty-one War. This rebellion was an attempt made by the

Irish to destroy the settlements, English and Scotch, that had been made under James the First, of England. A great many of the settlers around Maralin were killed and drowned by the Irish at this time as they broke down a bridge over the river Bann near Portadown and drove the settlers down to the bridge and pressed them into the river, where most of them were drowned.   While I was in England in 1886 I saw a work called the "Forty-nine." This contained a list of the men who composed a number of the regiments who served under Cromwell in 1649, when he was such a terror to the Irish who had destroyed the settlers eight years before. In the list I saw in England, were the names of Sir Hugh Magill, Lieutenant of one of the regiments, and James Macoun, Ensign. I take it that this James Macoun was the "old man" spoken of above.   These two men were apparently great friends, and it is stated that Sir Hugh married James Macoun's sister.   Sir Hugh was granted a large tract of land by Cromwell and the legend says that the men of Sir Hugh's regiment received land from him and had to do military service for it in later years.   This is possibly true because our property was freehold and given by Sir John Magill, brother of Sir Hugh, to James Macoun at a few shillings a year forever and this lease we held when we sold before we came to Canada.

The next record in connection with the family is in 1689 or '90, when Sir Hugh Magill at that date called out all the men in the neighborhood of Maralin and met King James' army at Dromore with such troops as he could raise, and was defeated and retreated to Coleraine, near Derry.   These men were in camp there all winter while the siege of Derry was in progress, and when William the Third came over in the spring they joined his army and marched with him to the Boyne, and in that battle one of the Macouns was killed.   This man was said to be the son of the original James Macoun, who emigrated from Scotland.   This fight of Dromore is given in detail in Macaulay's history of that time.   While this James Macoun was with the troops at Dromore his wife and two sons were left at Maralin.   After the fight at Dromore the French and Irish came down on Maralin and the people fled to the woods, some going to Armagh and from there to

Enniskillen. James Macoun's wife went with this party and lost her two boys. They had taken refuge in the woods and were on the point of starvation when they resolved to try and save their cows which had been taken by King James' troops and confined with many others in what was called in my day "The Miller's Holm." Oak woods surrounded Maralin at the time and at night the boys went to where the French and Irish had gathered the cattle in "The Miller's Holm" near Maralin. This was a narrow ravine down which a little stream flowed and the sentries evidently were close to the high road which passed the ravine, and the boys in the night went in and drove off their own cattle and took them into the woods. There they lived on their milk till their mother returned after the siege of Derry.

The next item of information I have in regard to the family is when these boys appear in history as church wardens of the parish of Maralin. This record my son, W. T. Macoun, found in the parish records of Maralin. These two brothers, Robert and James Macoun, were both church wardens in the year 1706. My father held another lease besides the one direct from Sir Hugh Magill, and this lease was made by Robert Macoun, the elder, to his brother James, in 1708, on condition that the latter would build a house in a given time. This house was built, and in it, several generations later, I was born. The terms of the lease I do not remember, but I read the parchment and distinctly recollect that the land was given by Robert Macoun, Gentleman, to his brother James at one shilling a year forever. This land, apparently, was not a portion of that which had belonged to James prior to this lease as the house stood outside of our land. The house and garden were quite distinct from our other property. Evidently our house was built as a gathering place for the people of the village, as it was the largest house in the village and built in such a way that an attacking force, without cannon, could not gain an entrance. The house was not very large but was four-square and its walls were two and a half feet thick and the windows on the ground floor were quite narrow and each had a part that was a lattice, and all had diamond panes of small size fastened with lead. Iron stanchions made it impossible to gain admittance by the windows.   The front door was double oak filled with large nails that were clinched inside.   This made it impossible to cut it down.   The key of the door was very large and as a boy I was not able to turn it, and the bolt was nearly an inch and a half across.

Over the door there was a stone inserted, giving the date, 1708, so that we had no doubts as to the age of it.   The walls were so solidly built that I believe the people in the early times understood how to make mortar very much like the concrete that is used today.   This is all the data I have of the erection of the house.   I might say that the garden as it was in my time, showed that it was the same garden that had been established when the house was built.   Inside, the garden was surrounded by a bank and outside, by a ditch of considerable depth so that the land was well drained.   In my father's time it had many rare shrubs of great beauty, of which my mother took advantage in our youth and sold to neighboring families to eke out her scanty means, due to the fact that the property had been willed away from our branch of the family.

My grandfather was born in 1737 and his family consisted of two sons and four daughters, my father being the younger son. Our property, being entailed, always descended to the eldest son and his heirs.   On this account my father enlisted in the army about 1796 and joined a dragoon regiment named "The Black Horse," being the Seventh Dragoon Guards, and were called the "Princess Royal's Regiment."   (That is, the regiment of King George Third's eldest daughter.)   Its commander for a long time was the Duke of York and my mother said that my father looked upon him as an exceptionally good commanding officer, so good that he called his eldest son Frederick instead of calling him after himself.   Two years after my father joined, the Rebellion of 1798 broke out in Ireland and his regiment was ordered there.   This led my father to take part in all the engagements that took place in the south of Ireland and I heard my mother say that he was wounded at the battle of New Ross, where his horse was shot from under him and that he took off the saddle and put it around his shoulders when making his escape from the battle.   Except for the Rebellion, my father saw no further active service, although the Peninsular War continued almost the whole time he was in the army. Preceding the battle of Waterloo, his regiment was under orders to embark but when the news came of the battle they were not required and returned to London. Before this time he had obtained a furlough and went home to see his father and found that in his absence his elder brother had died and he was heir to the property. After consulting with his father it was decided that he would cut the entail off the whole so that my grandfather could leave the property to whom he saw fit if my father did not return. This was before the battle of Waterloo, and my father, not returning again until about 1820, found that his father had made a will and died suddenly leaving the property to his daughters, except the house and a few acres of land which were left to my grandmother and a maiden sister as long as they lived. On their death it was to go to my father, if alive, and in case of his death to be divided among the other three. At the death of his mother and sister, my father got possession of the house and land, which we still owned when we left Ireland in 1850. My father married Anne Jane Nevin, (my mother) in 1824, and her family were Scotch immigrants of the usual fighting clans, who had come to Ireland after the battle of Bothwell Bridge. My mother's people, being Presbyterians, and having relatives acting as ministers, my father was married in their house by a Presbyterian minister. Before my brother Frederick was born my father was told that if his wife had a son that he would be illegitimate and could not be heir to the property as the law required the child to be born in wedlock which had been performed by an authorized minister of the Church of England, so my father was married the second time by a Mr. Dolling in the church in Maralin. I was born on April 17th, 1831, and my father died in October, 1837

I remember very little about him but there are a few incidents that happened that I recollect distinctly. My earliest remembrance is that Frederick and myself were playing along a ditch that ran outside of the garden. In it grew a grass that we gathered the leaves of and which when put between our teeth made a sound hence we called it "Squeal Grass." This grass turned out

2

to be *Glyceria nervata*.   While leaning out to gather the leaves, one day, that were floating on the surface of the water in the ditch, I tumbled in head foremost and Frederick ran away screaming.   My father, who was clipping the hedge inside, jumped over and before long had pulled me out.   I remember that I was so young at the time that I had not ceased to wear baby clothes.

Another thing I remember was that the Earl of Clanwilliam, who, by the way, was our landlord and a member of the Magill family, invited my father and Frederick to go to Gill Hall near Dromore and have lunch with him and they went and Frederick, like most youths, got sick from the quantity of food he ate and was taken in hand by the butler.

The last thing I recollect about my father was going with him, dressed more like a boy, to Moira, where he drew his pension and he took me to the Church and showed me a tablet that was placed there in memory of a soldier, named Lavery, who was killed in the American War.   I remember little more about my father, except that he was a tall man and frightened the boys on the street when he would get a little tipsy and dress up in his uniform.   After my father's death I recall many things that happened.   I remember the day before he died quite well.   The doctor had him sitting up and I saw him bleed him and take a large bowl of black blood out of his arm and the next day he died.   At any rate that was the only thing that impressed me about my father's death, except the pride I felt when being patted and such things by the friends that came to the funeral.

The next thing I can recall with wonderful clearness was what they called in the north of Ireland, "The Windy Night," when many farm houses and stack-yards were blown to pieces and innumerable trees uprooted and the whole country devastated.   It is remembered in Ireland to this day.   It took place on the night of the 6th of January, 1839.

I remember being sent by my mother to school to an old woman who had five or six young ones like myself and my impression is that she was acting as nurse for us instead of teaching us anything from books.   The chief thing I recollect is that on the 21st of June she marched us by a Saint's well near the village, called Saint Roan's Well, and there she undressed us and placed each one of us under the spout out of which the water issued. This was intended to strengthen our religious and physical nature —she was a good Roman Catholic.

My school days were like those of nearly all boys; the greatest impression of them that remains is the fights that we had with our fellows, and there are other pleasant memories, such as bookmakers tell of when they went to school. A boy that could not defend himself had a very poor chance of having pleasant times. Our school was the parochial school of the church and, therefore, we were taught by the cleric of the Established Church of Ireland. No Roman Catholics attended it and we thought it our duty to fight the members of their school every day, as we always made a point of seeing them as they went home. From what I can remember now I seemed to have been a terror, because I was left-handed and used my left hand while I was expected to use my right and looking back on it now I always seem to have come out the victor. I fought others as well and never seem to have ever considered myself at fault. I remember that on one occasion I came home with a black eye and a bloody nose and my mother upbraided me and I told her that a certain boy had attacked me and caused all the trouble. I was telling this to my mother just when we entered our house and as I had proceeded thus far the other boy's mother, who was behind me, said: "Mrs. Macoun, look at my son and see which of them has got the worst of it." Both my mother and I turned around and the boy, besides being far worse off than I, had his clothes almost torn off. Of course I was caught in a falsehood and had to own up that I was the aggressor but said that I fought him because he would not do what I wished.

Our school was in an old orchard which had been the Abbey garden of years before, and our chief occupation in the late summer was sneaking into the orchard and getting the fruit off the ground. I did my work in the early morning and got to the orchard before the other boys and generally had the largest share. A small river ran close to the school and our occupation part of the time was catching small fish, called sticklebacks. We used a string and a small stick and a bent pin to which a fish-worm was attached. I have no remembrance of having had any special companions in my early youth.

My mother was very particular and tried to keep us from the boys of the neighborhood and as we had a garden well fenced in she encouraged us to spend our idle time in it. She gave my elder brother and sister parts of the flower beds that my father had had to tend but I seemed to prefer taking an old knife and going out to the fields and digging up flowers and bringing them in and making a flower garden of my own. I only remember primroses and the wild hyacinth.[2]

About this time a sect of Methodists came to our village, called the Ranters, and preached in the village schoolhouse. They were troubled with idle men and boys. My mother was asked to allow the Ranters to preach in our kitchen on Sunday and she allowed them to do so. Later, a prayer meeting was established there and it was one of the old time meetings and the hearers would make responses when the speaker would bring out anything of an unusual or startling nature. One evening the speaker said, amongst other things, that if the people would not repent they would all be cast into Hell and tormented forever. One of the old men who frequently responded woke up as the preacher reached his climax and yelled at the top of his voice: "God grant it!" To crown it all I laughed so heartily that I fell over and caused a great deal of disturbance, in the midst of which a canary, we had, started to sing. This was only one of the many occurrences that took place in the meetings held at our house.

I do not wish to say that I could not tell a lie, like George Washington, but I remember well I had the moral courage, even as a boy, to not lie if I were caught in doing something wrong. I will cite one circumstance that gave me great credit with the good people of our neighborhood. One Sunday I was given the task by my mother of watching our garden, but as soon as the meeting commenced in the house I started for a stream at some distance and had a fine time wading and chasing fish. On my way home I turned up a lane which was crossed by another and as I reached the crossing I saw Mr. Montgomery, our Squire, and his wife walking arm in arm down the avenue and I ran across and he saw me and called out: "John, what are you running for?" I answered without hesitation that I was running for fear of his seeing me. The next day he called in to see my mother and told her how fortunate she was in having such a truthful boy, and made me a present of a piece of silver. I felt that I had done a very meritorious thing. Whether or not that event had a great influence on my boyhood and raised my status so that I was permitted to play with Mr. Montgomery's children in their own gardens, while others were completely excluded, I do not know.

My aunts were married to men called Spence, Kincaid and Murphy, but I only remember that Uncle Joe Kincaid, a widower, lived with my Aunt Spence, who had lost her husband. He seems to have been a man of more than ordinary ability, as he took charge of her boys and superintended the farm. One day he took me into the orchard and showed me the filbert trees and pointed out the male flowers (aments) and told me from his imperfect knowledge, that from these flowers, nuts would come in the autumn. This sank into my memory and, as I will mention later, bore fruit. I loved work so well that when I would go to "Edinmore," as their place was called, they could not get rid of me easily, as I wanted to work on the land and drive a horse; and this was in the dead of winter and very cold. I loved to live outside and be going into out-of-the-way places and later it became even a passion with me and I knew more birds' nests than any other boy in the country. I remember being credited with the knowledge of one hundred and eight birds' nests in one spring.

Owing to the death of my father, Frederick and I seemed to have done a great deal of the work on the land, as I remember more about that than anything else. About this time the Ulster Railway was built and Frederick and I went to Moira to see the "Iron Horse" when it first reached that village. There was a great crowd and I stood beside an old lady who, as the engine came along, exclaimed that it was going on without horses! Evidently she expected that it would be drawn by horses. At this time and for years afterwards carriages were not covered and when people, riding in them for the first time, came to a bridge you would see everyone bowing their heads, fearing that the bridge was falling upon them.

As time passed things became more serious and my life seemed to have been taken up with working at one thing or another. I was always a busy-body. One time, when I was a small boy, they were building a large oblong haystack in my Aunt's stack-yard and when the stack was nearly up the greater part of it slipped and fell down. When my cousin looked around I was missing, but as one of them had seen me gathering up the hay close to the stack at the time it fell, my cousin crept under and finally reached me and when I was brought out I was insensible but recovered shortly. Time passed rapidly and I grew up to be a boy of sixteen, and at this time a great flood took place in the Lagan, a river near where we lived, and carried off 1,600 webs of fine linen that were on the bleach greens. The flood had come so suddenly and it was of such magnitude that no one had ever seen anything like it before. It carried the cloth over the meadows that were flooded and strung the webs in bushes and along the banks and on every obstruction the water met with for fifteen miles down stream towards Belfast. I suspect that I took chances as I got great credit for getting four webs that others were unable to get at. I took these to the office and returned them and, of course, got the bonus that was being given to anyone who obtained a web. The wife of the gentleman who owned the bleach green saw my mother and myself in Lurgan some time after that and my mother told her that I was the boy who saved the webs and the old lady put her hand on my head and said that she had heard we were going to America and likely I would be President there before I died. Of course I was very proud.

My brother Frederick was now nearly twenty-one years old and he decided that as soon as he was of age he would sell the property and we would go to Australia. The year before he became of age a law was passed in England that was called "The Encumbered Estates Ireland Bill." This was in the year 1849. Under this Bill any entailed property in Ireland could be sold. In due time my brother attained his majority and sold our property and we prepared to start for Australia. My mother, however, whose brother had gone to America some years before, begged us to go to America instead of Australia, and by doing so we missed being in Australia when the gold fever broke out in 1850.

I might say something about the Irish Famine in 1848, but could hardly add anything to what nearly everyone knows already. I remember, however, that our potatoes were not larger than marbles and that the whole of the potato crop, upon which the people of Ireland depended, was practically destroyed in 1847 and starvation brought upon many thousands of the people. Often we would come across men and women lying by the road-side unable to walk, where they were dying either of fever or starvation. We had to pay, that year, 16 shillings on the pound taxes for Poor Houses and not one of the people of the vicinity was in them. They were filled by strangers that had been picked up dying by the road-side. At the time of Dan O'Connell's death in 1846, I was a clerk in a store on North Street, Belfast and recall that at that time the bell was tolled night and day for a month.

One other event should be related. My grandfather had built a church for the Roman Catholics and given a lease for fifty years. We received the rents and one day Father Matthew, the great Irish temperance leader was at the chapel when our rent was due, and came to our house with the clerk who was paying it and had a talk with my mother and put his hand on my head and blessed me and hoped I would grow up a good temperance man, which I am happy to say I did.

Before leaving my youth and Ireland, I may, in this place, mention some of the characteristics that I had as a boy and as I write this down, after seventy years, I find that I haven't changed much. My strongest characteristic was moral courage. I often took a whipping stoically when a weaker boy bawled so loudly that listeners would say he was being killed. I, without a murmur, received what I got and often two whippings upon my shoulders by telling what we called a "white lie," to enable some weak boy to escape it. I remember one happening at school that I think worthy of recording. The teacher was very strong on spelling and usually gave us forty or fifty words to learn, which we did each day. I never remember studying this lesson as, whether I succeeded or not, I was always whipped.   One day we had a hard lesson and nearly the whole class had failed and the law was that for each word you missed you got a slap on the hand with a ruler.   I saw that it was going to be serious and behind my back I shook my fist at a small boy who was our best crier, and let him understand that if he would not cry I would thrash him when school was out.   He understood me, as I had done it before, and he immediately began to yell at the top of his voice and the teacher could not stop him and eventually when there was quiet, asked him why he cried and the boy said: "John Macoun said he would whip me if I did not."   The teacher turned to me and said: "I intend to do the whipping today" and he gave me what he had intended for the whole class.   That was the kind of schooling we got in Ireland in the days when I was a small boy.

Every afternoon, when school was let out, we waited for the Roman Catholic children to come from their school and then we would have a decent set-to.   I, apparently, was a little savage as my forte was to dash in and catch a boy by the hair (they wore long hair in those days) and never let go until I had hammered him below the belt so severely that he would cry "quit."   Hence, I never remember losing a fight but I was often afraid.

I never attempted to smoke but once, when my brother got a clay pipe and tobacco and he and I and our younger brother had a good smoke.   Then we ate apples and suffered horribly all night afterwards.   My elder brother and I never touched tobacco after that.   I was always active and fond of work, whether I got pay or not.   I remember picking a field, that is, clearing it of stones.   I had taken the contract from my uncle for doing it, working hard for ten days or more at four pence half penny per day.

Another characteristic was the power of seeing.   I could find more strawberries and more birds' nests and got more fun out of our games than any other boy.   One thing I would never do, and that was to play with what was called a "bad boy."   In front of our own house a number of us were playing on the street one day when a "bad boy" attempted to join us.   I would not allow it, and when my back was turned he took a race at me and shoved me and I fell and hit my head on a stone and was carried in senseless. For years after that I was troubled frequently with head-ache, which ceased by my having bleeding at the nose so badly that they thought I was going to bleed to death. I have had no trouble with head-ache since. I was very determined in having my own way in our play and generally succeeded and at the same time I must have been fairly amiable because I was nick-named "Johnnie Goodfellow," by a half-witted boy who played with us, while my elder brother was named the "Hard Fellow."

CHAPTER II

1850-1856

EMIGRATION TO CANADA, 1850—INCIDENTS OF THE VOYAGE—
CLEARING A FARM—AMUSING EPISODES IN THE LIFE OF A
SETTLER—HIRING OUT—FIRST ACQUAINTANCE WITH CANA-
DIAN WILD FLOWERS.

TO please my mother, my brother gave up thoughts of going
to Australia and we took our passage for America and left
Maralin on the Second of May, 1850, for Belfast. We sailed
from there on the ship "Chester", which carried three hundred and
eighty-seven passengers. I do not recall any person being in the
first cabin. The steerage people, I do not remember seeing, and we
of the second cabin had the deck to ourselves. The night we left
Belfast a great gale sprang up and, the bow-ports having been
left open, the ship began to leak. In the middle of the night all
hands were called to man the pumps and the sailors shirked and
hid and there was a great commotion and the passengers were
called upon to go to the pumps. My brother-in-law and Frederick
started for the deck. Frederick returned in about ten minutes
and I asked him why he came back so soon and he said "I never
got there. When we reached the deck, the ship was rolling so that
I fell and when I was able to get up I came down. I would
rather die in bed than be drowned on the deck." Some of the
passengers went almost insane and the women cried and the children cried and there was an awful hub-bub. When daybreak
came it was seen that the ports had been left open when they were
putting the ballast into the ship. The ballast was pig-iron.

After this, the weather for three weeks was beautiful and fair
and we made a quick passage to some point between Newfoundland and Nova Scotia on a Sunday afternoon, the 27th of May.
This day, a big storm of wind and snow broke out and our bow-
sprit was carried away and all the sails upon it. There were fears
that the mainmast would be taken away also, so all hands, pas-

sengers and all, were called upon to take the sails off the ship, which we did in quick time. The storm soon subsided and the next day was fine and we lay to awhile till the jury bow-sprit was prepared and we passengers used to congregate at the bow of the vessel. One evening, we were discussing our position and the ship was pointing west and in the morning she pointed to the sun again and an Irishman called out: "By golly, the sun is rising this morning in the west." He had no idea that the ship was just merely lying at anchor and that the current had caused her head to swing round. After the storm, the Captain had taken his bearings and said we were so close to Newfoundland that he would put into St. Johns if the weather did not moderate. It moderated and we headed for the St. Lawrence and had fine weather all the way up to Quebec. The beauties of the St. Lawrence have been spoken of so often that I shall say nothing now about them.

When we reached Quebec we cast anchor in the stream somewhere about the Isle of Orleans. There were quite a number of ships at anchor at that time and our Captain took a boat's crew and some passengers and the boatswain up to Quebec when he went to report at the Custom House. It seems that they all had more whiskey while ashore than was wise and the boatswain and the Captain quarrelled coming back. As soon as the boat touched the ship's side, the Captain ran up the ratlines on to the deck, seized a marline-spike and, as the boatswain came up, struck him on the head and the man fell into the sea and was drowned. The crew held a meeting that night and decided not to work the ship any more and, a strong wind coming up, the anchor did not hold and the vessel fell off a long distance from where she was anchored. The Captain signalled up to Quebec and the river police came down and took charge of the ship. It took them a long time to get the vessel warped up to where she had been the night before. We heard afterwards that the Captain had been imprisoned and tried for the murder of the boatswain, but it was shown that he was not at fault.

The next day we left Quebec for Montreal. We went up on the "John Munn," evidently a flat bottomed boat, because all night long three men were occupied in rolling great hogsheads

from side to side to keep her on an even keel.   I paid more attention to the working of the ship that night than I did to sleeping.

When we reached Montreal we took the train from there to
Lachine, nine miles up and there we took the boat for Kingston
and went up the St. Lawrence river and the canals to that city.
We then took another boat up the Bay of Quinte to Belleville,
where we lodged with Robin Archer, a friend of my uncle.   One
thing I remember about the morning we reached Belleville.   Like
any other "tenderfoot" we were wandering up the street in the
early morning and a man was taking down the shutters and he
asked us if we were new arrivals.   We said that we were and he
asked us if we would care to take our "bitters" now.   We said
that we would if it were not too bitter, in fact, that we would
like to have some.   We went in and he put a bottle before us and
a cup and asked us to help ourselves and, behold, it was whiskey
of a very unpleasant taste.

Two days after we reached Belleville, Frederick and I arranged to start for my Uncle's place in Seymour, thirty-two miles
away and began to walk and succeeded very well the first part of
the day.   During the afternoon we got very hungry and we had
no idea as to where we could get any food, as we thought that the
public houses of Canada, like those in Ireland, only gave drink.
We spent the whole day walking in the hot sun without food, and
late in the afternoon reached a point in the road where I asked a
man if we were near Seymour.   "Oh," said he, "you are in Seymour now."   We asked him if he knew Alec Nevin, our uncle,
who lived in Seymour, and he said that he had never heard
of him.   He noticed we were tired and when my brother told him
that we were hungry too, and that we had had nothing to eat all
day, he told us to go up to his house and tell the wife that he sent
us and she would give us all the bread and milk we could eat.

We went up as he told us and the bread and milk greatly
refreshed us and we were informed that we had still ten miles to
go, as my uncle lived on the western side of the township, while
we were then on the eastern side.   We travelled on and had
various adventures and discussions with men we saw on the way
but late in the evening we reached my uncle's house and, behold,

it was a one-roomed shanty, although he had a frame house almost erected in which we could sleep during the summer. I may say here that by this time America had lost a large number of its attractions and we began to realize something of the hardships that lay before us.

The day after we arrived at Seymour a wagon was sent down to Belleville to bring up the other members of the family and in due time it arrived back, but on the way, in crossing a corduroy bridge, my mother was jolted out of the wagon and fell into the ditch; she was none the worse, however, except that her clothes were in quite a bad state. When we all got together at my Uncle's and realized that all our decisions, made while we were in Ireland and on the way to America, had come to naught, we felt very blue. In Ireland it had been decided that I was going to be the farmer and Frederick was to tend to certain other matters and James was to do something else. We now discovered that ploughing was impossible, because the land was all covered with trees. Almost all the land was taken up by settlers or others and no place was available for a person of small means and no opportunity for anything but manual labour. We stayed at my Uncle's for the better part of June without obtaining any kind of work, and it had begun to be talked amongst the people that we were just a useless crowd. It was finally settled that Frederick was to continue his efforts to try and buy one hundred acres of land and we were to go out to work.

I hired with James Ponton. My brother James went to a farmer to work in the harvest, and John Spence, my brother-in-law, did the same. Shortly after this Frederick bought one hundred acres with eleven acres of clearing and a small shanty on it. To this, he and my mother moved. It was about one and a half miles from where my Uncle lived and this was where Frederick lived during the summer. None of us knew how to chop and we were only fit for harvest work, that anyone can do.

There was a fine spring of pure water in the forest that Frederick bought and he was advised to build his house near it. Then, like a woodsman, he commenced to clear the land where the house was to be, but, never having seen a tree cut down, he did exactly as a beaver does, cut all around the tree and watched it till it started to fall and then ran away from it. Working alone and in the hot sunshine, with perhaps heavy old-land clothes on, and much troubled by the black flies, he had an awful time of it and was so discouraged that he decided to leave for Ireland and join the Irish Police. He intended leaving me what money remained after paying his passage and I was to look after my mother and the others. After some time, I persuaded him that this would be a mistake and induced him to stay one year and if things were not well at the end of that time I would take over the money and property.

Later in the summer he became more satisfied with the conditions and began to think about marrying and also building a house, the latter of which he did in the autumn. The house, by good luck, was built in the clearing that was on the place when we came to it and it was on this homestead that he lived until his death.[1]

I remember well the day the house was put up. At that time all buildings were erected by what was called a "Bee." The men of the neighborhood were invited to come and each man who came brought an axe, and was ready to do anything that was required of him. The chief men at a "Bee" were the four corner men. We had four excellent men on the corners and the building progressed finely and was completed before night. In the afternoon Frederick produced the whisky, which was a necessary accompaniment at all "Bees," men could go and take a drink when they saw fit. "Bob Stillman," a wise leader and a very religious man, said, when he saw the whisky, that the Devil was coming, and later in the afternoon "Tom Munroe," a Frenchman, lost his balance and fell off the corner where he was and "Bob Stillman" asked what the cause was and I answered at once: "It was on account of the Devil coming." Of course, in that day, everybody drank.

As I have observed, I went to work at the Ponton's and was called by the ladies "the young man," to distinguish me from the old people and a couple of others who were on the farm. I seemed to be the man of all work, but not able to do much as I knew nothing of work at all. My chief work was picking stones off the summer fallow and a yoke of oxen were hitched to a "stone boat" which slid over the ground and the stones were drawn to the fence corners by the oxen. A little boy, nephew of the women, drove the oxen but, one day, he was required for something else and I was asked if I could drive the oxen alone. I thought that I could and got along fairly well. In the evening the men questioned me and asked how I got along with the oxen and I said : "Oh, very well, 'Haw' gave me a great deal of trouble, but 'Gee' did whatever I wished him to." Of course there was a great laugh. I found that the names of the oxen were Buck and Berry and that Haw and Gee meant for them to come towards you or go away from you and as I had never heard the names of the oxen, but the other two words in constant use, I had decided that they were the names of the oxen.

Another afternoon, I was working in a field close to the woods when I heard something falling repeatedly from a large tree and I crossed the fence to investigate and found that there was a large butternut tree loaded with fruit and the squirrels were up amongst the limbs cutting the nuts off and letting them fall to the ground. I picked up over a bushel and piled them at the base of the tree and went back to my work. After supper, I took a large bag and went back to get my nuts, but behold, they were all gone. At first I thought some person must have stolen them, but I found out later that the squirrels had quietly carried them off.

Another incident of my farming experiences stands out before me. All the fields were enclosed by rail fences and usually a block was placed under the lowest rail. A pea field was alongside of where I was gathering stones and small pigs came along, and, to my astonishment, went into the field and I could find no way to get them out but by taking down the fence. I happened to look where they went in and found that the block of wood that had been placed to hold up the corner of the fence was hollow and the pigs crawled through the log and got into the peas. Something struck me that I could stop that and I took the log out of the corner and sloped it in such a way that it would appear to go into the field and the next time the hogs came along I watched them and they immediately crawled into the log and came out on my side of the fence.   After doing this two or three times they seemed to get frightened and ran away grunting and never tried the fence again.   Many other circumstances might be spoken of regarding the greenhorns when they come to a new country and, even to-day, the old settlers laugh at the ignorance displayed by the green youths from the old country.

After our summer's work, James and myself returned to our new house. The work that all settlers took up in the fall was called "underbrushing," which was to cut all trees, under six inches, at the base, down level with the ground and gather up the rubbish of every kind and throw it into a wind-row.   While "underbrushing" we cut all fallen trees into lengths and everything would then be in readiness for the cutting down of the larger trees when the winter set in.   James, Frederick and myself were all "underbrushing" one day when we came to a tree that had been blown out at the root and Frederick, being the best chopper, took the cut at the root, while James and I cut near the top.   Frederick, being handy with the axe, was soon ready to cut his length off, when he called to us: "Look out there!"   We looked and, behold, he was slung over the root of the tree and the stump was turning back to where it had stood. By good luck, it threw him so far off, that the stump went into its old place and he was thrown beyond it.   As soon as we saw that no harm was done we sat down and had a good hearty laugh, but, we had learned a lesson: under no consideration to stand on a log and sever it from the stump but rather by the tree above the stump.   After "underbrushing" and cutting and getting ready for the winter I went to a neighboring farmer for a month to chop wood and to thresh oats in the barn with a flail.   I received $7.00 for the month's work and worked from daylight or before it, until after dark.   One day, when I was out chopping it was very cold and I was wearing a pair of worsted gloves.   One of my fingers got frozen and we had been told that if any part of us got frozen we were to rub snow on that part until we had thawed it out.   As soon as I saw the finger was frozen I took the gloves off and commenced to rub the frozen one with snow and in a few moments I had five frozen fingers instead of just one and I immediately returned to the house and had them thawed out properly and was not injured by the freezing.

Another foolish thing that we did, I may mention, to show that it is only by experience we learn. At Christmas time we expected my uncle and his family to come with a sleigh and we would all have a great sleigh ride. We lived about two hundred yards from the road and, as we had no lane at the time, we got shovels and shovelled over a foot of snow off the ground all the way from the house to the road so that they, as we thought, could come up easily. Instead of helping them we had worked for nothing, because it was impossible for the horses to pull the sleigh over the bare ground and of course we were laughed at as green-horns.

After Christmas and before New Year's day, Josh Archer, Frederick's brother-in-law, arranged to go into the woods to cut and saw logs. I agreed to go with him as measurer of the logs and to keep the men's time. The first thing we did when we went to the woods was to find where there was a spring and clear a place and erect a shanty where the men were to live. A number of dead pines were cut down and the logs brought together and the shanty was put up almost in a day and roofed with boards. The men began to cut the trees around where the shanty was and another man and myself were inside the shanty filling the chinks with mud and pieces of wood to keep out the cold. While we were at work the trees were falling all round the shanty and I was frightened for fear a tree would fall in our direction and I asked the man what he would do if a tree fell on the shanty. He said he would be so scared that he would not know what to do. I told him that I would drop down just where I was and lie close to the log beside me. With that, we heard a tree crack and we listened and in a short time heard the first tree strike another tree and a tremendous crack took place and we very soon heard the swish of a tree coming our way and I did as I had said, and fell down at once beside the wall and with that a tree lit fairly on the top of our shanty and knocked the other man down; but he was soon on his feet again and ran out and was sure he was killed. He frightened all the men with his yelling and had not been injured.

3

I enjoyed the winter in the shanty very much and no accidents took place and no men were injured.

I left the shanty afterwards and engaged as clerk in the store of John Gibb, in Campbellford. I remained with him until late in the spring, when I got tired of being a clerk and hired with a lady called Mrs. Carlow, for a year, at $10.00 per month with my board.

During that summer my brother-in-law, John Spence, had hired out with a farmer named Fraser, who had been an old gardener in the north of England and was very enthusiastic about the flowers of Canada. I had been much interested in seeing the strange flowers the past summer but thought little of making a study of them, but his talks about flowers so roused my interest that I talked flowers with him every Sunday when I went to see John Spence. This was the first time I took any interest in the flowers of Canada and to encourage me he presented me with an old book, that is in my collection at Ottawa, which was a list of the plants of Northumberland and Durham in England, published in 1806. This book I studied like a child with a picture book and learned the names of the flowers of England before I knew those of our own country. During the next two years, I had many talks with this old man but he died and my visits to his place ceased. At odd times during the next winter, Frederick and I took out cedar rails from a swamp that he had on our place. I cut and split and he carried the rails on his back for nearly half a mile. These rails eventually fenced in the 11½ acres of the clearing on his farm. Our friends called us fools now instead of loafers, as they had done in the summer. A whole series of accidents took place while we were engaged with the rails, as we actually knew nothing about the work. One day, a cedar limb fell off a tree in the swamp and it had a sliver sticking out at the butt end of it and it fell straight on Frederick's back and penetrated between two of his ribs, close to the backbone. We thought little of it that evening but the next morning he was unable to move and had great trouble with the wound in his back. At that time, balsam gum was the great cure-all for wounds and I went to the woods and got a small vial filled with the gum and brought it home and his wife put a poultice on his back with the gum. After a time, when the wound cleared Jane, his wife, thought she saw something in the wound and discovered the end of the stick, nearly half an inch wide, protruding from between his ribs and she got a pair of tweezers that she had and pulled it out and found that it was over two inches long. We then thought there was considerable danger and so had a doctor brought to see Fred and he probed the wound and said, that if it had gone in much further it would have struck a vital part and advised keeping the wound clean and anointing it with the balsam gum, as I had done before he came.

My own mishap took place in the same swamp but it was more simple than was Frederick's. I was cutting a cedar log and in bending a small stem limb it broke and the part still on the tree bounced back and struck me clear in the eye and I was blinded at once, because my other seemed to be in sympathy with the one that was struck. Frederick led me home and I was in great pain with the eye and spent a very agonizing night of it. In the morning, Jane thought she would have a look at my eye and told me that she thought there was something near the eye ball and she saw something there and got her tweezers again and pulled out a piece of bark lying above and back of the eyeball and the pain was instantly relieved. In a day or two it was as well as ever.

Another mishap that took place years after this, I may relate, to show how accidents often take place in the bush. I had taken a contract to cut ten acres for one of the farmers and Frederick and I worked together part of the time. One morning, we cut down a large maple that had old limbs at its top and was hollow, although we had no knowledge of this at the time and cut it. We stepped back from the tree as it fell and a family of flying squirrels flew out of the top and we gazed up at them and did not remark the large limb that was falling right down upon us. Without any warning, Frederick's axe flew out of his hand and a large limb came between him and me, where we stood. The limb had been displaced with the falling of the tree and it fell with the large end downwards. The limb had fallen clear on the top of his axe-handle as he held it in his hand and he was not hurt, fortunately.

One other incident that happened in the same winter I may mention, to show the dangerous things new settlers in a new country had to pass through. One night, in the latter part of winter, a shower of rain had fallen and caused all the logs to be covered with a thin sheet of ice, I was chopping a beech tree that was about a foot and a half through and standing on it at the same time. My boots happened to slip off the log, the axe flew from my hands, and my head scraped over the log and I almost lost my senses, but soon found that no bones were broken, but a small bone about my "Adam's Apple" was dislocated and I could not get my head straight, until I shoved the bone back in place again. The curious part of it is that that bone came out occasionally for ten years after that accident happened.

I shall say nothing about selling goods, while I was a clerk in John Gibb's store, except in regard to one circumstance that shows that I was not very wide awake at this stage of my life. I had remarked that old ladies who came to the store to buy cotton and such things always wanted me to sell it at a lower price than the one fixed, so, to be even with them, when they came to the store, I always added a cent to the price set per yard, and, after due discussion and deliberation, I threw it off again, and got credit from these older people, of being a very accommodating clerk. Mr. Gibb noticed that the old ladies preferred me to wait upon them and asked me the reason and I told him what I always did, and he advised me to cease doing anything like that as he would lose custom if it got around that he had two prices.

After clerking, I went to Mrs. Carlow, who had an old farmer called Ivey, as foreman, and a young man to take care of the horses and I was just the young man that did odd jobs about the place and had charge of nothing. During the summer, Mrs. Carlow, being an Anglican, gave ten acres of her land, which was bush, for an English Rectory and Church and she asked Mr. Ivey to go and locate it. He reported that he was unable to do it and she then asked the other man and he said that he had no idea of how to go about it. In the end, she turned away in great indignation and said it was an awful thing for her to have three men about her who could not do a simple thing like that. I spoke up

JOHN MACOUN, SHORTLY AFTER HIS ARRIVAL
IN CANADA FROM IRELAND

at once and said: "But Mrs. Carlow, you have not asked me yet!" She then asked me if I could do it and when I said that I would try she ungraciously told me to do so then. I may say here that I was always able, when a boy and up to the present, to make out to do in some way or other what was required of me and in this case I thought I saw no difficulty.

I took my axe and went to the farm and, after some difficulty and a good deal of thought, I ran the lines and made a brush fence along three sides and the road allowance made the fourth and five years later, when it was surveyed properly and added to the church, I was found to be nearly right.

This piece of work established my character and ability with Mrs. Carlow. She had no children of her own and was bringing up a young man named Harry Denmark, the son of her brother. A private teacher came early every evening to give him lessons and I was invited into the library by Mrs. Carlow to take part in the lessons with the teacher and her nephew Harry. Apparently, I took advantage of this as the teacher told my brother that I was all mouth and eyes when I was receiving lessons. Harry was what would be called a "real sport" as he was on the river all day sailing canoes or going on rafts and taking innumerable chances. He built a skiff and, in the autumn, he and I went to the Trent River, north of where my brother lived, and fished and shot ducks all day long and returned to my brother's house at night. By the end of the week we decided to return to Mrs. Carlow's. I may say that the skiff had been brought up to the river north of my brother's place, by a team from the farm and we were now going to take the boat back by the river, which was a foolhardy thing to try to do as there were two falls and numerous rapids on the river below us.

We ran one slide (Helly Falls Slide) and, as there was scarcely any water on it, we went down it without difficulty; in fact, towards the bottom of it we had to pull the boat over the slippery boards as there was no water. We had then a mile and a half to Crow Bay where Harry's father lived, and below that another mile and a half and we came to the Middle Falls. Here, Harry got it into his head that we should run over the dam as the fall was not very high, but I advised him to take the slide which we did. On this slide there were about four inches of water running and, as we rushed down, the boat came too near the side and as I was in the bow I shoved it, as I thought, gently, but owing to the swiftness of the water and slipperiness of the boards the boat went broadside down the remainder of the slide and I was thrown out on the apron and Harry righted the boat and shot into the water again. By good luck, I caught a chain and was able to hold on till he came back and took me off. Another mile and we were home and I decided that that was the last time I would go out duck shooting with a "Sport."

I may just add a word here. The next winter Harry went home to his father's place on Crow Bay and he and the hired man went out in the spring with two guns and he was never seen again alive. Both were drowned in Crow Bay.

When I left Mrs. Carlow, I returned to my brother's and this was my last experience as a hired man. My brother attempted to work in a saw-mill, piling boards, but he worked two days and came home with blistered hands and told me that if he died of starvation he would never work again for anybody.

After leaving Mrs. Carlow, I bought one hundred and sixty-four acres from the Government and decided to become a farmer. I made an arrangement with my brother to live with him and help him at a certain sum per day and he was to board me at a certain sum per day when I was working for myself, and that was our arrangement for the next five years. At the time I am speaking of most of the land in Seymour West still remained bush and the roads were little better than paths. A wagon road was generally made through the easiest part of the country and not on the proper road allowance at all. During the summer, fires would take place and at times become dangerous to the whole country round and all the farmers would have to turn out and fight the fire. Other times, a fire would be on our own land and the fight there would be both severe and dangerous. I have known Frederick and myself to have been so exhausted that his wife would have to come to us with water at the risk of being burned herself, while my mother would stand and gaze at us and the fire. Everyone in the country went through such experiences as this and none escaped.

One thing was creditable to the settlers, they were all willing to help each other and "Bees" were the regular ways of helping a farmer who was in distress or who wanted help for a big undertaking. We were just as ready to go out and cut a man's grain or plow his land as we were to go and help him erect a home or a big frame barn. All worked and all helped. The slogan of the country was "Root hog or die!"

These early settlers made Canada! I do not remember an idle man; all worked and although the pay was poor and the returns very often scarcely anything, I do not remember a dissatisfied man.

CHAPTER III

1856-1860

TEACHING SCHOOL—RELIGIOUS EXPERIENCES—STUDY OF BOTANY
—ATTENDANCE AT NORMAL SCHOOL, TORONTO, 1859.

AS I said, my brother James went to Belleville the second year we were out and became an apprentice as a moulder and now, after six years farming and making very little, I decided to follow his footsteps and leave the farm and become a teacher. Two causes forced this upon me. One was an affront that my brother's wife received from a man who held a small mortgage on my brother's land and the other was my desire to study botany. When I announced to my mother that I was going to teach school and give up farming she laughed at me as, since I was thirteen, I had never been in school and she thought I was deficient in knowledge of books. However, I said that I would make a trial and I would pay off Frederick's mortgage at any rate.

I knew a little of a good many subjects but grammar was one I had never paid attention to and so I bought Kirkham's Grammar and gave it three days' study and decided that I could pass for a school-teacher without difficulty. After my three days' grammar, I decided I was fit to go before the County Inspector and discuss the matter with him. I walked forty-three miles to where the Inspector lived and, it being winter, he took me out in his cutter and questioned me on various subjects as we went along. He said: "Mr. Macoun, a very short time in school as a pupil with a good teacher should give you information as to how to govern a school that I shall give you, and with a permit you can try your hand at teaching." He advised me to go to the school in the village where he lived and board with the teacher and attend his school. I attended school for the next three weeks and then received my certificate and returned to my home triumphantly.

Now my troubles began. I thought that I would be engaged in the section where my brother lived but he was informed that it was out of the question as it was not possible for a man who had been farming a month ago to start out to teach school properly. That was my first rebuff. Next, I went to another section where they wanted a teacher and they employed one who took ten dollars a year less salary than I was asking, and so I returned home again somewhat discouraged. I now decided to strike out for the front, which was the township of Brighton, as I had heard they had schools which were vacant in that place.

I had walked twenty miles that day and was very tired and had made a number of inquiries, but no teachers were needed, but, as I walked along in the early part of the evening, I saw a man taking potatoes out of a pit and he told me that a teacher was needed in that district and directed me where to inquire. The trustees met the same evening and discussed the matter and one of them, who had been at college when he was young, asked me a few questions, which I answered in a diplomatic manner. One of them was on grammar of course and I gave two answers, one according to Kirkham and another from a book I had studied when at school. Thus I got credit for a knowledge of authors, and I doubt yet whether the authors or myself were correct in the rendering of the subject, but I learned from this experience that the trustee was rather more ignorant than I.

That same evening, the trustee's wife, in discussing school matters with me, asked me if I could teach astronomy. I said: "I have my doubts." "Well," she said, "Miss Spencer, our former teacher, taught it." I found that Miss Spencer had taught it from books and I told her that I could teach it that way all right. I thought, before she told me of teaching it out of books, that the teacher would be expected to take the pupils out and discuss the stars with them.

I was hired and my salary was the munificent sum of $14.00 per month for six months, and board around. The boarding around was that I had a headquarters where I could stay the latter part of each week and I would board a week at a time with the people that sent children to the school.

I may now make a review of my character as a boy. Up to when I was nineteen, at which age I came to Canada, I was called a "good boy," but did not go to Sunday School so far as I can remember. I made excuses which were really lies, told the truth when a lie would have been dishonorable, never went back on my word and hence was called "good," without having any of the characteristics that "good boys" are *supposed* to have now. I never swore; I never smoked but once; would not play with bad boys; read the Bible; believed in God, but all the time was a young heathen. Without any idea beyond the enjoyment of the present, I was confirmed in church and passed much better than any of the others, but still I was in the dark about religion, although I was always correcting my playmates in such things. I remember telling one boy that if he swore he would never get to heaven and he answered at once: "I guess I have as good a chance as Jock Osle." This man we boys used to call "Curse the World." He never spoke but that he swore.

These, then, were my opinions and actions before I was nineteen. When I came to Canada, a new world opened up before me and of course new ideas were added to many of those I brought from Ireland. I found that truth and honor were scarcer in Canada than in Ireland and many wore the cloak of religion that had not the remotest idea of the character of what they claimed to know. We were located in the country where there were no churches except Methodist and Bible Christians. There were three different shows, running against each other, and we boys and girls patronized each one whenever it suited us. My seven years in the country brought many new ideas about things, both spiritual and temporal. We attended church and all the protracted meetings that were held in the churches during the winter months, which an irreverant man of my acquaintance told me were held to *make over* the members each year. I remember well one protracted meeting that was being held and a number of young men who were attending "Bees" went nearly every night and one or two would be converted occasionally. One afternoon a young man, named William Henry Graham, told us jokingly that he was going down to the school house and intended to be "converted" that night. He went and, sure enough, he was converted, went and studied for a preacher, and in a short time had a church of his own. A year or two after his conversion he married a second cousin of mine and later in his life went to Brockville and filled the church there to the satisfaction of the people, so that they kept him for many years, and his son today is the Hon. Geo. P. Graham.

"Conversion" as it was called, placed you with the saints, who, in my opinion, were lying sinners in many cases. I was full of fun but serious at heart and did only what I thought was right. I tried to be a Methodist and attended class-meeting. One Sunday in telling my experience I felt I was not as good as I might be and the class-leader told me I ought to have as good a testimony as Brother So-and-So. I knew the Brother lied and I did not, so I resigned from the class-meeting. I had very serious thoughts at this time about religion but in examining the people by whom I was surrounded and who were spoken of as highly religious I had my doubts of them.

At this stage I shall digress and speak of my development in connection with the science of botany. In another place I have mentioned where I got my first idea in regard to botany, namely that when I was quite a small boy my uncle took me into the orchard and showed me a row of filbert trees and pointed to the aments, or barren flowers, hanging on the branches of the naked trees and said to me: "Jock, these that you see here will all fall off and in the autumn it is on these trees we get the nuts that we use at Christmas time." This lay in my mind and after we came to America I was engaged one morning in May splitting rails and while resting on a heap of the rails I noticed the hazel bushes at the edge of the woods and, like Moses, went to examine and discovered that these were identical with what my uncle had shown me in Ireland. I discovered that he did not seem to have known that on these same bushes there were other little objects that were pink and these I found to be only on the bushes that held the aments. Later, I knew that these were the female flowers and that the nuts were produced by these being pollenized by the male flowers. These were the first studies I made in Botany.

Next, I came across an old gentleman named Fraser, a farmer with whom my brother-in-law lived, and he told me the names of many of the highly colored flowers around his house and gave me a list that had been published in England fifty years before, which gave the plants of the counties of Northumberland and Durham.   For years this book was the spring from which I gathered my basic knowledge.   All these plants were named according to the Linnaean system.[2] I remember that when I would be returning from labour for my dinner I always aimed to pick up a plant that I did not know and then work on it to find out where it stood in the system.   As was well known at that time, the system in vogue was an artificial one but it certainly served a tyro and my object was to find out where each species was in the classification.   My only other book besides this list, that I can remember, was Mistress Lincoln's Botany, and it followed the same system so that I was enabled to make some progress.

I may mention here how I learned.   I would take a common species of roadside or garden plant of which I knew the name and then immediately endeavour to work out its correct name from the classification.   The Mullein was the species that I took first. I found it more difficult than I had thought on account of its long and short stamens, but I soon came to understand the arrangement of the stamens and pistils so well that most plants could be classified by their form alone.   We had a library in Seymour at this time and I obtained a small English Botany from it and learned the most of our common weeds from that book as in that early time all our weeds were immigrants from England, although I did not know it then.

Another book from which I learned a great deal was Agassiz's "Lake Superior."   This gave an account of the plants around Lake Superior and was the only information recorded from that lake until I went there twenty years later.   After my spending six years farming in Seymour, as already related, I decided to become a teacher, partly to study Botany and for another purpose that I have spoken of elsewhere.   Up to the present I never had had more than one holiday in the year and that was Christmas Day.   Frederick and I might take a day's fishing in the summer, but an eight-mile walk and scrambling along the river was not very restful.

From Seymour I went to Brighton, where I taught school two

and a half years, and in all my spare time, while I was there, I evidently kept botany to the front.   I remember sitting under the fence when I was boarding with my prospective father-in-law, Simon Terrill, who was a well-known Quaker in that district, and he found me with a plant in my hand and said: "John, what dost thee ever expect to make out of the study of botany?"   I told him that I did not know but that it gave me a great deal of pleasure.

During the first year I was there I would get a number of plants in the summertime and bring them into the school and sit and describe these plants to the best of my knowledge as I had not up to that time thought of drying them and making a collection.   I described them so that it could be told what I had found in years to come.   This record is in a quarto volume with a number of species described in it by me over sixty years ago.   In that same book is a list of 256 plants that I named and collected the first year I was there.[3]

In August, 1859, I went to Toronto to attend the Normal School for a Session and had the great fortune to board with a Mrs. Wadsworth, on Victoria St.   Her son was attending Toronto University and in his third year and a prize man in botany.   Very soon we became companions and on Saturdays would go off botanizing.   At that time the cemeteries were nearly all brush or woods and we generally went there.   I found that as I had learned botany he actually knew nothing of it.   He also showed me that I had much to learn.   His knowledge was that of the schools and consisted of structural botany and classification obtained chiefly from lectures while mine was of the woods and fields.   I knew the plants and where they grew.   I soon learned where I was deficient and paid more attention to fundamentals.   My experience in the Normal school was a new one to me as I never had heard a lecture or had seen a big school.   Looking back now I can see that I was very green, ignorant of many things, but had the power of thinking for myself.   I could not write fast enough to take lectures, but put down what I could and filled out my notes afterwards.   Doing this got me into difficulties sometimes, but I made progress and was even applied to by older men when in difficulty.   I could write many pages on my experiences, but will only mention two.   The students had to teach in the Model School to show their ability.   The third division was the terror of the whole class and one of the dreadful troubles young students had to meet.   One morning I was notified to teach it, the lesson was the Pigeon.   I came in and found myself in front of a gallery of boys that would average perhaps ten or more years.   Pandemonium reigned for a time as every boy wished to tell me about his pigeons.   I was nonplussed, but finally got in a word and asked them to tell me something about wild pigeons.   This caused the clamour to cease and as no one spoke I asked them to tell what wild pigeons ate in the spring when they came in such numbers.   One boy said "peas," I said that was right, "but what did they get in the woods," no answer, and I said: "I will tell you, the fruit of the elm."   I had seen them eat it.   At this point the Head Master of the Model School came in and the bell rang. I had never reached the lesson.   I believed I was a failure and would get no certificate.   Next week a student told me that I was all right for he had seen the teachers' standing in the Model and I stood high.   Some years ago I saw a book written about the teaching of that time and the author hinted that the Third Division was designed to test the teacher's ability to keep order.

The other episode was different.   Dr. John Sangster was our science master and he always questioned us before lecturing on the preceding lecture.   He had lectured one day on pneumatics and told the class about the atmosphere.   I was absent teaching in the Model School and knew nothing about what he said.   When he began to question this day, I took care to not catch his eye. He marked me and immediately asked me what was the weight of the atmosphere.   I was taken aback by the question, but promptly answered, if he found the number of square inches on the globe and multiplied them by fifteen he would find the weight. In his usual sarcastic way, he said that would do, but said, why did I not follow his lecture.   I said that I did not hear it as I was at the Model.   From this time forward I could see his eye twinkle every time he met me.

Time passed and we formed a football club at the Normal

and challenged the University to play a series of matches.   I shall mention how we played 60 years ago.   One of the Professors placed the ball in the centre of the ground and each party lined up at the end of the ground and at the word started for the ball. I was the best runner on our side (but a very poor kicker), and reached the ball first and met head-on the son of Alexander Mac-Kenzie (the rebel of 1837) and I, having more momentum, went over him and took the ball.   We were not allowed to touch the ball nor put a hand on any player, but just use the shoulder.   Late in the season we met for a match and it began to rain and we discussed the probabilities and a University boy said, it would rain all afternoon as it was coming from the East.   I agreed with him that it would but said that it was really coming from the west. Someone said let us go to Professor Kingston, who had charge of the Weather records.

We were where the Parliament buildings stand now and the Professor lived quite near.   A few of us were admitted and the Professor asked what he could do for us.   The young man said that he claimed the rain came from the east and another said from the west and we wished to know who was right.   He said it appeared to come from the east, but this storm was coming from the west as it was now raining from Detroit to Toronto. He asked for the student who claimed the rain came from the west, so I stood up and he asked me how I knew,   I told him I had Maurie's Geography of the sea, and he said, "that is the best book on the subject of air circulation."   I mention these instances for the purpose of impressing upon any young person reading this that anyone desiring earnestly to attain knowledge can attain it without any teachers.   Without any teacher I had succeeded so well that I was now a marked man, both in the Normal and among University students.   My five months at the Normal School had opened my eyes, and I saw that being self-taught gave one a great advantage over those that had only studied what pupils are told, especially in lectures.   Many young men were so busy writing they had no time to think.   I could not write fast and only took short notes.   I had taught myself, in studying plants, to ask why such things were so and applied the same test to the lectures in the Normal and so came out with an A1 certificate of the Junior Division at Christmas.   Dr. Robertson, Head Master, offered me the Village school at Brampton near Toronto, and I offended him when I said I was already engaged for the School at Castleton, Northumberland County.   If you were recommended by the Normal teachers in those days it was as great an honour as to be mentioned in despatches in war time.

CHAPTER IV

1860-1871

CONTINUATION OF BOTANICAL STUDIES—FIRST APPOINTMENT AS
A TEACHER IN BELLEVILLE, ONT.—MARRIAGE, 1862—RELA-
TIONS WITH OTHER BOTANISTS—BOTANICAL EXCURSIONS—
ACCEPTS THE CHAIR OF NATURAL HISTORY, ALBERT COLLEGE,
BELLEVILLE, ONT.

THE scene now shifts to Castleton, where, beginning with
January, 1860, I spent ten months teaching and studying
botany. The village doctor (Dr. Gould) was an Eclectic,
as many doctors were at that time and understood botany. Very
soon he and I were friends and I went with him when he was
visiting on Rice Lake Plains. I usually rose at four in summer
and made a large collection before breakfast. During this summer
I progressed greatly in my studies and made excursions in all
directions. Up to this time I made no attempt to do anything
with carices or grasses. I had no microscope nor glass, of any
kind, and had to depend on my eye alone and, as a result, I learned
to depend on the eye even in taking in the meaning of a book. I
collected a few species this year which I could make nothing of,
and sent them to Professor Hincks, of Toronto University, who
named them for me. One of them was a puzzle (*Ambrosia artemi-
siaefolia*) to me and I have never forgotten the pleasure it gave
me to know its name. Doctor Gould, of Castleton, was a great
help to me and took me to many places I could not go on foot.

In the autumn I heard through my brother who lived in
Belleville that one of its schools would be vacant in November
and I applied for it. The late Sir Mackenzie Bowell was Chairman of the Public School Board at that time and obtained my
appointment. On November 1st, 1860, I became teacher in No.
1 School, Belleville. There were four Public Schools in that
town at that time. My removal to Belleville was the real turning point of my life. Before the winter was over I had discovered

I could hold my own with the best of the teachers and stood well with the people. I then decided to devote all my spare time to natural history and as a commencement bought a few books. I remember the first one I bought was Goldsmith's Natural History and began its study, but soon gave it up. When I learned from it that ants laid up corn for winter, I knew better. Next I took geology and read Lyell's First Principles and bought Humboldt's Cosmos' and Hugh Millar and other works of like nature and many on physical geography. By reading and observing in the open, and from my habit of thought, I began to see the causes which had produced all the changes in the world. My vision widened and I saw how to apply my knowledge in school. I began to give the scholars lectures on physical geography and covered the land with plants and animals that I knew were there. It was easy to show why cities grew up by the sea and on navigable rivers and to explain about the trade routes of long ago. What I said was not all fact but none of us knew any better and the children were interested and I was learning. The first year in Belleville I had established my reputation as a teacher and had no trouble with pupils or trustees. My botanical studies were ever before me and I made great progress in collecting. I made a very large collection of Carices and named many of them, but had a number I could not name. I wrote to Professor Dewey of Rochester, New York State, and he answered at once that he would name my collection for me, which he did. It turned out that I had nearly ninety forms and some of them quite rare. One of my species was *Carex mirata* Dewey which was dropped later by the United States botanists, but has been taken up again in late years. Two forms were considered new and named by him *Carex Bellivilla* and *C. Canadensis*. This year I began to collect every moss I could see, but I knew little about them.

My chief difficulty all through my earlier days was the lack of basic knowledge. I did not know how to commence, never having received a lesson in botany. Structural botany I learned from Woods Botany. I studied the Linnaean System from English books and used it in placing plants all through the sixties.

After getting a home of my own in 1862 I at once commenced a more permanent herbarium.

I was married on January 1, 1862, and felt the value of a home of my own.   I now had more duties, my mind was maturing and I had made more progress in my collecting and general study. I obtained a text book on geology that, after describing the various rocks of a great period, gave a chapter on the animal life of that age and another on the plant life, also.   This book opened my eyes and I immediately saw the connection between the "Six Days' Creation" that we all believed in at that time.   I saw at once that whoever wrote the Pentateuch saw pictures of the earth in the making just as geology and astronomy teach now, but these were not believed then.   Since then I never doubted the authenticity of the Bible.   I still doubt many of the expounders of it.   After this time I could never see how a naturalist could doubt the existence of a God.   By this I don't mean one who created things en bloc, i.e., in six days.

I had started on a new life and I put my powers at work and I now became a *real* collector and thinker, but far from being a botanist, though called that by my friends.   This year (1862) I did so well in collecting Hepaticas that I sent a series of collections to Sir. Wm. Hooker, who was then Director of Kew Gardens. He was so well pleased with what I sent that he presented me with his great work on the British Jungermannia a quarto volume containing 91 plates.   This work is in my library at Ottawa.   In collecting mosses and liverworts I was also alert and had my first new moss named and figured in 1861, by Professor Sullivant, the father of American Bryology.   I kept adding to my flowering plants, but could make nothing of grasses at that time.   Two causes prevented this knowledge of fundamentals.   I was self-taught and had no microscope.   In 1863 Mr. C. F. Austin was working on the *Hepaticae* and mosses of the United States, especially the former, and I sent my material to him and for over ten years I supplied him with my specimens and he determined them. This year I had a visit from Mr. George Barnston of Montreal, an old Hudson Bay Chief Factor.   He was an excellent botanist and a special lover of mosses.   He made me many visits after this and was a very esteemed friend until his death. This year, also, Professor George Lawson of Queen's College, Kingston, who formed the Botanical Society, came to visit me and asked me to join? That summer we had a great meeting in Queen's College and I met for the first time young men who were botanical students. The leaders among them were Dr. Robert Bell and his brother John; A. T. Drummond, of Montreal and J. K. McMorine, of Kingston and others whom I have forgotten. These young men were a part of the class which Professor Lawson was teaching and I called him "the father of Canadian Botany." All the other botanists whom I heard of or knew were taught outside of Canada. These young men were a great inspiration to me when I saw their enthusiasm, and a spur to keep ahead of them. I was older than they were, but they had been taught and I was an outsider. The older men and the professors seemed to take pleasure in some remarks I made and I lost my diffidence and we all became very sociable. Of course I was only a schoolmaster to the young men at first but very soon we were all young botanists together. Dr. John Bell had made a collection of plants on the Gaspé Peninsula and these were discussed, and it was decided that I was best able to decipher them. I took them to Belleville and named them and my part of them is now in the Herbarium at Ottawa. My visit to Kingston opened my eyes and I saw better than I had in Toronto in 1859 that independent thought was the power that always won. At one of our meetings in Kingston I read a short paper on bog plants. In this paper I stated that the bog produced Arctic conditions and plants from a bog should not be included in speaking of the flora in Canada when climate was under discussion. Shortly after, the editor of the "Whig" said, in speaking of our meeting that in my paper I applied some of Professor Tyndall's statements in his new book on "Heat as a Mode of Motion." I had not seen the book, but I was always looking for causes, and by this time I was ready with an answer for almost any natural cause, right or wrong.

The years 1863-64 passed and I was adding to my herbarium by exchanges with botanists in the United States. Doctor Vasey and many others exchanged with me, and I began to have quite an extensive herbarium. This year I visited Professor Dewey in Rochester, New York, and had a very pleasant and instructive visit. He was nearly eighty years of age and wanted his mantle to fall on someone and told me that I was, with the exception of Dr. Asa Gray, better fitted to take up his work after his death than anyone else he knew. I told him that my knowledge was self-acquired and I was deficient in many branches of education and that I could not think of such a thing. Loaded with specimens and blessings I took my leave. My standing in botany was now getting well established and the next year (Sir) Mackenzie Bowell who was publishing a Directory of the County of Hastings, asked me if I would write a sketch of the Botany and Geology of the County.[3] This I did to his satisfaction and my own, and by it added to my rising standing as a teacher and scholar. I now planned a series of excursions that added greatly to my botanical knowledge and unconsciously prepared myself for the future. My purpose was to make a botanical trip every year in my summer vacation.

This year (1865) I made an excursion up the Hastings Road into sparsely settled country and brought back many species I had not hitherto found. I had learned that soils produced certain plants and I now found that rocks, lakes and ponds and river bottoms had distinct floras, and there was no chance about where things grew. I could now tell what I might expect in any locality so I always aimed to go where conditions varied. My school prospered and gave me no trouble. The year 1866 was an off year in many ways. The Fenian Raid took place in June and I was in camp at Prescott for some time.[4] The same summer gold was discovered near Madoc and people went mad over gold hunting, and even the children in the school would bring me rock specimens showing traces of mica and others, iron pyrites. These I classified as fool's gold. In the late summer Dr. Robert Bell, of the Geological Survey which was then located in Montreal was sent up to examine Richardson's mine and report on it. He did so and like a wise man gave a neutral report which pleased nobody. The excitement increased and men came from all over Canada and the States. Richardson's mine sold for $40,000.00

and chiefly to local men. One of the shareholders, Mr. Robert Patterson, asked me in November if I would go out to Madoc and report to him what I thought of it. I told him that I knew very little of geology and less of mineralogy, and that he had better get someone who knew more. He said that he would risk me, so I made the "Pilgrimage" as we called it. I had three ideas about how to distinguish gold and with these and a jack-knife I became a specialist. I knew that iron pyrites and quartz were too hard for my knife, that calcite or limerickite would cut or crumble and that gold would cut readily but not crumble. With this primitive knowledge I entered the lists in a hotel in Madoc Village and found all sorts and conditions there. The people generally had samples which the farmers called "Quartz." I asked to see the specimens and found, as I expected, calcite, which cut easily and looked like quartz. I told them that it was not quartz, and at once I had a crowd around me. Quartz, iron pyrites and calcite were disposed of in short order, and I was the centre of a crowd. A man came up and produced a nugget of pure gold, but lighter in color than the Madoc gold. This was the Quebec gold, which I had seen in Belleville. I immediately said that it was not found here and told him he got it before he came to Madoc, and that it came from the Chaudiere. It was seen that I was a specialist and took precedence at once. I may say that that was the first and last time I ever claimed the role of a mineralogist. The upshot of my investigation at the mine next day was that gold was there, but in small quantities. Mr. Patterson unloaded and I rose in public favour.

The year 1867 was spent without special incident and in 1868 a grand expedition was planned to the source of the Trent River. I. I. Tenill a teacher in the Deaf and Dumb Institution in Hamilton, Ont., Henry Reizen, School Inspector of South Victoria and myself were the explorers, I being the botanist. Details of our trip and how we left Lindsay and reached the Muskoka Lakes and our adventures by flood and field would fill a book itself. In this connection I will only say that I made very large collections of many species hitherto not seen by me.[5] I made a very large collection of potamogetons and rushes and other genera and as these species required the work of specialists I wrote to Dr. Robbins of Vermont, regarding the potamogetons and Professor Englemann of St. Louis, Missouri about the rushes. These gentlemen answered promptly and I had their help in all my difficulties as long as they lived. Before this year I sent my difficult species to Kew, but Sir Joseph Hooker had ceased to work on American Botany and had left the work to Dr. Asa Gray of Harvard.[6] I wrote Dr. Gray and I suppose recited my successes. His answer was very caustic and he plainly told me that others might accept my statements, not Asa Gray. Of course I made good and I found a kind, generous, and noble man. Years after, I met him in Montreal, and remember the merry twinkle of his eye when he told how he sat on my assertion of knowledge.

The upshot of my ten years or more of botany had given me standing in England and Scotland as well as in the United States, and I was becoming known even in Canada and my own town of Belleville. This year, Albert College rose from an Academy to a University[7] and the necessity arose to increase the staff and the range of subjects. Bishop Albert Carman, Principal of the University asked me if I would undertake the chair of Natural History, and give my lectures in the morning. I fell in with the arrangement and took up the work. I had never heard a lecture in College, but I was a teacher and succeeded to my own satisfaction anyway, and as there were no complaints, I went on in my own way making sure of the statements I made. My knowledge of botany and geology, physical geography and meteorology was all first hand and I could give as much in half an hour as the average student could swallow, if not digest. I had unconsciously been preparing myself for the future in the above studies and it soon became apparent.

At this time Canada was often looked on as the "Lady of the Snows,"[8] and we helped that opinion by our winter sports. One section of our people maintained that Canada was a mere fringe along the Great Lakes and the arable land only fifty miles in depth at the most. The other had a wider outlook. I confess I belonged to the majority, or the first section. My reading the accounts of explorations and travellers' tales led me to believe this.   This winter, I read Professor Agassiz's Lake Superior and adopted his view of that Lake.   He gave a real picture of it as it was and I noted his statements carefully.

I was now known outside of Belleville and Mr. George Barnston and Mr. David Watt[9] of Montreal asked me if I would make a botanical trip to Lake Superior and collect everything in that line.   I was glad of the chance.   They agreed to furnish the money if I would give them the greater part of the specimens.[10] At this time there were few inhabitants around the Lake, except at the Hudson's Bay Co.'s trading posts.   Mr. Donald A. Smith (Lord Strathcona) was then Commissioner of the Hudson's Bay Company and he gave me a circular letter to each officer around the Lake to receive me as a guest and help me in every way, which all did without exception.

Early in July, 1869, I sailed from Collingwood on the "Old Algoma" and had a wonderful time for nearly two months.   I collected at many places around the Lake and stayed for two weeks at Fort William with Mr. John McIntyre, who was in charge, and, being an old traveller, was very entertaining.   In Agassiz's Lake Superior, he spoke of seeing the cows and their calves swimming across the Kaministikwia every morning to feed and returning at night.   He saw them in 1848 and I saw them do the same thing in 1869.   They may do it yet.   My collections were very large and contained many rare species, which I picked up everywhere we stopped.[11]   We had sixteen horses and a large lot of lumber which was intended for Mr. Dawson who was just starting the "Dawson Road" that cut such a figure during the next ten years.   The lumber was used to build the first house at Port Arthur, as it was named afterwards.   There I saw the first specimens of *Rubus nutkana*, which is so common on Vancouver Island.   Besides going to many places of interest I made observations on climate and gained light on one problem.   Agassiz placed the flora around as mostly subarctic, but I found that that statement only held close to the lake, while I found the plants a few hundred yards back from the lake almost identical with those north of Belleville.   I saw the cause at once, the lake water according to Agassiz was 48° F. at midsummer and 120 miles of cold water accounted for the change in flora on its shores.   Later on in these notes I will speak of what this led to.

Many of the species I found on this trip were rare and a number new to science.   Mr. C. F. Austin named the mosses and hepaticas and named one of them *Jungermannia Wattiana*.   The lichens I sent to Professor Tuckerman and found him a gentleman and a friend in need.   Until his death he named every one of my lichens.   But what was most valuable to me was that he presented me with all his works and assisted me in many other ways.   When I look back at this early time, I found that every specialist helped me in every way they could and I was now, thanks to them, on my feet and could do my own thinking without the aid of a master. The more I read the less I believed in many notions that prevailed about climatology, but had no knowledge to contradict them.

I decided to spend part of my vacation this year (1870) in North Hastings about 50 miles north of Belleville.   I took a companion, one of my pupils, and we spent two or three weeks amongst the lakes and streams of that region.   No difference was found in the general flora except one that I had noted before, namely that the Laurentian rocks produced generally a distinct flora from that of the limestone.   I considered the plants on limestone lands as showing a warmer climate than the Laurentian. I would say now that the soils were warmer and more southern forms were to be seen.

The year 1871 opened with an invitation to spend my holidays at Royston Park near Owen Sound, and I gladly accepted, as I wished to visit Lake Huron.   Mrs. Roy was an accomplished botanist and corresponded with all the leading Scotch botanists. Besides, she knew where most of the species, for which Owen Sound was famous, grew.   July of that year saw me a guest at Royston Park, and for the first time having communion with a botanist day after day.   Mr. Roy called himself our man Friday and carried a basket.   We collected many mosses and flowering plants, the former of which were sent to Professor James, who was then preparing his Manual of North American Mosses.   The ferns of that region were fine and a number of species were collected in quantity.[12]

CHAPTER V

1872

IN 1857, the British Government sent out an expedition under Capt. Palliser, to explore in Canada. This expedition spent four years in the country and made a report stating that it was impossible to make a railroad through the Rocky Mountains. Their report also said that the largest proportion of the prairies was nothing more than part of the Great American Desert. This report gave the country quite a setback.[1] In 1867, Nova Scotia and New Brunswick joined Quebec and Ontario, forming a united Canada. As soon as this took place, the ideas of Canadians were apparently enlarged, for immediately they asked England to arrange for the purchase of the Hudson's Bay Company's claims for the North West Territories. This purchase was accomplished in 1869. These efforts caused a good deal of irritation amongst the Company's servants in the North West and especially amongst the half-breeds at Fort Garry. This resulted in the "Riel Revo- lution," which took place in the winter of 1869, which led to the expedition of the Canadian Militia under General Wolseley, and the revolution was suppressed in 1870. Next year, British Co- lumbia joined the coalition and on July 20th, 1871, signed the agreement. Immediately after the signing by British Columbia, survey parties started work both at Victoria and Ottawa to survey the route of the first Canadian transcontinental railway, which was subsequently called the Canadian Pacific.

In the winter of 1871, I was asked again by Mr. Watts[2] of Montreal, if I would go to Lake Superior the coming summer and make another collection for him of the plants that grew around

the Lake. I made arrangements at the College for permission to
stay away longer than the holidays should opportunity offer to
go to Manitoba, as I wanted to see the prairies. On the 15th of
July, I started for Toronto and the next day went to Collingwood
to take the boat for Lake Superior. On the way out I noticed a
company of gentlemen in peculiar dress and thougt they were
English sportsmen. I took passage on the "Francis Smith," and
so did they.

As the boat left for Owen Sound, I was standing on deck looking at the scenery we were passing when a gentlemen came up
where I was and we began talking. I told him I was admiring
the beautiful trees and shrubs. He said that he was considering
the strategic importance of the hills. I saw at once that he was
a military man.

Mrs. Roy, of Royston Park, at Owen Sound, where I had
spent my holidays in 1871, had promised to meet me in Owen
Sound and give me a few boxes of strawberries. I walked into
the town and the gentleman that I had talked with on the boat
overtook me and fell into step. I told him I was about to meet
a lady who was going to give me some strawberries and, sure
enough, in a few minutes we met Mrs. Roy with the strawberries,
and I introduced the gentleman as a military friend I had met on
board the "Francis Smith." He bowed and said, "Colonel Robertson Ross, at your service, madam," and she said, "Am I speaking to the Adjutant General?" And he said, "Yes." Mrs. Roy
said, "My husband told me yesterday that you were coming
West." We had some conversation and came back to the ship.

On board, a gentleman in semi-clerical costume (Rev. Dr.
Grant), came up to me on deck and began to converse. He talked freely with me and shortly retired. He had hardly gone until
a fine looking man appeared and entered into conversation and
asked me a few questions. I told him what I was intending to
do, and he said, "What would you think of going across the prairies?" I said, "Nothing would please me better." In a few
minutes I found he was the Sandford Fleming who was the chief
engineer of the Pacific Railway which was to be built in agreement with British Columbia. He invited me to go with him to

the Pacific Coast and act as Botanist to his party which was now on the way. I now found that the men who were peculiarly dressed were his party. I became one of the company: the Chief, Sandford Fleming, C.E., Ottawa, the Secretary, Rev. George M. Grant, Halifax, the Doctor, Arthur Moren, M.D., Halifax, the Botanist, John Macoun, M.A., Belleville, and Mr. Horetzky, Photographer.

I soon felt myself at home in their company and was told by Mr. Fleming to keep my eyes open and make a note mentally or otherwise of the productions of the part of the country we passed through. My observations on the trip are found in my report to the Government.[4] I made a practice of going on shore at every opportunity, showing that I was on the job, and very soon attracted the attention of the party and the passengers on the boat, among whom there were a great many tourists. The following extracts are given word for word as they are found in "Ocean to Ocean," which was written to record events of this expedition by Reverend Dr. Geo M. Grant, later Principal of Queen's University.[5]

"Two or three days previously, the Chief had noticed, among the passengers, a gentleman out for his holidays on a botanical excursion to Thunder Bay, and, won by his enthusiasm, had engaged him to accompany the expedition. At whatever point the steamer touched the first man on shore was the Botanist, scrambling over the rocks or diving into the woods, vasculum in hand, stuffing it full of mosses, ferns, liverworts, sedges, grasses and flowers, till recalled by the whistle that the Captain always fortunately sounded for him. Of course, such enthusiasm became known to all on board, especially the sailors, who described him as "the man that gathers grass" or more briefly "the Hay-picker or the Hay-maker." They regarded him, because of his scientific failing, with the respectful tolerance with which all fools in the East are regarded, and would wait an extra minute for him or help him on board, if the steamer were cast loose from the pier before he could scramble up the side. This morning the first object that met our eyes on looking out of the stateroom window was our Botanist on the highest peak of the rugged hills that enclose the harbor of Gargantua. Here was proof that we all had time to go ashore and most of us hurried off for a ramble along the beach, or for a swim, or to climb one of the wooded rocky heights.   The beach was covered with the maritime vetch or wild pea in flower, and beach grasses of various kinds.   When the Botanist came down to the shore he was in raptures over sundry rare mosses, and beautiful specimens of *Aspidium fragrans, Woodsia hyperborea, Cystopteris montana* and other rare ferns that he had gathered.   The view from the summit away to the north, he described as a sea of rugged Laurentian hills covered with thick woods.   In the meantime some of the passengers went off with the Botanist to collect ferns and mosses.   He led them a rare chase over rocks and through woods, being always on the lookout for the places that promised the rarest kinds, quite indifferent to the toil or danger.   The sight of a perpendicular face of rock, either dry or dripping with moisture, drew him like a magnet, and, with yells of triumph, he would summon the others to come and behold the trifle he had lit upon.   Scrambling, panting, rubbing their shins against the rocks, and half breaking their necks, they toiled painfully after him, only to find him on his knees before some "thing of beauty" that seemed to us little different from what we had passed by with indifference thousands of times.   But, if they could not honestly admire the moss, or believe it was worth going through so much to get so little, they admired the enthusiasm, and it proved so infectious that, before many days, almost everyone of the passengers was so bitten with "the grass mania" or "hay fever" they had begun to form collections."[6]

On July 22nd, we arrived early in the morning at Prince Arthur's Landing (Port Arthur) and landed at the commencement of the Dawson Route which was being started when I was there in 1869.   We halted only a very short time there as preparations had been made for us and we almost immediately started for Lake Shebondowan, forty-five miles distant. We travelled in wagons up this road and found it very good indeed after what I had seen three years before.

At Lake Shebondowan we took a water route to the North West Angle.   At this stage I may mention how the party was taken through the Lakes and Rivers from this point to the borders of Manitoba. When we reached the Lake we found a small steamboat ready to take us across and ahead of us had been a number of immigrants who were going by that route to Manitoba. Our party had three large Hudson Bay birch-bark canoes and canoe-men who were brought all the way from Montreal, being the pick of the Iroquois Indians. One of them, Ignace, had been Sir George Simpson's chief guide and the others whom we had were equally as good. Of the three canoes one was a five fathom canoe equal to 30 ft., and the others were four fathom. Besides our canoes there were a number of others and the flotilla was arranged as follows. The barge with the immigrants was tied to the steamer and each canoe was attached in single fashion to each other and it. Of course, Mr. Fleming's was in the lead. This was the order of progression at any time during the trip while we were attached to a steamer.

After we crossed the Lake, the country passed through was very varied and, in fact, was apparently more water than land and caused great difficulty afterwards to the engineers to make a railway location through it. The following extract from "Ocean to Ocean" will suffice in showing the character of the region passed through: "We now entered a lovely lake twenty-two miles long; its name explains its characteristic. As the steam launch stationed on it happened to be, unfortunately, at the west end, the Indians again paddled the canoes for the four miles, when we met the launch coming back; it at once turned about and took us in tow. After a smart shower the sky cleared, and the sun shone on innumerable bays, creeks, channels, headlands and islets, which are simply larger or smaller rocks of granite covered with moss and wooded to the water's brink. Through this labyrinth we forged our way, often wondering that the wrong passage was never taken, where there were so many exactly alike. Fortunately, the fire-demon has not devastated these shores. The timber in some places is heavy; pine, aspen and birch being the prevailing varieties. Every islet in the Lake is wooded down to the water's edge. Our Botanist, though finding few new species not obtained on his holiday, looked forward with eager hope to the flora of the plains.

"This expedition," he said, "is going to give me a lift that will put me at the head of the whole brigade." But, as we drew near our third portage for the day, his face clouded. "Look at the ground; burned again." One asked if it was the great waste of wood he referred to. "It is not that, but, they have burned the very spot for botanizing over. What is a site for shanty and clearing, compared to Botany!"[7]

"July 20th, the Chief awoke us early in the grey, misty dawn. It took more than a little shaking to awake the boys; but the Botanist had gone off no one knew where, in search of new species. As we emerged from our tent, Louis and Baptiste appeared from theirs and kindled the fire. We had commenced the programme intended to be carried out while on the way to the Pacific. This was to rise at day-break, have first breakfast, make a certain distance, then a halt for second breakfast. Then another halt for lunch and to camp early in the evening after having proceeded as far as Mr. Fleming had planned we should go that day." This rule was carried out as long as I was with them. For the next few days, the scenery and the conditions were just as I have described. On the 25th, we had a terrible rain-storm and we lay part of the day under the canoes and, from an extract, I will tell in a few words the conditions under which travellers existed at that time. "After taking a swim, we rigged lines before huge fires, and hung up our wet things to dry, so that it was eleven o'clock before anyone could lie down. 'Our wet things,' with some meant all. The Doctor and the Secretary had stowed theirs in water-proof bags, kindly lent them by the Colonel, but, alas, the bags proved as fallacious as our 'water-proofs'! Part of the Botanist's valise was reduced to pulp but he was too eager in search of specimens to think of such a trifle, and, while all the rest of us were busy washing and hanging out to dry, he hunted through woods and marshes and, though he got little for his pains, was happy as a king."[8]

"On the 26th, we were up at three a.m., and off within an hour and made very good progress. We were now drawing towards Fort Frances on Rainy Lake, but owing to head winds and the little steamer having such a large number of canoes and barges we were unable to make the west end of Rainy Lake and so were forced to camp on the shore of the Lake after we had made only thirty miles." Our steamer was small, the flotilla stretched out far and the wind was ahead. We therefore determined to camp; and, by the advice of the engineer, started to the north shore to what is called the 15 Mile House, from Fort Frances, said house being two 'deserted' log huts. In a little bay here, on the sandy beach, we pitched our tents and made rousing fires, though the air was warm and balmy, as if we were getting into a more southern region. The Botanist, learning that we would leave before day-break, lighted an old pine branch and roamed about the place with his torch to investigate the flora. The others visited the immigrants to whom the log huts had been assigned, or sat around the fires smoking, or gathered bracken and fragrant artemisia for our beds."[9]

Next day, we reached Fort Frances and for the first time saw the Colorado Potato Beetle and noted its power of destruction as most of the potato plants were destroyed. We spent a few hours at the Fort and then started down Rainy River which was very beautiful and showed that in the future it would be a valuable and attractive country. The following extracts will give a general idea of its appearance. "Rainy River is broad and beautiful; and flows with an easy current through a low lying and evidently fertile country. For the first twenty-five miles, twenty or thirty feet above the present beach or intervale, rises in terrace form, another, evidently the old shore of the river, which extends far back like a prairie. The richness of the soil is evident, from the luxuriance and the variety of the wild flowers. Much of the land could be cleared almost as easily as the prairie; other parts are covered with trees, pines, elms, maples, but chiefly aspens."[10]

We had now reached the Lake of the Woods and it being Sunday we intended to proceed no further, but, the steamer came along and we had to hook on. In a short time we reached the Lake and a thunder-storm coming up we were compelled to take shelter behind a small island. The crew, the immigrants and ourselves constituted a large number, so we moved to a smaller island, and hauled the canoes out of the water, and later had the usual Sunday service.   We had dinner on this island and there I found the ash-leaved maple, the nettle tree, *Celtis occidentalis*, and an abundance of flowers, twenty-four kinds that I had not seen since joining the expedition and of these, eight with which I was unacquainted.

Early the next morning, July 29th, we arose early and got ready for the journey.   The captain was afraid to take the passage as it was still very rough.   The Indians were afraid also and it was finally decided that instead of travelling as we had been used to in a long line, one behind the other, two canoes should be fastened to two barges that were in front of us, thus travelling in a more compact body and, by this means, we passed the 'traverse.'   The sun came out and we were enabled to travel the remainder of the day and reached North West Angle in the evening and immediately retired to rest.

Early in the morning of the 30th, the wagons arrived to take us to Oak Point, the commencement of the prairies.   We had now eighty miles to travel by wagon to Oak Point through a new road, the country being chiefly covered with light forest.   For the first twenty miles we travelled over a flat country, much of it marshy, with a dense forest of scrub pine, spruce, tamarac and here and there aspens and white birch.   In the open parts of the country many kinds of wild fruit grew luxuriantly, such as strawberries, raspberries, black and red currants, and so forth, and many flocks of wild pigeons and prairie chickens, were sitting on the branches of the different trees by the road side.

The next section of the country was totally different in character.   It was light and sandy for more than ten miles or so west.   The following extract will give a general description of the country passed through.   "This total change in the character of the soil afforded a rich feast to our Botanist.   In the course of the day he came on two or three distinct floras; and, although not many of the species were new, and, in general features, the productions on the heavy and light soils were similar to those of like land farther east in Ontario and the Lower Provinces, yet, the luxuriance and variety were amazing.   He counted over four hundred different species in this one day's ride.   Great was the

5

astonishment of our teamsters when they saw him make a bound from his seat upon the wagon to the ground and rush to plain, woodland, or marsh. At first, they all hauled up to see what was the matter—it must be gold or silver he had found. But, when he came back triumphantly waving a flower or bunch of grass, and exclaiming: "Did you ever see the like of that?" "No, I never," was the general response from every disgusted teamster. The internal cachinnation of a braw Scotch lad from the kingdom of Fife, over the phenomenon, was so violent that he would have exploded had he not relieved himself by occasional witticisms; "Jock," he cried to the teamster who had the honor of driving our Botanist, "Tell yon man if he wants a load of grass, no to fill the buggy noo, an' a'll show him a fine place where we feed the horse." But when one of us explained to the Scot that all this was done in the interests of science and would end in something good for schools, he ceased to jibe, though he could not altogether suppress a deep hoarse rumble far down in his throat—like that of a distant volcano—when the Professor, as we now called him, would come back with an unusually large armful of spoil. The bonny Scot was an immigrant who had been a farm servant in Fife five years ago. He had come to the Angle this spring, and was getting thirty dollars a month and his board, as a common teamster. He was saving four-fifths of his wages and intended in a few months to buy a good farm on the Red River among his countrymen, and settle down as a Laird for the rest of his life. How many ten thousands more of Scotch lads would follow his example if they only knew how easy it would be for them."[11]

After leaving this point, we pushed on as fast as possible but found when we stopped for dinner we were still thirty-three miles from Oak Point, and, after some discussion, we decided to push on again, which was a foolish move as it turned out later. When we were about half way clouds formed and a heavy rain began to fall and our horses were very much jaded by their long haul, and owing to the heavy nature of the road our progress was very slow. Shortly after, it grew dark and the darkness was so dense that we could scarcely see the road and the teamster was unacquainted with it in the dark, but a halt was called and Mr. Fleming, Dr.

Grant, and myself got out of the wagon and took hands in front of the horse. Mrs. Fleming[12] in the centre of the road and Dr. Grant on his right and I holding his left hand. For some miles, and I thought hours, we tramped when suddenly the teamster called, "All right, I see a light." We were actually through the woods and onto the prairie and, sure enough, there was a light. The teamster stopped and we got on board and asked him if he could see the road now himself. He said no road was necessary now that we were on the prairie. We just headed straight for the light and, though we were two miles off, we started for it even though there was no road, and arrived a long time after midnight. The following is another extract from "Ocean to Ocean." "Arrived there wearied and soaked through. We came to what appeared to be the only building, a half-finished store of the Hudson's Bay Company. Entering the open door, barricaded with boxes, blocks of wood, tools and so forth, we climbed up a shaky ladder to the second story, threw ourselves down and slept heavily beside a crowd of teamsters whom no amount of kicking could awake. That night drive to Oak Point we 'made a note of.'

"July 31st. Awakened at eight a.m. by hearing a voice exclaiming: "Thirty-two new species already; it is a perfect floral garden." Of course it was our Botanist with his arms full of the treasures of the prairie. We looked out and saw a sea of green sprinkled with yellow, red, lilac and white. None of us had ever seen the prairie before and behold, the half had not been told us. As you cannot know what the ocean is without having seen it, neither can you in imagination picture the prairie."[13] I may say that Dr. Grant's expressions only conveyed a slight opinion of my own thoughts in the matter. I was really astounded by the number of species and their luxuriance that I beheld on that morning when I first saw the prairie. And for nearly a thousand miles the same thing was repeated, at intervals, with variations chiefly in color. The impressions then made have never faded from my mind.

We were now thirty miles from Fort Garry and struck out on a straight road across the prairie. In that one ride I seemed to have lived half a lifetime. When we reached the Red River we crossed it in a scow and walked up to Fort Garry, which was to be our home during our stay, one altogether too short.

Captain Palliser in his exploration, 1857-1862, seemed to have adopted the views of the American people, who, at that time, had condemned the whole of the centre of the United States, from the hundredth Meridian to California, to sterility and called it "the American Desert." And the desert was said by Palliser to extend northward of the 49th parallel to the Saskatchewan.[14] Such a view was adopted at this time by our Government, and, when we reached Winnipeg, all the leading men were discussing the subject, pro and con. Archbishop Taché took a leading part on one side and a Mr. Taylor, the American Consul, took the other side. While in Winnipeg, or at Fort Garry as it was known at that time, this was the constant theme of discussion. Archbishop Taché spoke of a "fertile belt" extending from Winnipeg northwestward to Edmonton, but maintained that the Saskatchewan country was a dry, poor affair and it was "*not* fertile." In 1868, Archbishop Taché had published a pamphlet at Ottawa,[15] in which he stated this very thing, that the Saskatchewan was not fertile but that a belt of country extended from Winnipeg to Edmonton in which wheat and other cereals would grow. At this time, the Canadian Government believed that the "Great American Desert" extended into Canada north of Latitude 51° and hence the only part of the country of value would be that from 52° northward, hence the term, "Fertile Belt."

Consul Taylor, on the other hand, lived most of his life in St. Paul, Minnesota, and knew the value of the prairie country, and, having heard great accounts of the black soils to be found in the Saskatchewan Valley, he maintained that in the future it would be the wheat producing country of the American continent.

I heard both expositions and thought little about the results, as ,at that time, I had no idea of the country talked of.

After leaving Fort Garry, we travelled nine miles beyond Portage La Prairie and stopped there over Sunday. The afternoon we left Portage La Prairie we had an awful storm and, to show what a storm on the prairie really is, I make the following extract from "Ocean to Ocean": "At 4 p.m. we started for Rat

Creek, ten miles off (from Portage La Prairie).   The sky was threatening, but, as we always disregarded appearances, no one proposed a halt.   On the open prairie, when just well away from the Hudson's Bay Company's store, we thought we were in for a storm.   Every form of beauty was combined in the sky at this time.   To the south it was such blue as Titian loved to paint: blue, that those who have seen only dull English skies say there is nowhere to be seen but on canvas or in heaven; and the blue was bordered in the west with vast billowy mountains of the softest, fleeciest white.   Next to that, and right ahead of us, was a swollen black cloud along the under surface of which greyer masses were eddying at a terrific rate.   Extending from this, and all around the north and east, the expanse was a dun-colored mass livid with lightning, and there, to the right, and behind us, torrents of rain were pouring and nearing us every moment.   The atmosphere was charged with electricity, on all sides; lightning rushed towards the earth in straight and zig-zag currents and the thunder varied from the sharp rattle of musketry to the roar of artillery; still there was no rain, and but little wind.   We pressed on for a house, not far away; but there was to be no escape. With the suddenness of a tornado the wind struck us—at first without rain—but so fierce that the horses were forced again and again off the track.   And now, with the wind came rain—thick and furious; and then hail—hail with angular lumps of ice from half an inch to an inch across, a blow on the head from one of which was stunning.   Our long line of horses and carts was broken. Some of the poor creatures clung to the road, fighting desperately; others were driven in to the prairie, and, with their backs to the storm, stood still or moved sideways with cowering heads, their manes and long tails floating wildly like those of Highland Sheties. It was a picture for Rosa Bonheur; the storm driving over the vast treeless prairie and the men and horses yielding to or fighting against it.   In half an hour we got under the shelter of the log-house, a mile distant; but the fury of the storm was past, and in less than an hour the sun burst forth again, scattering the clouds, till not a blot was left in the sky, save fragments of mist to the south and east."[16]

Three miles further on was our camping place, Rat Creek. We were now ten miles from Portage La Prairie and to that date no settler had crossed it. Mr. MacKenzie and Mr. Grant were the only settlers there at that time. The whole of the country west of this to Edmonton was called the "Great Lone Land," and extended from here eight hundred miles without an inhabitant except a few half-breeds and Indians.

I may as well mention now our mode of travel. Our caravan consisted of six Red River carts and two buck-boards which had been bought at St. Paul. The carts were all of wood and no iron in them at all. From this time forward, the Chief decided that we would make three spells a day and must make at least forty miles each day for the next month. We had attached to one of the carts an odometer which gave the number of revolutions of the wheel and from that was measured the distance travelled on each spell. By such means, we knew without any difficulty how many miles we had travelled. The cavalcade was arranged so that one buck-board went in front and then the six carts one after the other. My buck-board was the last of all. We had over forty horses and, as we were going so fast most of the time, they were changed three times a day. This was our regular mode of travelling for the whole trip. We would rise at sunrise and have some breakfast; take a second breakfast after going about ten to fifteen miles; then take our mid-day spell of the same distance and, after dinner, take another spell and camp early in the evening. As we were passing over the whole distance through the "fertile belt," we were seldom on a very extensive prairie so that we had feed, wood, and water most of the time.

Just as we were about to start and leave Rat Creek (the men of the party had gone ahead), a band of Sioux, noble looking fellows, came sweeping across the prairies in all the glory of paint, feathers and Indian warlike magnificence. They had come from Fort Ellice, having recently travelled the long road from Missouri, and were now on their way to Governor Archibald to ask permission to live under the British flag, and that small reserves or allotments of land be allowed them, as they were determined to live no longer under the rule of "the Long Knives." All had guns

and adornment of one kind or another.   A handsome brave came
first with a painted tin horse hanging down from his neck to his
naked bronze breast, skunk fur around his ankles, hawk's feathers
on his head, and a great bunch of sweet-smelling mint *Monarda
fistulosa* on one arm to set him off the more.   I went up to the
leader and made signs to him that he was a fine fellow and slap-
ped him on his bronze thigh, as he sat like a king on his horse.
They were the first wild Indians I had ever seen and, when I looked at those magnificent fellows, I felt that their day was about
ended and was sorry to think of it.   They were dressed, just as I
had read in .books, with breech cloths around their loins and a
few beads and ornaments about their bodies and all the rest was
naked and the color of bronze on account of the sun shining broad-
ly on their naked bodies.   This was the first and last time I have
ever looked on such splendid looking Indians.

The prairies, we had been passing through in Manitoba, were
then called weedy prairies on account of the number of tall flowering plants that grew upon them.   Before us, while we stayed at
Rat Creek, extended a flat plain, twelve miles wide without a
house, and one unbroken mass of tall flowering plants; sun-flowers
penstemons, asters, golden-rods, and many other compositæ.
This prairie that we now entered upon was the last of the Manitoba plain and, in rainy weather, was a very difficult region on
account of the richness of the soil and wet ground.

For the next few days we were travelling from Rat Creek to
Fort Ellice, a distance of 150 miles.   During that time, we passed
through a beautiful country and to us Easterners it looked as if
it were a perfect garden with the rich soil and great numbers of
autumn flowers.   When we reached the Assiniboine, at Fort
Ellice, the ford was only three feet deep but the bottom was a
shifting sand so it did not do to let the horses stand while crossing.
I waded in and led the company across as the Chief of the party
had gone to the Fort.   Curiously enough, I led my party across
the same place in 1906 and close to the crossing of the Grand
Trunk Pacific.

After crossing the river, we moved west for the first few miles
along the north bank of the Qu'Appelle and I went down into the

valley and among the sand hills near the stream to inspect the flora and came back rewarded by finding half a dozen new species.

For the next few days we were passing through a very fine country and still we felt that there were no signs of the want of fertility. All the land was good. After passing through the little Touchwood Hills and the greater Touchwood Hills, which are not hills at all but merely a succession of beautiful little lakes and forests of poplar that had been kept from fires by the lakes, we shortly came to the widest expanse of prairie we had yet seen. Away to the west and south it extended without a break as far as we could see. Before descending to the plain, the half-breeds, on horse-back, rode into the thickets and pulled down some small poplar trees that were there, put them on their shoulders and rode to our camping place out on the prairie.

The day after we crossed the Touchwood Hills, when out on the prairie south of Quill Lake, we saw two white cranes, on a ridge, that looked to me like two ostriches, they stood so high. Willie, the boy that got our horses and Frank Fleming, immediately started out to catch the cranes. Frank carried a gun and Willie carried a lariat. I, being at the rear of the train, had a good look at the pursuit. As they galloped towards the cranes, the cranes ran for their lives along the ridge and, as the boys approached the ridge, one of the cranes took to flight and the other one, which may have been a young one and unable to fly, ran like a race horse. Willie went after it and eventually ran up close enough to throw his lariat around its head and brought it to the ground. The old one returned and seemed to attack Willie, but was beaten off by Frank Fleming. In a few moments, Willie came riding past him with the crane over his shoulder and, at the camp fire, it was cleaned and got ready to eat at our first camping place. In extent its wings were at least six feet; a most excellent specimen. The flesh tasted very good, but was of a dark color.

Day followed day and, on the fifteenth of August, we arrived at the South Saskatchewan. At this time there was no established ferry. When travellers came to the shore, if the boat were on the far side, they would send over a man on horseback, and if the boat were on their side they just took it over and left it when through.   This was the point that was afterwards called Batoche's Crossing.   It was thirteen years after when General Middleton, with the Canadian Militia, fought with the half-breeds at this point.

At Duck Lake, a few miles further on, we got a great many wild fowl, and later passed on to Fort Carlton.   Fort Carlton at this time was a renowned Post, as all travellers to the north passed it. The Post itself was of very little importance. It was just the usual square of four or five wooden buildings surrounded by a high fence.   This constituted the Fort, and, having been designed and intended against the Indians only, it was of little consequence that it was built on the low ground almost by the river.   At Fort Carlton, we crossed the North Saskatchewan and took what was called the Northern Trail for Edmonton.   Our reason for doing this was that, if we took the more southern route, we should be liable to run against the Blackfeet Indians, who were frequently fighting with the Crees, and all travellers to Edmonton kept to the north.   This is a quotation from Mr .Grant: "After crossing the Saskatchewan we did not move the camp till about eight o'clock.   This delay gave the Botanist an hour or two to hunt for new species, which he did with all diligence and the rest of us had time for a swim or a ramble up and down the river.   Our Botanist had been slightly cast down of late because of finding few new varieties.   The flora for the five hundred and thirty miles between the eastern edge of the prairie at Oak Point and the Saskatchewan is wonderfully uniform.   The characteristic flowers and grasses are everywhere the same.   We expected, however, to meet with many strange varieties after crossing the two Saskatchewans."[17]

The distance from Fort Garry to Edmonton is nine hundred miles and is usually regarded as consisting of three portions: two hundred and fifteen miles to Fort Ellice on the Assiniboine; three hundred and nine more to Fort Carlton and about three hundred and eighty up the North Saskatchewan to Edmonton. On this third part of the journey we are now entering.

Before writing any further of the trip, I may now repeat some opinions in regard to the prairies held at that time.   Some observers, long resident in the country, declared that the fertile belt practically meant the whole distance between the North and South Saskatchewan and other vast regions to the east, north and west, especially a broad belt along the bases of the Rocky Mountains to the south of Edmonton, two hundred miles long by fifty broad, the home of the Blackfeet, and pronounced by many to be the garden of the North-west.   Others maintained that, as far as the Saskatchewan country was concerned, only a narrow belt along such rivers as the Battle, Vermilion and Red Deer could be cultivated with success.   It is not necessary to decide between those views now.   We knew, at this time, on the authority of Captain Palliser, who crossed and re-crossed the plains several times, that the central American desert extended a short way into British Territory, forming a triangle, having for its base the forty-ninth parallel from longitude 100° to 114° W., with its apex reaching to the 52nd parallel of latitude.   But the first emigrants would naturally select land along the courses of streams, especially the navigable rivers, and they would soon find out all about the intervening districts.

While at Edmonton, I found quite a number of miners at work on the bars of the river.   From one of these miners I bought an ounce of Saskatchewan gold and, on my return to Ottawa, had it made into a ring for my wife, which she still wears.

While we were crossing the prairie we read "Butler's Lone Land"[18] and discussed a pamphlet which was published by a Mr. McLeod of Ottawa[19] immediately before we left.

When we reached Edmonton, Mr. Fleming decided that it was important that this pamphlet should be taken into account and asked Mr. Horetzky and myself if we would try and reach the Peace River and come through the mountains to Fort McLeod this autumn, and we said that we would try.   It was decided that as soon as Mr. Fleming's party left for the West, Mr. Horetzky would arrange the outfit for our trip.   The following is from "Ocean to Ocean.":

"We had to say good-bye (Mr. Fleming's party) not only to the Indians who had come from Fort Pitt and to Mr. McDougal and the gentlemen of the Fort; but also to Horetzky and to our Botanist, as the Chief had decided to send these two on a separate expedition to Peace River, by Fort Dunvegen, to report on the flora of that country and on the nature of the northern passes through the Rocky Mountains. We parted, with regret, for men get better acquainted with each other on ship-board, or in a month's travel in a lone-land, than they would under ordinary circumstances in a year."[20]

The quotations from "Ocean to Ocean," written by Dr. Grant and published in 1873, are now followed by quotations from Mr. Horetzky's book, named "Canada on the Pacific," published in 1874,[21] dedicated to Mr. Mackenzie, who was then Premier of Canada. Mr. Horetzky's descriptions and observations of certain parts of our trip are freely given and I put in a few of my own observations to fill up the hiatus. The first quotation I make is a part of the Preface.

"To the officers of the Hudson's Bay Company, without exception, the best thanks are due for the hearty welcome and aid extended to Mr. Macoun (my colleague), and myself, during our journey. Mr. Macoun, Botanist, of Belleville, Ontario, has also contributed very important data regarding the flora and growing capabilities of the Peace River country. In the section covering Lesser Slave Lake to the Fraser River the reader will kindly bear in mind that absolute correctness is not to be expected."[22]

The next quotation is in regard to the start to the Pacific: " 'Hurrah for the Peace River!' Such was the joyous exclamation of our Botanist, as, after waving an affectionate adieu to our late travelling companions, he turned upon his heel and remarked to me in a manner peculiarly his own, 'Now *we* shall soon settle McLeod's theory!' It must here be remarked, by way of explanation, that, in the early part of 1872, a pamphlet, styled 'The Peace River' had been published in the City of Ottawa, setting forth the possibility of a line of communication between the Eastern and Western parts of the Dominion of Canada, by the Valley of the Peace River. The author of the article in question had been aided by extracts from an old Hudson's Bay Officer's Journal and Diary. The Chief Engineer of the Canadian Pacific Road, struck by the possible advantages of such a highway, chose the writer of these notes (Horetzky) to make a *reconnaissance* of that pass, and ascertain as nearly as possible its actual elevation. With this object in view, I left Edmonton in the beginning of September, 1872, accompanied by Dr. Macoun, an eminent botanist, *en route* for the Pacific coast."[23]

CHAPTER VI

1872-74

Continuation of Journey to the Pacific Coast—The Peace
River—Over the Mountains in Winter—Arrival at the
Coast—Homeward Bound—Report and Conclusions in
Regard to Climate Based on Growth of Plants—Many
Episodes Described.

HAVING, as already remarked, bidden adieu to our late
companions, and having seen them fairly under way for
Jasper House, it now behooved me to make preparations
for the Peace River journey, and as the season was already advanced no time was to be lost.

A circumstance which lent an additional zest to our contemplated trip was the fact that we were in complete ignorance as to
the proper means of procedure and the time necessary to accom-
plish the journey. Nobody at Edmonton could tell us aught
regarding the Rocky Mountain Passes north of Tête Jaune Cache.
In vain, did we seek for information as to our proposed journey.
All the positive information we did obtain was that a Hudson's
Bay Company's boat annually descended the Peace River to the
Rocky Mountain Portage for the supply of leather required for
the Indian trade in New Caledonia (a part of northern British
Columbia), but that boat had already been down and long since
returned to the west side of the mountains, and our chances of
getting through to McLeod's Lake before the winter set in were
very slim indeed. In fact, everybody was only too willing to
impart what knowledge he possessed, but, as that was generally of
a negative and contradictory character, we derived but little
satisfaction or advantage from it. We were told by one party
that such and such a route was not to be thought of; by another
that we would possibly make a very slow and tedious progress on
foot through the dense forests of the Peace River but that it would
be folly to think of taking horses; and a third and veritable Job's

Comforter coolly affirmed that we would never be able to cross the the Grand Muskeg which was described as being infinitely worse than the famous Dismal Swamp of Virginia.   We were filled with all manner of conjectures.   One would tell us we could not cross the rivers on our way and others said we would never get through the Rocky Mountains.   The end of it all was that Horetzky decided to take the bit in his teeth and do what he thought best. I may say here that it was Horetzky who had charge of Mr. Fleming's party all the way from Fort Garry and, as he was an old Hudson's Bay Company's clerk, he knew how to deal with the half-breeds and Indians; therefore I was quite safe in being his companion.

"These conflicting and adverse statements, although rather disheartening, did not prevent my choice of some well-defined course and I determined to strike across the country to Fort Assiniboine on the Athabasca and thence over the swampy and barren grounds intervening between it and the Lesser Slave Lake. But we had to bide our time.

"Two Hudson Bay clerks, then at Edmonton, had received peremptory instructions from their superior officer at Fort Garry to immediately proceed to New Caledonia by way of Peace River and, as a matter of course, all the resources of Edmonton in the way of horses, men, and provisions were laid under contribution in order to expedite their journey.   Notwithstanding these drawbacks, I set about making preparations for the journey as fast as it could be done under the circumstances, but little assistance, however, could be expected from the Company until Messrs. Young and King had been disposed of.   On the second of September, these gentlemen's preparations being completed, they took their departure, kindly promising to smooth the way for us by leaving advice of our expected advent at every post they should pass, and, whilst bidding us farewell, expressed the wish that we should meet again, only on the west side of the Rocky Mountains, as they would travel with customary Hudson Bay celerity.   The Botanist, whose countenance during our affecting leave-taking of Messrs. Young and King had assumed a rueful and comically sad expression, especially upon their allusion to our keeping the rear

all the way to Fort McLeod, remarked, after the last of the cavalcade had disappeared through the main gate of the Fort. "It is
too bad to be left behind in this offhand manner." "Never mind,
my dear Mac," said I, "We may not be so far behind them after
all, and, as they intend to proceed by canoe from Fort Assiniboine
to Lesser Slave Lake, we may steal a march on them and possibly
get ahead of them yet."

"The fact that provisions could not be readily obtained when
once on the way from Edmonton until we reached Fort McLeod,
rendered it imperative to carry supplies in quantity sufficient for
a journey of nine weeks' duration. I accordingly packed two hundred and thirty pounds of flour, twelve pounds of tea, twenty-four
pounds of sugar and sundries besides one hundred and fifty pounds
of pemmican (equal quantities of finely pounded dried buffalo
meat and grease). Meat and tea we expected to find at any of
the solitary establishments of the Hudson's Bay Company which
we might pass. Pack saddles and sundry horse trappings had to
be made and fitted, men had to be chosen, the horses picked out
from amongst the somewhat ill-conditioned animals left at the
Company's horse guard. In the meantime Mr. Macoun, who
was to be my fellow traveller as far as Stuart Lake, whence he
was to proceed to Quesnel and Victoria, busied himself by scouring
the surrounding country in search of further botanical additions
to his already bulky collection."

"Our party, when ready, consisted of four persons, namely,
the Botanist, myself, and two hired men, one of them an Irish
miner, by name Armstrong, recently arrived from the Omineca
diggings on the Peace River; the other an English half-breed
named Thomas, who turned out to be as lazy a rascal as ever
munched pemmican. Of horses we had six to pack and four to
ride, making ten in all."[1]

After saying good-bye to Mr. Hardesty, I went on with the
horses and left Mr. Horetzky to settle up business at Edmonton.
At one p.m., Mr. Horetzky overtook our little train, which had
stopped by the side of a small creek, and found us busily and
pleasantly employed preparing dinner. The preparation of this
meal, indeed, of all our meals, was unvarying in kind and quality

and simply consisted in the pounding up with an axe of a couple of pounds of buffalo pemmican, which, after receiving an addition of water and a sprinkling of flour, was placed in a frying pan and heated. This mixture, together with tea and bread, was our daily food during the whole journey to McLeod's Lake and, though very uninviting to a tyro, is the strongest food and the best for the traveller. One great advantage of pemmican is its portability. It can be compressed into very small bulk, a bag, containing one hundred pounds net weight, measures but three feet in length by about ten inches in width, and will serve four men over a month. My mode of eating it was to receive my portion while it was hot and eat it up at once. I never took a second helping!

For the next few days, we had very bad weather. It was raining most of the time, but on the sixth of September the morning broke bright and clear and we packed up and were off in a short time and reached the Athabasca in the afternoon of the next day. When we arrived there we found that the two clerks from Edmonton were then starting for Little Slave Lake and going down the Athabasca. We crossed the river to the Fort and Mr. Calder, who had charge, said that his son William could guide us across the barren ground to Little Slave Lake, as he had crossed that way with a cow six years before. Here, Thomas, the lazy half-breed, was dismissed and William remained with us until we went to McLeod's Lake.

For the next ten days, we were passing through a country that was almost impassable, swamps and marshes and difficulties of all kinds, and the following quotation from Horetzky's book will show what we went through. "For nearly the entire distance the trail was hardly discernable. Our animals mired at every swamp we came to and these were by no means a rare occurrence, the Botanist, having counted twenty-seven separate and distinct ones during the course of but one day's travel. We seemed during these nine days to have experienced all the misfortunes incidental to pack-train travelling. One of our horses was impaled on a sharp stump and almost bled to death. Our provisions got materially damaged and, to crown all, the weather, which had been so propitious during our journey over the plains, seemed now bent on making us pay for former benefits and enlivened us with continued storms of wind and rain, which alternated to sleet and snow.

"Upon the whole, we had a remarkable time of it and were not sorry to catch the first glimpse of the lake, which we reached on the afternoon of the twentieth."[2]

My opinion of the whole country was that it was a continuous muskeg with islands of spruce through it, and our trail led through the islands. When we reached the lake we were all tired out and immediately camped and settled down for the evening, but not to sleep because at this time (late in September) the whole lake, as far as we could see, was covered with wild fowl of every description; in fact, no water was to be seen, it was all water-fowl. This was the condition of the lake the whole time we passed along it.

We had gone through one series of difficulties only to meet greater obstacles. I may say that I preferred walking to riding as I was unused to it, but now, with a river to be crossed, I had to mount my horse and, by good luck, I had a Mexican saddle with a pommel in front, and when my horse got into difficulties I held on to it.

"The river, at our crossing place, was about thirty yards wide and each rider, before making the ford, drew his knees up to his chin, fondly hoping that in this position he would be enabled to reach the other side comparatively dry, but, entering the middle of the river and sinking deeper and deeper in the cold element that hope was rapidly dispelled and the individual temperament of each member of the party was pretty well shown. Ejaculations and more than direful expletives were heard uttered in an ascending scale and equally plaintive tones as the ice-cold water first reached the boots, then filtered into the trouser pockets and higher still in case of the most unlucky ones. This difficult little prelude to the day's work having been gone through, we dismantled, and, having emptied our boots and rid ourselves of the surplus water, we resumed our way on foot for the double reason of restoring circulation and of sparing our animals."[3]

Next day we came to another large creek, or river, where our horses, losing bottom for a few yards, were obliged to swim.

6

Again we camped on the other side.   Next morning, after travelling a mile, we came to a much larger river and this time we had
to make a raft of dried trees and took our baggage across and
drove our horses.   In this manner we travelled over land by the
lake for four days.   On the evening of the fourth day we camped
in a meadow of very tall grass and at this point was the crossing
to the Little Slave Lake Post, which was close to the head of the
lake.   Mr. Horetzky fired off a gun to let the people at the Post
know that we wanted help to get across but we got no word from
the Post.   Two Indians who had been out hunting came up just
then; each had an old flint-lock gun of the Hudson's Bay Company's type.   The following quotation is Mr. Horetzky's description of this meeting:

"Those fellows were dressed in the unmistakable Hudson's
Bay *capot* and were each armed with an old flint-lock gun with
which they rather astonished our Botanist.   A flock of grey geese
happening to pass at a short distance, Mr. Macoun pointed to
them, and by signs signified his desire to see them shoot.   The
two aborigines motioning to us to keep quiet immediately began
to imitate the cackling of geese and looking up we saw the flock
swerve slightly in their course and turn in our direction.   When
within shooting distance, although to our unpracticed eyes were
yet too far off, bang, bang, went the guns and a couple of plump
geese fell into the grass beside us.   A plug of tobacco each, in
payment, was received by the Indians with evident marks of
pleasure and they good-naturedly set to work collecting fire-wood
and doing other little chores of the camp."[4]

While we were setting out our supper the Indians pointed to
a canoe which was coming up and we found that it was our two
friends, the Hudson's Bay clerks, Messrs. Young and King, who
said we would not see them again until we got to Fort McLeod.
We hailed them and they promised to have a boat sent over for
us in the morning.

On the twenty-ninth of September we started from Little
Slave Lake for Peace River Crossing with a set of new horses.
As usual, I took the lead and went forward a day ahead of Mr.
Horetzky, and made very good progress and, after an uneventful

LOOKING DOWN THE PEACE RIVER FROM THE ESCARPMENT.
PEACE RIVER, ALTA., AS FIRST SEEN BY
JOHN MACOUN IN 1872 [5]

trip, we reached the vicinity of Peace River on the first of October. "Quickening our pace to a gallop, and lost in admiration of the landscape and the sudden transformation of the scene, we at length came to a dead stop on the brink of the Great Peace River Valley which now barred our progress westward. We had at last reached the long-looked-for goal of our hopes and, resting our nags for a little, we feasted our eyes on the glorious landscape now mapped out before us. Throwing the reins over our horses' necks we let them feed there a few minutes while awaiting the arrival of the others, who, with the pack animals, were still a mile or so behind. A strong westerly gale was blowing, but the air was so warm and balmy that to recline on the beautiful grassy sward full face to the blast was positively delicious.

For several miles to the south-west, the noble river, flowing eight hundred feet beneath us on its silent course to the Arctic Ocean, could be distinctly traced as it meandered through its mighty valley. Several large and wooded islands dotted its surface here and there causing eddies and whirlpools, which, in their turn, made long faint streaks of foam, barely visible in the distance. With the exception of these disturbing causes the bosom of the mighty river looked perfectly unruffled at our high altitude and failed to give any idea of the great velocity with which it flowed."[6]

On the morning of October first, it was decided that Mr. Horetzky should go right up to Dunvegan, fifty miles above, and I would bring our baggage and the boat which the Hudson's Bay Company sent down to take us up. This boat was one of the large Hudson's Bay barges which were used at that time on all the rivers to carry freight. It had a crew of six men and myself and Armstrong. Our mode of progress was, by all the men, except myself and the steersman, going ashore and hauling the boat when the wide beach called a "Batture" was on our side of the River. When the Batture was on the other side we crossed over and took it. In going up the river I had nothing to do but make observations and eat. This I did in a fashion altogether my own. On the boat, the men got a bundle of dried meat and each man turned over the lot and selected his own piece and so the selection went on until it was all taken.   I asked the guide why they did that and he said: "We know that we will get no more until this bundle is eaten and hence each man makes his own selection of what he is going to eat."   I decided I would try the dry meat in preference to raw pemmican and had a piece selected for myself. At this time, I always carried a little bag of salt with me and I remember that this day I hung the bag around my neck, sat on the boat and cut a bite off my dried meat, dipped it in the salt and sat there and chewed.   It kept me busy until nearly dinner time to eat my breakfast.

At nightfall we camped on the edge of the river and fastened the boat to a tree on the bank although the boat was nearly one hundred yards from the tree.   Most of the men slept on shore. The guide and myself slept on the boat, and, being tired and possible sleepy, I never woke during the night.   When I raised my head in the morning I found the boat was close to the shore. In the night the river had risen rapidly and, as the water rose, the boat was hauled in and I discovered that I was the only one of the party who did not realize the danger we had been in.   The flood came so unexpectedly that the boats that were at Dunvegan were all carried away and we saw them sail past in the morning. As far as we knew, they were lost.   After a consultation with the guide I climbed the bank and ascended to the trail and took my way for Dunvegan, which I reached in the evening.   The men with the boat did not arrive until the next day.

The next day after my arrival at Dunvegan a council of war was held between ourselves and the Hudson's Bay people.   Owing to the great rise in the river and the loss of the boats it was decided that, as we could not get assistance to go up the river by boat, owing to the high water, and as we wished to proceed further, we would have to go overland to Fort St. John.   The Hudson's Bay clerks, Mr. Young and Mr. King, decided not to proceed any further as it was too late in the season, in their opinion, to pass the mountains before winter.   Mr. Horetzky wished me to return also to Edmonton as he thought he might be able to get through even if winter did set in.   I said at once that I would at least attempt to continue the journey and was prepared to leave my bones in the mountains rather than fail. From that time forward, I saw that Mr. Horetzky believed that I would be an encumbrance to him in getting through and he laid his plans, without my knowledge, as I was not able to talk French. When I decided to proceed onwards with him a number of horses were collected and we crossed the river and took the trail for Fort St. John on the sixth of October. On that day the Hudson's Bay clerks returned to the south.

For the next ten days, we were crossing through a fine section of the country bordering on the Peace River.[7] The trail often led us into ravines cut nearly one thousand feet into the valley but good soil was found in every part.

We crossed Pine River on the sixteenth and, in a short time, were in sight of St. Johns Hudson's Bay post. While there I discovered that Mr. Horetzky had a scheme to not go through the mountains by Peace River but to ascend the North Pine River where we found there was a pass that led through the mountains. We discovered it in this way: While in conversation about the mountains, the Beaver chief, Mastie, said that there was a canoe route up the Pine River into a lake in the mountains from which a stream discharged into a river flowing to the west. He showed us a plan made with a pointed stick on the floor of the cabin. I asked the guide to tell him to let us know what the borders of the lake were like. I knew if he said it was rocky his statement was wrong, but that if it were marshy along the lake his statement was correct. He answered that it was marshy all round the lake and I said at once, "No doubt it is a new pass."

Not understanding French I was not aware that Mr. Horetzky was trying to get the Indians to lead him up the Pine River while I would be sent with the baggage up the Peace River, through the Rocky Mountains, and up the Parsnip to Fort Mc-Leod. In other words, he would shake me off and I would be left for the winter in the mountains. That was evidently the scheme he had in his mind as the sequel will tell. This quotation is Mr. Horetzky's own explanation of this: "Here I found Mr. Kennedy, the clerk in charge, and, having expressed my wish to cross the mountains by the Pine River Pass, we soon had engaged

the services of three other Indians who, with Mastie, were to
conduct me to McLeod's Lake by that route, while Mr. Macoun
was to proceed by the River to the same point. But all my arrangements were soon broken through by one of my chosen band,
a newly married man, backing out and his example, being con-
tagious, decided the others to refuse, point blank, to go on the
journey, which they now pronounced to be hazardous and
difficult."[8]

Before proceeding up the river, it was decided that we should
make a supply of pemmican for the passage of the mountains.
Being interested in the making of it, I decided to watch the pro-
cess. To make fine pemmican, thirty pounds of pounded lean
meat, then thirty pounds of fat are taken, and in our case, thirty
pounds of Saskatoon berries as well, the three making a total
weight of ninety pounds. A small trough was obtained and the
thirty pounds of pounded meat thrown into it with the thirty
pounds of bear's grease, or moose grease, and then the thirty
pounds of Saskatoon berries which had been dried. With a scoop,
we mixed it all up together. Then a bag, which had been made
of green moose skin with the hairy side out, received this mixture,
by being shovelled and pounded in and, as soon as it was cold,
it became almost as hard as rock. Pemmican made, as this
was, is almost impervious to water. While at St. Johns we did
not eat pemmican because there was an abundance of moose
meat and before we started on our trip each man was given a
supply of eight pounds a day moose meat for rations. I, myself,
got thirty-two pounds of moose meat for a four-day trip, which
we now took up the Peace River.

It was fifty miles from St. Johns to Hudson's Hope by the
river and we were expecting to go up in four days. Our start
was not very propitious. We had two canoes, two Indians in
each canoe, myself in one, and Armstrong in the other. Mastie,
the chief, steered my canoe, and Armstrong had charge of the
other. The population of the post came down to see us make
our start. When I gave the word to shove off, Armstrong's canoe
gracefully turned down the river, while Mastie turned up and of
course we had to go on shore again until the other canoe had been

brought up to the landing. For the next four days, going up that river has always, as I look back upon it, been like a nightmare. The current was strong and the men were awkward, and the canoes were dugouts made of poplar. The most I can remember about it is that it was moonlight when we were on the river and we seemed to have worked day and night because I do not remember sleeping at all. The Indians were fresh at the work and were bound to go up in four days and they gave me no rest and took little themselves.

On the evening of the third day, we reached Half-Way River and fell in with a company of miners from the Omineca who were then on their way to Liard River where they expected to find a lot of gold. They had come through the mountains in a large boat and had left it above the canyon of the Peace River and I hired it from the leader for twenty dollars to take us through the mountains to Fort McLeod.

The next evening, we arrived at Hudson's Hope and camped on the slope of the bank while the cabin, called Hudson's Hope, was on the other side of the river. My men immediately left for the other side after piling the luggage on the bank and I, as night fell and a storm arose, was all alone. The trees were falling around me in all directions as it was a "brule" and there were many dead poplars. Long after dark, Mastie came back and we had our supper while the storm continued. I almost gave up hope of being spared during the night as the trees were falling all around. Mastie rolled himself in his blanket and lay down beside a log and I got myself fairly under another log. At any rate, I resigned myself to my fate and fell asleep and in the morning there was a dead calm.

Since our discussion at Dunvegan I had a feeling that Mr. Horetzky was dissatisfied with me because I would not go back. It again became apparent to me that he had decided not to go through the mountains with me but that I should go through alone. The following extracts from his book show this conclusively:

"After vainly essaying all manner of inducements I had finally to give up the project of going by the Pine Pass and take the only remaining alternative which was to proceed to the Rocky Mountain Portage and take my chance of finding a boat or canoe with which to ascend the river."[9]

"Several days having been lost in getting men and horses for the trip and collecting large supplies of fresh moose, pemmican, and other provisions, it was three o'clock in the afternoon of the nineteenth when Mr. Kennedy, William, two Indians and myself crossed the Peace River with part of our baggage, and seven horses, *en route* for the Rocky Mountain Portage, distant some fifty miles. The stream being three hundred yards wide with a very strong current the usual difficulty and loss of time was experienced in getting the horses across. I ascended a hill on the north side ahead of Mr. Kennedy and took an excellent point from which to look over the country.

"The appearance of Mr. Kennedy with the horses caused me to abandon the delightful prospect and, taking a last look at the Fort and river, I saw two "dug-outs" (canoes) pushing off with Mr. Macoun and the rest of the luggage. "They have a strong current against them all the way to the portage," said Mr. Kennedy.[10]

I had wondered at the time why we did not all go overland, but Mr. Kennedy told me, three years later, when I was there in 1875, that Mr. Horetzky intended to go ahead of me as it was a doubtful matter whether we would get through or not and he thought he would get through whether the winter set in or not.

When he reached the far end of the portage beyond Hudson's Hope, he found that, with the exception of the boat which I had engaged, he could not proceed and required more men to navigate than he had with him. He then decided to send over the portage for me and the men whom I had with me. This is his account of the situation: "At eight o'clock Kennedy and I, having turned in, were about composing ourselves to sleep when the wind, which had latterly been unsteady, veered to the south and blew with such terrific violence that we were obliged to turn out and fell several large pine trees which stood in the vicinity and threatened us with destruction. The cracking of falling trees was heard all night and effectually banished sleep. The following evening, Mr.

Macoun, Armstrong and the Indians, with the horses, arrived. We pushed off at one p.m. on October the twenty-fourth, on our one hundred and forty-mile trip."

"The boat being heavy and the Indians perfectly unused to pulling an oar, we started with three men on the line while William steered the unwieldy craft by the aid of a long sweep, and I took up a station in the bow with a pole. In this manner we proceeded up stream for the whole one hundred and forty miles."[11]

During the first two or three days we had little difficulty in getting along; the weather was mild and pleasant, but on the night of the twenty-seventh it suddenly changed and began to snow. At this time we were entering the main chain and, for the next few days, we hardly ever saw the sun.

Our last day in the mountains, I shall never forget. About the middle of the afternoon when the snow was falling very thickly, Mr. Horetzky called to me to look up and I looked and apparently right over my head I saw a mountain top over a mile high in the bright sunlight with fleecy clouds tossing over the sun. In a few minutes, the mountain was obscured and we saw the sun no more until the next day at five o'clock, when we turned out of Peace River into the Parsnip and faced south and in a few minutes we were in the bright sunlight. Three years later, I discovered the cause of our trouble of the day before. We were then passing through what is called the real Peace River Pass, called by the Hudson's Bay Company, "Hell's Gate," and the mountain that we saw turned out to be the same mountain I named, in 1875, Mount Selwyn.

We were now on the Parsnip River, seventy miles from Fort McLeod, and, at this time, we were certain the winter was about to set in as we found the water was thirty-three degrees when we tested it with a thermometer, and, indeed, the next day, after we entered this river, little films of ice were to be seen floating. The stream was very tortuous and shallow in places with a strong current in others.

The second day on this river, William, our steersman, missed his stroke and swung into the river and would have been drowned had he not held on to the oar which we kept still in the boat. We

immediately put ashore, built a fire, and he put on dry clothes;
and was none the worse for his bath.

Next day, we saw two cabins on the bank and of course stopped
to have a chat with the occupants.   They turned out to be
cabins belonging to Pete Toy and Bill Southworth, the former
owned a bar at the mouth of the Omineca and was noted all over the
country.   He told us he dug for gold and hunted for beaver and
martin in the winter.   We asked him where we were and he told
us twenty-two miles from Fort McLeod and that we had just
come up in the nick of time, for the river was going to freeze right
away.   He said he was going up to the Fort the next day and
wished us to stay with him all night.   We preferred, however, to
push on as the ice was floating in the river.   "Mr. Toy gave us
some delicious fresh bread made from British Columbia flour.
We, in turn, presented him with a chunk of pemmican, manufac-
tured at Fort St. John, of which we had an ample supply.   De-
clining his offer to make use of his cabin for the night we pushed
on and camped a mile above.   Pete promised to join us the next
day as he too wished to go to the Fort.   'Gentlemen,' said Pete,
as we were shoving off, 'You may consider yourselves very lucky
to have got through as well as you did, but I see you are prepared
for the worst.' pointing to the snow-shoes and other paraphernalia
requisite for winter travelling, with which we had taken the precaution to furnish ourselves, 'And mark my words,' added he,
'before three days, this 'ere river will be running ice, but you are
all right now!'

We arrived at Fort McLeod on the 5th of November and the
next day the winter commenced.   For the following four days, we
were waiting for the ice to form on the lakes and, finally, on the
ninth, Mr. Sinclair, who had charge of the fort, agreed to go with
us to Fort St. James on Stuart's Lake, over eighty miles distant.
We got ready on the ninth and started, Sinclair, Horetzky, myself and four dogs which drew a toboggan upon which was placed
our baggage.   The thermometer marked nine degrees above zero
and the morning was beautifully clear.   This was my first time
to travel with dogs and hence was a new experience.   The snow was
hardly a foot deep and the dogs had no road to follow.   It was

necessary that one of us should travel in front of the dogs and they would follow. This was our mode of travelling: a runner going in front of the dogs and they following.

Late in the afternoon, I was the leader and we came to a little hill. I was feeling tired and thought I would drop out and let the dogs go on; but instead of that they ran up the little hill after me and struck a log and upset the machine and then they turned on each other and had a fight. When we camped that night, we decided that the dogs with the toboggan were of no use to us and we resolved that after this the dogs would be packed and so we would travel in that way. This evening, while at supper, I complained of feeling somewhat sick as I was shaky all over and Horetzky said, "Well, let us see what the thermometer is." We found it was down to zero.

"The weather had now become very cold, the mercury standing at zero at sundown. This night, we made our first winter camp of the season. Having chosen a convenient spot with plenty of green spruce and a sufficient quantity of dry wood at hand, one of us cleared away the snow while another cut spruce branches and a third chopped dry wood in lengths of eight or ten feet. Spreading the spruce on the ground to a depth of six inches or so, we arranged the wood in front and soon had a roaring fire by which we boiled water for tea and were presently in the enjoyment of a good supper of pemmican, bread, and scalding hot tea. After supper, we all spent half an hour in getting an extra supply of wood which was piled up close at hand to replenish the fire, and spreading our blankets we lay down with our feet to to the blaze and were soon snoring with faces upturned to the clear and glittering sky. In a winter encampment, a covering is rarely, if ever, used although sometimes a piece of thin sheeting cotton is spread behind to break the force of the wind."

"The following morning at six o'clock the mercury stood at ten degrees below zero and the air was sufficiently keen to render heat from about a cord of blazing logs perfectly enjoyable."[12]

Our camp was by a lake which we designed to cross in the morning. While they were packing up, I went down to the lake shore with an axe and tried the ice and found it three inches thick and prepared to cross. Our dogs carried about twenty pounds and each of us had a load to carry also. I found that the ice was so smooth that I could draw my pack along on it, which was easier than carrying it, and the others did the same, excepting the dogs. We had noticed, when starting, that cracks would run across the ice, out, apparently, for miles, and we heard them running along. I took little notice of this at first but soon saw that when a dog would cross a crack with his load the ice on one side would sink and the water ooze up. I thought little of it, but the guide, Sinclair, in changing his pack let his gun fall and the butt broke a hole in the ice and the water flowed up. He immediately yelled to us to separate and try to make shore as the ice was very dangerous. By God's help, we reached the shore without any mishap and ventured no more on ice for some time.

For the next few days, we struggled on, crossing difficult country until we came to Muskeg River where I was exhausted owing to the load that I had to carry. Here, we hired three Indians to take our loads to Fort St. James and we plodded on.

On the evening of the 13th, we reached Carrier Lake where we camped and the night was bitterly cold. As we lay in the open camp by the lake, the ice on it, and the trees around us, kept cracking and between them they caused me to lie awake and the brightness of the night, added to the intensity of the cold, made it a night long to be remembered.

In the morning, we started to cross the lake with a strong wind in our backs and on the way my cap flew off and went at a terrible rate across until it was nearly out of sight and, under the clear ice beneath our feet, could be seen water and occasionally fish and this caused me to almost lose my nerve and I could scarcely keep my feet as we plodded on towards the shore. We reached it almost where my hat had arrived sometime before and in a short distance we had to cross the discharge of another lake where the ice was very thin. I, being without a load, crossed first to see if it would bear and I reached the shore in safety, while an Indian of the party broke through and in a moment, almost, we had a fire lit and he changed his clothes and moccasins for dry ones and was none the worse. If we had all been white men he would have tramped on with his wet feet and in a short time would have had them frozen.   As Mr. Horetzky looked at the thermometer, when we stopped, he found it to be twenty-six below zero, Fahr.   The same evening we reached Fort St. James and this part of our journey was over.

The next morning, Mr. Gaven Hamilton, who had charge of the post, came to me and apologized for the bad quarters I had had the night before and told me that Mr. Horetzky was arranging for my departure for Quesnel, and was putting up supplies. He said he had heard from Sinclair that I was on an equal footing with Horetzky on the expedition and he wished to know if this were so.   I told him it was correct and showed him my credentials. He was greatly surprised; "Why," he said, "he is ordering all manner of luxuries for himself but, for you, he has just ordered what we usually give to our men."   I told him that I did not care what I got as long as I got away from Horetzky with my life.[13] He then assured me that in giving me the provisions for my trip my food would be as good as that of the head of the post.

Next day, I left for Quesnel, one hundred and forty-four miles distant.   My companions were a half-breed called Murdoch, a splendid man, and with him a young Indian.   These two were to be my companions down to the Fraser and with us we took provisions for ten days.   This was carried on the backs of the two Indians and I had nothing to carry but my overcoat.   The following is a quotation of Mr. Horetzky.

"Here, Mr. Macoun, my fellow-traveller, immediately prepared to leave for Victoria and, having procured for him a couple of Indian guides to carry his baggage and provisions, we said good-bye and he took his departure for Quesnel on the 17th."[14]

On the morning of the 17th, we started for Stuart river, but, before leaving, Mr. Hamilton took me aside and asked me if I had any matches.   I told him I had none, so he supplied me with some and gave me besides a light skin coat so I could travel in it.   Each one of us, when we started, carried a pair of snowshoes, mine were nearly seven feet long, and, as I had never worn a snow-shoe in my life before, I felt very awkward, even in carrying them.

We walked along rapidly and reached Stuart river by dark and crossed it on the ice and slept in the cabin of the ferry-man as we were travelling on the Omineca trail. Of course, the ferryman was not there, but we went in and made ourselves at home.

The next day, we walked along and, in the evening, reached the Nechaco. The river was nearly three hundred yards wide and covered with great hummocks of ice with the current rolling between. We were very doubtful as to whether we could cross it and Murdoch got a large pole and walked in front, trying the ice at every step while I came up in the rear in perfect safety. Some miles beyond the river we camped in a little hollow and, as this was our first camp, I may as well describe how we arranged matters the rest of the journey.

Every evening, when we arrived where we were to camp, which was always in a thicket of green timber, with lots of dry wood in the neighborhood, my business was to take a snow-shoe and clear the ground of snow where our camp was to be. Murdoch took his axe and went to the wood to get wood for the night. I always got a few small twigs for kindling. By the time Murdoch got the supply of wood for the night, the Indian boy and myself had finished getting the supper ready. I forgot to mention that my bed was the first under way and it was arranged so that my head would be away from the fire and my feet towards it.

I left my snow-shoes at Stuart river but the others took theirs with them. We were blessed with fine weather; very cold nights but no storms during the whole trip and we pushed on day after day as fast as possible but camped early in the afternoon and laid in a good stock of firewood for the night. As we passed southward, the snow got deeper and at last it got so that it was just an inch or so above the knee cap, and only then did I find it fatiguing. As I had no burden to carry, I walked in front and broke the road for the other two. One afternoon, when it was almost time to camp, we suddenly came across the track of a snow-shoe in the snow and, without ado, we followed the snow-shoe till we came to a sylvan lodge in which we found an Indian, and his wife and daughter, and we were greeted with all the friendliness we could expect. I may make this remark, that all the

Indians at that time, west of the mountains, could talk Chinook, and, no matter of what tribe they were, they always understood each other. We talked Chinook and enjoyed ourselves very much and remained there for the evening. In the morning, when we were leaving, Murdoch said to me that they had a number of fine fish there and thought it would be wise if I should purchase a few as our rations were getting low. I hadn't a cent of money with me, but I did have a red bandanna handkerchief, that cost twelve and a half cents, in my pocket. I pulled it out and held it out to the old wife and let her know that I wanted fish for it, and she brought out a pile of fine trout and Murdoch, who stood by, took out all he wanted.

Next day, we crossed the summit and began to go down towards Quesnel, and we found the travelling much better, but the cold increased. Our last night, before we reached Quesnel, was the coldest we had experienced and it was hard work to keep ourselves warm before we started to walk. Early in the afternoon, we reached the Fraser opposite Quesnel and found the river choked with ice moving slowly down with the current. The ferry-man refused to cross and, as we had finished our provisions, we were desirous to do so. He considered and then said, "If you will take the risk, you may have the canoe and go over yourselves, but I will not take you." Murdoch went out and took a view of the river and said to me, "If *you* are not afraid to go I will risk it." I said, "Certainly, I will go if you say you can cross." After getting directions from Murdoch as to what I should have to do, we entered the canoe and ran up alongside of the ice about a quarter of a mile and as soon as we got an opening, steered straight for the other side, but we were forced down greatly by the accumulation of ice packs until, when we got past Quesnel, we were still fifty yards from the shore and the whole population of the village watched us. By hard work and God's help, we reached the shore about one hundred yards below Quesnel and were soon landed and my long journey had ended for I had now only four hundred miles to go by stage and another two hundred to Victoria and I would be in civilization again.

I may as well mention now that I had been the ward of the

Hudson's Bay Company ever since I left Edmonton as, when I left there, I had no money and they paid my way through until I reached Ottawa. Knowing this, I immediately went to the Hudson's Bay store there and explained to Mr. Williamson, the factor at Quesnel, that I had arrived and would expect him to take charge of me until I could get passage to Yale, on the Cariboo stage. He was very kind and arranged everything for me, promptly and effectively, so that in a few days I was on my way to Yale with a company of miners who were returning from the Omineca and Cariboo gold fields. The only exceptions in the company were myself and Judge Sullivan, who, three years after, was drowned in the wreck that took place off Cape Flattery. We had the usual difficulties that are experienced in travelling in winter but the road was good and the horses were in excellent condition and the Barnard Stage kept up its repute and Joe, our driver, was a host in himself and careful of his passengers. I will mention only one or two of the adventures that we had on the way. One that stands out very prominently in my mind was going down a steep hill with a precipice at one side and a mountain on the other. We were in a wagon by this time (we had started with a sleigh), as we were passing south, and the whole face of the hill was covered with clear ice upon which neither man nor beast could stand. Joe stopped the stage and said, "Gentlemen, you can do as you see fit, ride down the hill with me, or go down each for himself and I will pick you up at the bottom." We one and all decided to leave the stage and Joe kept his seat and took the lines of his four horses and said, "Good-bye, boys," He knew well that if he went over the precipice he and the horses would be killed and he knew, at the same time, that if he could steer the stage, he could steer the horses. So Joe, the stage and the horses, slid down the hill. We watched their progress and when Joe disappeared around a turn we knew he was safe. Then we began to descend and each man had his own plan and his own difficulty. We all got down safely. I remember that I kept to the cliff and held on to points of rock when it was too difficult to stand.

The next episode I think of was when we reached Lytton.

Joe asked me if I would like to see an underground Indian house. I remember saying: "Of course." "Well, come with me then," said Joe, and I went and found a number of Indians living below the surface of the ground close to the old village. The mode of descent was difficult. Joe asked me if I would like to go down, and I descended the pole by means of cleats nailed to it and when I reached the bottom I found a circle of Indians sitting round, apparently quite comfortable and warm. However, the stench was so great, I immediately caught my nose and closed my nostrils and rushed for the pole, up which I scrambled in a great hurry. I had never seen an underground house before and I have never seen one since.

Without any mishap, we reached Yale, and, as we carried the mail, we immediately embarked in a canoe with two Indians sitting abreast paddling, and another man who steered. It was a large Indian canoe and was quite comfortable and carried at least ten passengers, perhaps more. In due course of time, we stopped at Langley and stayed over-night at Harrison River. Here again, Joe was willing to show us around and asked us to go and see a tribal house which then stood near the landing. We found this to be a large building like a shed, roofed over and built of split cedar logs, and in it we found at least a dozen different families of Indians. Each of these families had their own private fire and sleeping place but no partitions whatever. All this was so new to me that the impression which was formed then has stayed with me ever since. I never saw a tribal house again.

When we reached New Westminster, we could telegraph to Victoria and I learned that the San Francisco boat was there and about to leave shortly. We asked them to stay over at the outer wharf until we could reach it as a number of us were going on at once to California. At this time, this was the quickest way to the East. They told us they would. In the evening, when we arrived at Victoria, we found the boat was just passing out. My friends asked if we were to be left and the Captain said, "Oh, we will get you when we come back again." This left me with fourteen days to spend in Victoria and I immediately took up my quarters with Mr. Watt, who had then charge of the Dominion
7

Government Stores in Victoria. Being without money, I went, the next day, to the Hudson's Bay Company's headquarters and interviewed Chief Factor Graham who was then in charge and said that I wished for some money to enable me to pay my passage through to Ottawa. He looked up and said: "Are you one of the men who left Edmonton early in September?" I told him that I was and he said: "Where are the clerks that started with you; did they not get through?" I told him no. "Well, how did you get through?" "We determined to risk it and here I am." "And where is your mate?" "Oh, he has gone down the Skeena and will be here shortly." He drew a long breath and then said, "Well, that is the first time that an employee of the Government accomplished what a Hudson's Bay Company's clerk failed in."

The evening before we sailed for San Francisco, one of my friends turned up to go with me and the other came to bid us good-bye. And he said, with tears in his eyes, that all his money was gone and he was unable to go with us. And yet, he said, he had not seen his mother in seventeen years. Three years after, I saw him at Cache Creek where he was a man-of-all-work at the hotel and hardly had a rag on his back. This was the fate of many miners that I met in the early days.

Christmas was spent in Victoria, and Johnston, my friend, the miner, and myself, reached San Francisco in due time and the only thing I can remember, that took place there, was my exchanging gold with a Jew for paper, and he, with a very sober face, said that there was four per cent discount, and I, being a tenderfoot, was about to give it when the miner said: "Look here, old fellow, it is you who gives that discount." This was perfectly true. It may be asked why I was changing gold for paper. The reason is very simple. The Union Pacific had been open just four years and the road was infested with robbers and confidence men, and no man's life was safe, and so I changed my gold for paper and, at the hotel, before I started for the east, I put the bills under the soles of my feet and then put on my socks and from that time till we reached Ottawa, the chief part of my money was under the soles of my feet, except what little I kept out to spend on the way. Johnston and I bought five days' provisions and a large lunch basket at the same time and had our five days' food no matter what happened. At this time, there were no sleeping cars and each man sat up or slept as it best suited him. We had many adventures in crossing to Chicago but only one I will note.

Late one evening, a man came on board with the usual belt around him. We saw a brace of pistols in it and the miner said to me: "That is a highwayman for sure and we are in for it to-night." And I said to him: "We will not both sleep at the same time," and we agreed that one of us would sit up awake while the other slept. We did so and the man disappeared in the early morning but no damage was done to any of the passengers, although all seemed to be aware of their danger.

In due course of time, we reached Chicago and there we encountered our first confidence man. The station was placarded with notices: "Beware of confidence men." When we reached Chicago, I had a bag of wearing apparel and odds and ends that I wanted to express and went into the express office. When I came out I found Mr. Johnston talking with a spruce looking young man to whom he introduced me as the son of Judge somebody in Stratford. We had a pleasing conversation and, as it was time for the train to pull out, we took our seats in the train and Johnston said: "That young man is the son of one of my friends and it is a great treat to have his company with us to Canada." A few minutes before we started, the young man came into the car and tapped Johnston on the shoulder and asked him to walk to the door with him, and, as he asked Johnston to come out and shut the door after him, Johnston said: "Oh, no, I wish to sit in the car. What do you want?" The young man said: "I want to see if I can borrow a little currency from you as I am short on change." Johnston at once put his hand behind him as if to draw his pistol and said: "Nary a red," shoved the man out, shut the door and came back to me. We had been sitting only a few minutes when a man came in with two valises. He peered into every man's face and went out of the car into the next one in front. Shortly after in came the conductor and he said: "There is a bad case! Did you see that man going down through the car? Well, he fell into the hands of one of these confidence men and he actually gave him a cheque that he had so that he could pay for some goods which he was buying and he would make it good when they got home, as they both were from Vermont!" Johnston and I proceeded on our way and were the best of friends going home and I have never seen him since. I may say that the basket fell to my lot and it has been in the family ever since.

On my arrival home, I found everything in order. My wife had conducted the affairs of the establishment in an efficient manner. My family having increased from four to five, in my absence, I decided that it was now necessary to have larger quarters and I immediately set about putting up a large front to my house with a centre hall and tower three stories high. This, being a new undertaking for me, was given to a carpenter to carry out. I was shortly summoned to Ottawa to give an account of my trip and, on consultation with Mr. Sandford Fleming, I returned to my home and commenced to write a complete report of my extended trip.[15] After this, I took up my duties in school and college and continued my work. When my report was completed, I sent it to Ottawa and got a reply from Mr. Fleming's assistant that my report was considered the best given for the season and that it would be printed in full. I was satisfied with this and troubled myself no more about it.

My summer's experience had opened my eyes to the necessity of knowing more about our country than I had known before and I took up my studies of physical geography and climatology with greater vigour, at this time, than ever before. I was lecturing at this time on physical geography and geology to the students and it only added to my knowledge and not to my work. I may say that I lectured also on meteorology. In the course of my lectures, many questions came up that I could not solve and others I solved in my own way but was uncertain of their accuracy. One or two conclusions that I came to may be here expressed. Up to this time, when speaking of the climate of a country, the statement was always made of the annual temperature. For years, I had been studying the growth of things and I found that the climatic conditions of the growing time had to be the proper standard. At this time, Canada was looked on as, "Our Lady of the Snows," owing to the fact that all our public sports were held in the winter: tobogganing, snow-shoeing, and occasionally ice palaces and carnivals. On this account, even men writing in England had stated that Canada was merely a lump of snow.

While crossing the continent between Winnipeg and the Pacific, I noticed a wonderful sameness in the flora and concluded at once that there must be a sameness in the amount of heat given off in each district and, therefore, the plants of one district give a key to the climate of another that produced the same plants and the result was that I published the statement that it was only the growing months of the season that should be counted. Many other problems came before me and, in thinking them out in after years, I came to certain conclusions that were expressed in future years.

While Mr. Fleming and myself were absent, a change of Government took place and Mr. John A. Macdonald gave place to Mr. Alexander Mackenzie, and, upon our return, Mackenzie reigned instead of Macdonald. Mr. Fleming and myself were both conservatives and he at once told me that my allegiance was to Mr. Mackenzie and to do what was right in my report.

CHAPTER VII

1874-1875

EXPLORATIONS FROM VICTORIA TO THE PEACE RIVER—NEW
WESTMINSTER, YALE, SPENCE'S BRIDGE, QUESNEL, NECHACO,
FORT ST. JOHN, McLEOD'S LAKE, PARSNIP AND FINLAY
RIVERS, HUDSON'S HOPE—DESCRIPTION OF THE ROUTE—
BOTANICAL NOTES—EPISODES AND INCIDENTS.

IN the spring of 1874, my report on the expedition of 1872, was
published in the Railway Report, and Dr. Selwyn,[1] who was
then at the head of the Geological Survey, when he saw the
report, said at once: "I must have that man with me when I go
out next year."[2] He was going to make an examination of the
Peace River Pass, and the country adjoining, for the Mackenzie
government, who were then thinking of sending the railway
through by the Peace River. Dr. Selwyn wrote to me, asking if
I would go, and, having got permission from the College and the
school authorities, I answered yes, but had doubts of being acceptable to the government as my political principles were known.
In the winter, I saw Dr. Hope, of Belleville, who had the patronage
of that city, and asked him if he thought Mr. Mackenzie would
give me the position and he said he thought he would because,
"Macoun," he said, "I, myself, tell you, we have no one else so
well fitted for the position." It turned out as he had said.

On the 14th of April, 1875, I left home again, for the far west,
travelling by railway as far as Laramie City in the state of Wy-
oming, where we were detained six days by a washout owing to a
rain storm and the melting of the snow. Ours was the first train
stopped and each day another train came in heavily loaded. A
Scotchman and his sister were with our party, and, in conversation, he advised that we immediately put in a stock of provisions
as there was a scarcity in the city. We did so and eight of us
arranged with a boarding-house keeper to give us dishes and the
ladies that were of our party did the cooking and serving and our

meals were taken after the boarders were through. We moved after six days, and had six miles to walk through the mud and then took the train for one hundred and fifty miles to Green River, where I saw the most extraordinary sight I had ever seen. Bars of silver, so heavy that none of us could lift them, were piled up like cord-wood on the platform and the sight of so much white metal has never left my eyes since. After this, we had no more stoppages but, the last day we were on the train, we took dinner on the top of the Sierra Nevada with fully ten feet of snow on all sides. After leaving the station, we immediately began to descend and, although we were in snow-sheds, I, and two or three other men got out on the steps and watched. We soon passed out of the snow and into spring and could see the buds on the bushes. In another minute or two spring flowers were seen; later on flowering shrubs appeared and, as we were passing towards the plains, summer was upon us and before we came to Sacramento the hay was cut in the fields. This was all seen in just half of one day.

Nothing of importance took place after this until I reached Victoria where I commenced my duties. I had been appointed Botanist to the party with instructions to make note on all the country passed through, in regard to its flora, climate and agricultural capabilities. This I performed to the best of my ability from Victoria to Peace River Pass and the whole length of the Peace river and nearly one thousand miles more before I reached Fort Carlton on the prairie.

I purpose, when speaking of matters in connection with this trip, to quote largely from my report to the government on all matters coming into my line of work. This report was published in 1876 and will be found in the geological report for 1875.[3] I shall speak little of the botany on account of its being the subject that I fully dealt with in the report alluded to. I shall deal mostly with my observations in connection with the climate and productiveness of the country passed through. I shall also speak of incidents that took place on the journey not mentioned in the report.

I reached Victoria, B.C., on the second of May and began at

once to carry out the instructions already referred to as given to me before I left Ottawa. I carefully examined the flora in the vicinity of Victoria and collected on Cedar Hill and Mount Tolmie and many other localities. I noticed that, on these two mountains, there were many species that seemed peculiar to them but which plainly indicated that a part, at least, of the California flora had worked its way thus far to the north. Since writing the above, I have found that such is the case and that the flora in the vicinity of Victoria has many species that are also found at San Francisco.

Two facts regarding the climate of Vancouver Island and indicated by the flora are: dry summers and abundant rainfall. The former is shown by the annuals being all in bud and flower by the first week in May and the latter, by the luxuriant growth of succulent vegetation in the low grounds. The general character of the flora, therefore, proves that the climate is warmer than that of England and that the rainfall is periodic, rather than distributed throughout the year, and corresponds with the decrease and increase of heat, the summer being very dry. It is a remarkable fact that July, the month of least rainfall on the coast, is the season of the greatest precipitation in the dry region along the Thompson. The difference in the time of blossoming of apple trees on Vancouver Island and that of Belleville, Ontario, is about three weeks. In the beginning of May, 1875, vegetation was said to be unusually backward, and yet it was three weeks, in advance of Ontario.

Owing to the wetness of the soil, many apple trees, though young, were beginning to show signs of decay, but draining would remedy this and, if the advice I gave to plant orchards amongst the rocks where the oaks abound is followed, no more complaints will be heard about the apple trees dying young.

Although spring was so far advanced, scarcely any plowing had been done owing to the water in the soil due largely to lack of drainage, and over a month of the best part of growth for cereals was gone. In many places, I saw grass a foot high and expected to find cabbages and other vegetables proportionately advanced but there was nothing to be seen. The climate is

everything that can be desired and a larger number of settlers
with more advanced ideas of agriculture is alone required to make
Vancouver Island what nature intended it to be—the Garden of
Canada on the Pacific Coast.

In accordance with my instructions, I left Victoria on May
14th, on the Steamer "Enterprise," for New Westminster. Our
approach to the mouth of the Fraser was indicated, before we
reached the light-ship, by the muddy appearance of the water,
while extensive mud banks and low marshy grounds gave evidence
of the immense quantities of detritus brought down by the Fraser.
As we passed up, marsh gave place to meadow, and soon, the
meadow, to a thick jungle of willow and other bushes which gradually merged into forest that would vie with a tropical one for
luxuriance.

Early on the morning of the 15th, we were again under way
and reached Harrison River about dark. I found the vegetation
further advanced here than at Victoria. The white thorn (*Cra-
taegus*) was in flower and the shoots on the trees had made more
growth.

"I may mention here what seems to me the cause of the mild
climate of the Pacific Coast, and, in my opinion, it is precisely
the same as that of Western Europe. A stream of warm water, a
little south of the Island of Formosa on the southern coast of
China, a current analogous to the Gulf Stream, is observed moving
to the north east. It passes east of Japan and, while a part of it
enters the Behring Sea, the remainder passes through to the
Aleutian Islands and ameliorates the climate of Alaska to such a
degree that the annual temperature of Sitka, in latitude 57 degrees,
is higher than that of Ottawa, in latitude 45 25', the mean annual
temperature of the former being 44.8 degrees Fahr. while the latter
has 37.4 degrees. Esquimalt, within three miles of Victoria, in latitude 48 25', has a mean annual temperature of 47.4, only three
degrees higher than that of Sitka which is nine degrees further
north. With these facts, the temperature of Sitka and Esquimalt,
it is very easy to forecast the future of the whole region west of
the Cascades between Victoria and the Stikeen River. The
Queen Charlotte Islands, being more insular than Vancouver

Island, must have a milder climate, and hence they may be set down as of equal value. A careful examination of a map of the world will show the close relationship existing between Europe and western America in the same parallels. A warm current of water flows down the coast of the latter, while the shores of the former are bathed in the tepid waters of the Gulf Stream. Both regions have their shores deeply indented by inlets, "Fiords," in the one case and "Canals" in the other. The oak and pine forests of the British Isles and of Norway are simulated by the oak and fir forests of British Columbia. In both, the moist climate is caused in the same way—the vapor, rising from the warm sea water, is blown inland and, being condensed by the cooler air over the land, falls in rain or fog upon the slopes and valleys. The old forests of Great Britain and Ireland, including those of Norway, are a product of the Gulf Stream, while the mighty forests of our western province, including the Queen Charlotte Islands, are certainly a product of the "Kuro Siwa" (Japan Current). It only remains for me to add that as years roll on and our possessions become developed, the value of this second Britain will come so vividly before our people that men will ask with astonishment how such ignorance prevailed in the past! Today, there are four hundred miles of coast line in our western possessions north, with a forest growth superior to anything else in the world at present. Its shore is indented with multitudes of harbours, bays, and inlets, teeming with myriads of fish. Its rocks and sands contain gold, iron, silver, coral, and other minerals. And besides all this, a climate superior to England in every respect, both as regards heat and moisture, and yet, men ask me what it is all worth? I answer: "Worth more than Quebec, and all the Maritime Provinces thrown in, and skeptics may rest assured that the day is not far distant when my words will be found to be true." (1875).[4]

The boat reached Yale at noon and, after resting for a short time, I went out to examine the neighborhood. Tempted by the close vicinity of the mountains, I climbed the nearest and found it by aneroid to be about 1,000 feet above the river. At the base, many plants were in flower which, as I neared the summit, ceased to show blossom.   On the middle slopes there were quite a number of eastern species and those noted at Victoria were congregated around a little moisture on the top."

During the next day and a half, I employed myself by climbing among the rocks and collected many interesting forms; amongst other rare things, I had the good fortune to re-discover *Saxifraga ranunculifolia* Hook.   This species seems never to have been found since its discovery by the lamented Douglas.   I found it in the high cliffs some distance from where the road turns to go up the Fraser.   Dr. Gray told me there were no specimens in American herbaria and that my discovery was interesting.   While climbing amongst the rocks I came across a crevice filled with ice, within less than fifty feet from the river, and from which a large supply could be taken.

On the afternoon of the 18th of May, I started on foot up the Cariboo road expecting a conveyance to overtake me and carry me to Boston Bar that afternoon.   A few miles on the Yale side of Boston Bar we turned the point of the mountain and, almost immediately, the plants showed that there was less precipitation and, on looking back, I at once detected the cause, in the mountains acting as a barrier to keep out the superabundant moisture of the lower Fraser Valley.

"May 19th.   This morning, we were on our way long before the sun shone above the horizon.   As we proceeded, the vegetation gave more and more indications of dryness, and at Butcher's Flat, *Pinus ponderosa*, the pine of the interior plateaux, was to be seen in some abundance.   After crossing Jackass Mountain, which intercepts whatever little moisture goes up the valley from Boston Bar, just as the range below that locality shuts out the moist winds of the coast, the traveller will see by looking back that it blocks up the valley while the river, much compressed, winds round its base.   Now all is changed; the sage brush (*Artemisia tridentata*) becomes frequent and, at Lytton, a group of Nevada plants is the characteristic flora.   Vegetation was far advanced here, in fact ahead of Victoria, as roses were seen in flower for the first time a little above Lytton.

Proceeding up the Thompson river, the land gets dryer, so

that, before we reached Spence's Bridge, we were prepared for the change that is so marked as one rises on the terrace beyond the bridge.   All trees have disappeared except those on the mountain summits or in sheltered valleys, with a northern aspect.   Below the line of trees, beautiful grassy slopes are covered on the lower parts with bunch grass and above was sward with a few *Compositae* and other plants while the benches near the river are altogether destitute of flowering plants.

I spent a week on the Thompson at Spence's Bridge and Cache Creek and collected many species of rare and interesting plants which were not observed in the low country.   One fact showing the similarity of the flora with that of Nevada and Utah was the actual discovery of two species of plants, supposed by Mr. Serrano Watson, of Harvard, who has ably explored there, to be peculiar to those states.   The species were *Astragalus Beck-withii*, T. and G., only detected in the neighborhood of Salt Lake, Utah, and in Ruby Valley, Nevada; the other *Crepis occidentalis Nutt, var. Nevadense* Watson, was supposed to be peculiar to Nevada, but here it was found in company with the type of the species.   Dr. Selwyn noticed a similarity in the rocks with those of Nevada also.

It was very interesting in ascending the mountains to notice the change from early summer to late spring and to observe the shrubs which at the riverside were in full bloom and 3,000 feet above it were only bursting into leaf.   A similar change was also noticed on May 26th when crossing the high plateau between Clinton and Bridge Creek, and showed most conclusively the contrast between the climate of the Thompson and that of the country between Clinton and Lac La Hache."[5]

Many interesting discoveries were made as we went north, but none of particular moment until we reached Quesnel.

On the 28th of May, I commenced my examinations of the flora around that part and found many of the common eastern species in full flower and nearly as far advanced as at Belleville on the 24th of May, in 1876.   Nearly all the species observed were eastern ones or western plants that reach the wooded country west of Lake Superior.

On June 4th, we crossed the Fraser and, I may say, launched at once into the wilderness.   Up to this time, I had travelled from Yale on foot, in a stage, or by boat, to Soda Creek and then by boat to Quesnel.

At Quesnel, a pack train was waiting for us to take ourselves and goods on the overland journey to McLeod's Lake.   The pack train consisted of twenty-six pack animals besides a horse for each one of the company.   Our company, on leaving Quesnel, consisted of five members.   I elected to walk all the way as I could thus make observations at my leisure and collect plants. A horse, however, was set apart for me when I wished to ride, but I handed it over to a Scotchman who was attached to the pack train.   Our mode of travel from now on to McLeod's Lake may be stated as follows: Owing to the large number of horses to pack, we were always late in getting away in the morning, but we never took the packs off the horses until the evening.   I would start on ahead on the trail and make notes and enjoy myself, having learned from Dr. Selwyn where the proposed stopping-place for lunch was to be, the same course taking place in the afternoon.   Many observations were made on the way and the most exciting circumstance on the trip was—one day when I was some miles from the train of horses, I looked up and saw three gray wolves, with their tongues hanging out, calmly looking at me from a little height of land on one side of the trail.   Like the hunters we read about, I immediately looked for a tree to climb, but I could see none that suited my ability, so I loosed a sheath-knife I carried in my belt, and did the next thing that a hunter does—I yelled at the top of my voice, but they looked as uncon-cerned as if I had never made a sound.   We faced each other there for some minutes, when they quietly sneaked off into the bush and I felt so relieved that I was unable to walk any further and waited for the pack-train to overtake me.

The country travelled through for over ten days after leaving Quesnel was rather rough, but, after we crossed a ridge that I remembered crossing in 1872, the country showed marked signs of improvement and was drier and richer, and, apparently, well suited for agriculture.   I was very much struck by the grasses of the region.   They consisted chiefly of three Genera, *Poa, Bromus* and *Triticum*, all three first-class hay and pasture grasses, and I may say that these were the grasses that we found the whole way to Peace River, everywhere forming a splendid sward and were very tall for the species.

When we reached the Nechaco, we found the country very rich and worth more extended notice than the other parts that we had passed through, but I may just write one incident that took place at the river to show how some people value the things they own.

We had been at an Indian camp the preceding night and an Indian and I went ahead of the party and reached the Nechaco before they arrived.   A thunderstorm came up and, as there was no shelter, I put on my waterproof and sat down on the green, but, to my surprise, the Indian took the saddle off his horse and turned him loose and sat on the saddle and spread what little coat he had over it to try and protect it.   He protected his saddle while I tried to protect myself.

We had now reached the crossing of the Nechaco and the meadows on the right bank of the river were full of meadow plants resembling those of Ontario and there was nothing in the flora to indicate a cold climate except that it was ten or fifteen days behind that of Ontario in 1876.   The familiar plants in our meadows and fields were everywhere and not a herbaceous plant or shrub reminded one of being more than ten degrees north of Belleville, except the want of our forest trees.

The 16th of July was occupied in getting our baggage across the Nechaco, a broad and rapid stream two hundred and fifty yards wide, and, late in the evening, we pitched our camp on the left bank.   I may mention here that Dr. Selwyn had had a canvas punt made somewhere in the east and with this he intended to cross the various rivers that we might meet in our exploration. This river was the largest we had come to and the boat was put together and found to be quite buoyant, and with it, our baggage and ourselves, were taken across the river without much effort. Our boat was named "Nechaco," and will be spoken of later.

The land between the Nechaco and Stuart River was of

the very best quality, it being both prairie and forest and quite level and not difficult to clear. The next day, we crossed Stuart River, two hundred yards wide, and followed the trail without difficulty to Stuart Lake. Late this afternoon, when within six miles of Fort St. James, I suddenly came upon a limestone cliff and immediately the flora changed. Many beautiful flowers that I had not seen since I left the lower Fraser Valley were in full bloom and, on the rocks at the base of the cliff, they made such a charming picture that I sat down in my loneliness—but not alone—and drank in the surpassing beauty of the scene; hunger and weariness were forgotten and I resumed my march with the light, joyous step of the morning, feeling that in the realm of Nature, God's hand was ever open to strew one's paths with beauties and fill one's heart with praise. While others cursed the road and the flies, I, in my simplicity, saw nothing but Nature decked out in the springtime loveliness and, instead of grumbling at the difficulties of the way, I rejoiced in the activity of the animal and vegetable kingdoms. For nearly a month, I had kept travelling with spring, but now, with one bound, we had passed its portals and stood on the verge of summer.

"Sunday the 20th. Looking back over the 146 miles which lie between Fort St. James and Quesnel, I am struck with the resemblance of the flora to that of the forest region west of Lake Superior. There is not a species in this whole distance which in any way indicates either an Alpine or cool climate except two, and these were only observed once. The dry summer climate, which is indicated by the flora, proves the rainfall to be inconsiderable, and, therefore, the prospects are good for the successful cultivation of grain. Tomorrow, I accompany Dr. Selwyn and two Indians in a canoe up Stuart Lake for about eight miles for the purpose of climbing Pope's Cradle, or Stuart Lake Mountain. Our friends at the Fort said that we would be unable to climb it as it was quite steep and very difficult.

"We commenced to ascend from the lake shore and, after a fatiguing climb of three hours in the hot sun, we reached the summit, which we found to be 2,600 feet above the lake, or nearly 5,000 feet above the sea. I obtained an enormous collection of interesting plants and had quite a pleasant day while Dr. Selwyn attended to the geology.   After a rapid descent, we reached the lake and started for the camp, propelled by the wind, against the bear skin, which one of the Indians held up to catch the fitful breeze.   It would have been less labour to paddle but that would have been 'work.'   Late in the evening, we reached camp and were soon oblivious to mundane things."[6]

On the 22nd of June, we left Fort. St. James for McLeod's Lake, and had much difficulty on our way, on account of the bad trail through burnt forest.   Some days we had to cut our way for miles and made little progress.   I quote the following from my journal.

"To-day, that is the 26th of June, I had a lonely tramp along the shores of Carp and Long Lakes, to the discharge of the latter lake.   When a few miles on the way, a pelting rain came on and continued without intermission the whole afternoon.   I trudged cheerfully on believing that I would meet Indians at the ford of the river and get myself dry and warm.   What was my chagrin to find the Indians gone and their fire burning on the other side of the rapid river.   Without hesitation, I undressed and plunged in, but the current was so strong and the water so deep my courage failed and I returned to the bank.   Shivering and cold, I contemplated the situation and at last determined to do or die and waded across.   Soon, I had a rousing fire and its genial warmth brought back life and content to my frozen limbs."[7]

I was unaware of the depth of the river when I started in to wade across.   As the water was very clear, with a gravel bottom, it seemed quite shallow, but, as I proceeded, the depths increased and, on my second effort, I took a large pole that I found on the shore and, with its support, I gained the other side in safety.   Now, I learned that there was a fall in the river of one hundred and twenty feet only a couple of hundred yards below me, and, doubtless, if I had known this I would have lost my nerve and been carried away in the swift water.   Later, I found that the ford was said to be four to five feet deep.   The next day, we reached Fort McLeod and I spent a few days collecting around the country.

On the 3rd of July, all our preparations were made to start for the Peace River and now our company was reduced to eight. In the "Nechaco" were myself, Mr. Webster, the geologist, and John Mclennan, who had charge of the commissariat. In a light skiff were Dr. Selwyn and two young Indians, and, in a dugout made of poplar, were Anderson and Hillier, the cook.

About two o'clock in the afternoon, we started and all the inhabitants of the post and a number of Indians who were there came out to see us make our start, and they all expected that we would never reach Hudson's Hope alive as our boats were frail and the capacity for river work that had been shown by us at the Fort was of no account.

Dr. Selwyn gave orders, at the start, that he was going to micrometer the river and instructed Anderson and Hillier what they were to do. The "Nechaco," being a large boat and carrying the most of the baggage, was not required to do anything but only to proceed with the rest. All went well for about half an hour, when Hillier and Anderson stopped at a bend of the river to give Dr. Selwyn a sight. At this point, the current was very strong and ran with great force under the bend. They stopped and the current caught the canoe and caused it to turn over and both men were thrown into the rapid river. We, in the "Nechaco," were opposite the men when they were thrown into the water and, as they were carried off in the current, we worked hard to overtake them, but failed. However, Anderson was thrown on the shore some distance below and we found that he was only slightly out of breath, and Hillier kept hold of the canoe and was caught some distance further down by Dr. Selwyn and the boys. This ended our survey of the river—it was never attempted again as long as I was with the party. We made camp right away and felt consoled for the loss of the bacon when the men were saved, but each man felt from that day forward that he was in more than common danger.

On the evening of the 8th, we reached the forks of the Finlay and Parsnip rivers and camped. During the evening, I told Dr. Selwyn that when I came up the Peace in 1872 I was told that there was a very large eddy at the junction of the two rivers and, by

8

all means, to keep close in shore as we passed out of the Parsnip into the main river.   I had my note book and showed Dr. Selwyn what we did and how we passed the eddy three years before.   He paid no attention to what I told him and, after breakfast the next day, he gave orders that we were to proceed down the river and ignored what I had told him about the eddy.   I refused to start and told Mclennan to hold on to the bushes where we were and let Dr. Selwyn proceed first.   The other men in the canoe stayed with us and Dr. Selwyn and his two Indians went on and rounded the point out of our sight.   In a short time, we saw them going at a great rate backwards into the middle of the river and they were pulling with all their might to get out of it.   By good luck, the eddy was nearly full at this time and it burst and they made the shore in a short time.   We waited to see what would happen next and Dr. Selwyn and his men came back looking rather pale and said that it was impossible to pass the eddy, at this stage of the water, on that side.   He now gave orders that we were to cross the Parsnip and we went along the right bank of the Finlay and when we got about a quarter of a mile up, Dr. Selwyn said that we were far enough and that now we would cross and run down the left bank of the Finlay.   We all crossed and went up the Finlay and he, with his two Indians, went first and crossed the Finlay, and ran down and were in safety.   Then, they called to us and the canoe started and they succeeded the same way; we in the "Nechaco" had a big punt to handle and she would never steer or go anywhere but with the current and when we reached the far side of the Finlay, we found the trees had fallen into the water and we couldn't make the shore and had to keep out in the current.   However, we were able to round the point with the aid of a rope thrown to us by Mclennan.   Late in the afternoon, we ran down to the rapids about a mile below us and camped. Here Dr. Selwyn thought that it was a good place to fish and got on his long rubber boots that reached to his hips and waded in and stood on a stone, but received no bites except from mosquitoes, and, in his efforts to beat them off, slipped and sat down on the stone.   When he got on his feet again, he found that he was anchored as his boots were full and he was unable to walk out.

We were all amazed at the Doctor's mishap and looked very serious when Mclennan very slowly made his way to his assistance and brought him to shore.   I believe that made us all happy again as I remember the misfortunes of the morning did not seem to stay with us.

I will now give Dr. Selwyn's version of the same event. "July 9th.   Started at 7 a.m. and at 9.15 reached the Finlay forks.   A very swift eddying current ran along the right bank of the Parsnip and to avoid this and reach the opposite shore without being shot down the rapids below we were obliged to go some distance up the right bank of the Finlay.   We then crossed over and were swept rapidly down the left shore, when, rounding a sandy point which the angle, formed by the two rivers made, a few vigorous strokes brought us into still water."[8]

Later in the day, we moved down the river for about four miles and camped just at the mouth of the pass, called by the Hudson's Bay people, "Hell's Gate."   The mountains on either hand rise here to about 6,000 feet almost perpendicularly from the water.   We were now under the mountain to which Horetzky had called my attention in 1872, when we were passing upstream. As it seemed to be the highest mountain in the vicinity, Dr. Selwyn determined to climb it the next day and asked me to accompany him while he took observations and decided on the route that we would follow.   I quote from his report:

"After a critical survey of the mountain from the opposite or left bank, I thought we could reach the summit; at all events I determined to attempt it, and we accordingly crossed to the right bank and selected our camp.   It was too late for our ascent of the mountain, but in the afternoon, Mr. Macoun and I ascended a rocky spur a short distance in our rear to reconnoiter.   We reached a height of 950 or 1,000 feet above the river.   I took several bearings from this point and was also able to determine the best route for our ascent the next day.   This seemed to be a leading ridge on the very side of the valley of a small brook which entered the river about one and a half miles below our camp.   We accordingly made our way across to this ridge and on reaching the axis of it, I was surprised at finding what appeared to be a well-worn Indian trail. A closer examination, however, showed that it was a path made by the rocky mountain goat and I at once concluded that it would lead us up the easiest path to the highest summit of the mountain and therefore determined to follow it on the morrow.

"Next morning, after breakfast, I called for volunteers to accompany Mr. Macoun and me up the mountain and at 8 a.m. we set out. There had been considerable discussion in camp upon the probability of our being able to reach the summit. One of our party confidently asserting that it was quite impossible. So far as his own power of climbing was concerned, his opinion proved quite correct as when we still had some 1,500 feet to ascend he gave it up and lay down to await our return, reiterating his opinion that none of us would ever reach the summit, and doubtless to persons unaccustomed to alpine climbing, the undertaking might appear somewhat formidable. At about 2 p.m., however, we arrived there and, though it cost us five and a half hours of continuous toil, we were amply repaid by the magnificent scene around us. We were now 4,590 feet above our camp and about 6,220 feet above the sea. To the north, the river lay directly beneath us at probably less than three-quarters of a mile of horizontal distance and beyond it, from northwards to northeast, stretched away for twenty or thirty miles, a perfect sea of alpine peaks and ridges." [9]

Early in the morning of the 11th, as quoted above from Dr. Selwyn's report, we started in high spirits to climb "Mt. Selwyn," in company with Mr. Webster and Mr. Mclennan. I started by carrying my botanical box and, in the latter, my portfolio containing a large quantity of paper. We started from the mountain stream which Dr. Selwyn and I had seen yesterday. When we reached the stream, I asked as a favor that a halt of a few moments be made while I examined the banks which I did with astonishing success. In a few moments, I had collected a large number of alpine species which had been brought down by the stream from far up the mountain. From the very base of the mountain, we followed the path formed by the mountain goat spoken of by Dr. Selwyn. On the lower slopes, there was no change in the vegeta-

tion, but gradually there came a change, at first scarcely notice-
able. A few mountain forms were intermixed with the forest
flora of the valley. Gradually the valley species ceased, alpine
ones became more common, until at last none of the former
remained.

The day was very hot, being 84° Fahr., in the shade, when we
left the base and it seemed to get warmer instead of cooler as we
ascended. We had some steep climbing on the first part of the
route and our progress was both wearisome and slow. About
1,500 feet from the summit, we reached the limit of trees and here
also came upon our first snow. We were all very thirsty and I
scraped out a hole below the snow and it was very soon filled with
water and each one of us lay down on the ground and drank his
fill. Mclennan, who, by the way, was a man accustomed to his
drinks, could not resist the temptation of swallowing more than
his share and lost all hope of reaching the top and so lay down
and enjoyed himself while the rest of us plied our weary way to
the summit.

About two hundred feet above where we left Mclennan, the
slope got much easier and we found a real spring of beautiful
water and I thought that it might help Mclennan to bring him up
to it so I went down and asked him to go up the two hundred
feet where the good water was. He said he was d——d if he
would, so I left him and followed the others.

I am saying nothing about the flora of the mountain for, as
it has been spoken of so often by others, it is useless for me to
add to the beauties by which I was surrounded. Our trip was
very hurried, but I noticed that, on the moist places where the
snow lay longest, there were the greatest number of species and
many were observed there that did not appear in drier spots.
Where the heaviest drifts of snow had lain, and where much of
it still remained, one or two anemones and *Ranunculus hyper-
boreus* were blooming and in fine condition., To show the progress
of the spring, four yards from the snow the petals had fallen and
between that and the snow the plant was in all stages of growth,
from its springing out of the soil to the faded flower. A number
of drabas and arenarias absolutely plastered the ground with

multitudes of flowers. Five hundred feet below the summit, Mt. Selwyn stands first, in my imagination, as the highest type of nature's flower garden. None of the plants, except the peduncularias, rose above the general level, which was about two inches or possibly less, and all was a flat surface of expanded purple, yellow, white and pinkish flowers. The peduncularias were about four inches high and stood singly amongst the others and each was nearly two inches broad with expanded blossoms.

The summit was quite level, with a little parapet in front, upon which we stood overlooking the river as we gazed upon a wondrous scene. Leaving others to take in the picture in detail, after a few minutes of close scrutiny, I turned away from the entrancing sight and busied myself with what more concerned me; the flora of the peak. With sad and reluctant steps, I turned from the summit and commenced to descend, intending to examine the different points more fully than I had done in the ascent. About 1,000 feet from the summit, I was overtaken by the others and, after a slight halt at the last patch of snow, where we had left Mclennan, we hurried on, reaching camp in a more or less exhausted state about 7 p.m., after nearly thirteen hours of incessant and continuous labour.

When we left the river in the morning, the thermometer stood at 84° Fahr.; on the top of the mountain in latitude 56 north, over 6,000 feet above the sea it stood at 82°. I had supposed that we would find it cold on the mountain top but the very opposite was the case—I had actually to take off my coat and hat and bathe my head in the snow to cool myself. Looking east from where we stood, a blue, sultry haze hung over the mountains and the river, while to the west the atmosphere seemed clearer and colder. The mountain, upon which we were, seemed to close in on the river valley and shut out the vapour of the western plateau in exactly the same way as the Cascade range below Boston Bar does that of the Pacific. We had this amply verified the next day for we had scarcely gone six miles—the distance along the base of the mountain—before we all noticed the change to a drier and warmer climate. Mt. Selwyn thus closes the Peace River Pass and stands as a portal barring the way against the

Pacific breezes carrying moisture, the alleged cause of the mild climate and luxuriant vegetation of the Peace River Valley. Later on I shall attempt to show the true cause of the mild climate of the eastern base along the rocky mountains.

The next day, Anderson and I climbed a limestone mountain, 3,000 feet high, on the other side of the river, and found the ascent both toilsome and dangerous. We got little to repay us for our trip. We did not see the slightest sign of an alpine plant and I confess it with a feeling of disappointment. I looked about me and found them not. We ate our lunch on the very verge of a cliff, from which we could look down on a little mountain tarn 1,000 feet below, and our hearts yearned for water, but there was none to be had. We reached camp at 6 p.m., exhausted but well pleased with our trip. I had settled one point that, in this region, Arctic vegetation is not to be found on a limestone mountain in latitude 56°, at a height of 5,000 feet above the sea.

At noon on the sixteenth, we reached the Rocky Mountain Canyon and, from sheer exhaustion, I was scarcely able to ascend the bank. Our tents were pitched and I commenced to change my plants and dry my papers. This had been part of my daily work for nearly three months so that a halt always found me busy. The cause of my great weariness was more from pulling our unwieldy boat in making the wide crossings that we had to make from side to side of the river to suit Dr. Selwyn's ideas about camping, than from climbing. I quote the following from my report: "On the afternoon of the 17th, Mclennan and I ascended the Buffalo's Head, the view from which is so graphically described in Butler's "Wild North Land."[10] We, too, found the base of the mountain lying "thick with brule and tangled forest," but, worse thant his, was the mass of pea vine, vetch and various weeds and grasses which covered the logs and made our progress both slow and laborious. Before Butler, "there rose abruptly a mass of yellow grass and blue anemones," and before us, the same steep; but the grass waved green on the hill-side, and the herald of spring (*Anemone patens var. Nuttalliana*) had already perfected its seeds and disappeared under the wealth of grass that covered its grave. We also stood on that hill-top and looked on the wondrous panorama that lay stretched out before us. But our occupations were more prosaic; we were there to see and faithfully report what we observed regarding the soil and productions of the country. Sitting, possibly, on the same rock on which Butler sat, I mentally attempted to contrast the region we had left west of the mountains, with that in which we now were, and I could find no points of agreement. West of the mountains, the climate was cold and moist and the land generally covered with a coniferous forest, but here we found prairie and aspen forest and a climate dry and warm. Here, 3,000 feet above the sea, the mountains are actually without forest and covered with grass and vetches over two feet high. *Botrychium lunarioides,* a *Lychnis* and *Are-naria propinqua* we found on the highest point. There were many signs of the grizzly bear being in the vicinity as there was scarcely a log which had not been turned over or torn to pieces in their search for ants and their larvae. *Aquilegia coerulea* and *Parnassia palustris* were obtained on our way to camp, and a considerable number of eastern species which were not observed west of the mountains.

During the four following days, we remained in camp close to the canyon, and I employed my time in making excursions in the vicinity, drying, packing and labelling plants. We had now passed the mountains, and I closed my western observations and commenced a new series."[11]

On the morning of the 21st, we started to cross the portage to Hudson's Hope. The morning was very warm and walking over the sand hills was not pleasant. While crossing the portage, I found quite a number of eastern species, and, amongst others, *Linum perenne.* On reaching the Post, we ate a hearty dinner of moose meat, Early Rose potatoes, turnips and onions, and rejoiced in the thought that we had accomplished so much of our journey in safety.

While the rest of the party were getting ready to proceed down the river, I employed myself, as usual, making a thorough examination of the flora in the vicinity for the purpose of comparing it with that further down the stream. The following extract from my journal, written on the spot, will give a truthful picture of Hudson's Hope as I found it on the 22nd of July, 1875: "I have been extremely surprised at the rankness of the vegetation around here, although there is very little rain at this season and has been little all spring.   Wild peas and vetches grow to an amazing height in the poplar woods, and form almost impenetrable thickets in places.   Vetches, roses, willow-herb and grasses of the genera *Poa*, *Triticum* and *Bromus* fill the woods and cover the burnt ground, and surprise Canadians by their rankness and almost tropical luxuriance.   Charlette, who is in charge of this post, has two small gardens, in which he has growing, potatoes, onions, turnips, beets, carrots, cabbage, and various other vege-tables.   Yesterday, we had new potatoes for dinner, of a very fair size, which were planted on April 28th.   Numbers of the onions were one and a half inches across, raised from seed imported from England and sown about the first of May.   Growth is extremely rapid, owing partly to the length of day and cloudless skies sup-plemented by heavy dews, and possibly, also, in part, to the great range of temperature during the twenty-four hours, from about 45° at sunrise to 80° Fahr., at noon.   Sometimes the range is even more, but the above may be taken as the average.   The rankness of the vegetation on the west shore of Lake Superior has frequently been alluded to, and may be caused by the some-what similar great range in the temperature there."[12]

For the next few days, I employed myself around Hudson's Hope examining the flora of the country.   The others were busy during this time in making a raft on which we were to float down to St. John's.   During the afternoon of the 25th, and the forenoon of the 26th of July, we floated down the river on our raft, and, although we had ample time to admire the magnificent scenery, there was no opportunity to botanize.

"At St. John's, a few minutes' observation tended to show that this point was much warmer than Hudson's Hope, that the soil was richer, and that the vegetation was in a far more advanced state.   Raspberries and service-berries were fully ripe and in great abundance.   Potatoes, oats, barley and many varieties of vegetables were in a very flourishing state in "Nigger Dan's" garden.   The oats stood fully five feet high, and the barley had made nearly equal growth.   After the tents were pitched, Anderson cut a quantity of wild grass for our beds which was over three feet in length; it consisted principally of species of *Triticum* and *Poa*.   On your decision (Dr. Selwyn's) to build a canoe for the ascent of Pine River, I found I would have several days at my disposal, and on the morning of the 27th, accompanied by Anderson, I started up the hill in rear of the fort, for the purpose of examining the region north of the river.   We found the level of of the country above the river valley to be about 700 feet.   On the plateau, the surface is either a dead level or slopes away from the river.   For nine miles, the distance travelled, the whole country was covered with the most luxuriant vegetation.   Clumps of willows and poplars of various ages were interspersed with the most astonishing growth of herbaceous plants I ever witnessed. Willow herb, cow parsnip, *Geum strictum*, *Triticum*, *Bromus*, *Poa* and a number of other tall-growing species covered the whole region with a thick mass of vegetation that averaged from three to five feet in height.   Wild larkspur (*Delphinium scopularum*) was found over seven feet high, and many vetches were even taller. In many places, the climbing *Leguminosae* were in such abundance as to completely cover up all other plants, and cause the country to look like a field of mixed peas and vetches.   The species were *Vicia Americana*, *Lathyrus venosus* and *ochroleucus*, the first named being the most abundant."[13]

THE VICTORIA MEMORIAL MUSEUM, OTTAWA.[14]

CHAPTER VIII

1875

Down the Peace River 700 Miles in a Dugout from Fort St. John to Fort Chipewyan—Provisions run out—Reaches Fort Chipewyan Sick and Starving—Returns East via Athabasca River, Buffalo Lake, Clearwater River and Lake, Isle-a-la-Crosse, and Green Lake—Across Country to Fort Carlton and on to Winnipeg—Many Interesting Incidents en route—Home on Nov. 13th after Travelling about 8,000 Miles.

WHILE at St. John's, Dr. Selwyn decided to build a canoe so that he could proceed up the Pine River on his exploration.[1] The canoe was made out of a poplar tree and was thirty-six feet long and very unwieldy but it served its purpose. He decided that the canoe was not large enough to take all of the party and he left Anderson and myself behind. I was to go down the Peace River with Mr. King,[2] who was going down the river to meet the Hudson's Bay boats bringing up the outfit for the posts on the river. Dr. Selwyn permitted me to accompany him with the understanding that I should not be away more than forty days and that I should rejoin his party either at St. John's or Dunvegan. I was supplied with forty days' provisions and from the time Dr. Selwyn left till the morning of the 4th of August I was busily engaged drying and packing plants and had little time to think of the arduous journey of seven hundred miles that loomed before me. Had I known what was to occur, I would never have thought of going on such a foolish errand with a man who was on his way to meet his wife.

Early on the morning of the 4th, we packed up and proceeded to load our canoe, which was just an old cotton-wood dugout, but found that it was so small that three men and our provisions were too much for its capacity, so a man and a bag of pemmican were left behind. With light hearts, we pushed off, believing that our trip was going to be a pleasure excursion and that we should sail down about 300 miles and return leisurely with the boats.

On the evening of the second day, we reached Dunvegan, and found the people at the post living on bear meat, so I charitably gave them some of my flour, which Mr. King agreed to replace when we met the boats. On the morning of the 5th, we left Dunvegan and floated down the river. After passing Smoky River, game became plentiful and black bears were very numerous along the river margin, feeding on berries; while beaver, lynx and geese were quite common.

Later, we fell in with a camp of Indians who had a large quantity of berries and these, to go with the flesh of a black bear, constituted their sole diet. A dainty dish composed of berries fried in bear's grease was served up but my appetite for such food being very poor, I declined to partake of it. My flour did duty again as, in a few days, we expected to meet the boats.

We reached Battle River on the 8th and, it being Sunday, we remained with Mr. Macaulay, the gentleman in charge of the post, until next morning. We fared sumptuously on cabbage, green peas, radishes, moose meat, bacon and flour, the latter being taken from my stores, but this could not last, and, after breakfast on Monday morning, we were again floating down the river.

We slept on a sand bar above Wolverine Point, and at dawn on Tuesday, August 10th, were again at work paddling with all our might until the afternoon, when, the wind blowing strong up the river, our frail canoe was in danger of capsizing, and we were compelled to keep close in shore to avoid the waves.

I had learned by this time that my trip was to be one with constant hard work and little opportunity to study the vegetation along the river.

On the 11th, we started early and toiled all day with the paddle. The river, by this time, was very wide and the wind had a great sweep and generally blew in our faces. Late in the evening, when rounding a point, we saw buildings in the distance and knew we were approaching Vermilion. The following is from my diary:

"Having decided to rest one day at Vermilion, I employed it in a botanical survey of the neighborhood.   I first examined the field and garden, and found with the utmost astonishment that, although more than two degrees further north than Dunvegan or St. John's, the barley and vegetables were much further advanced. Barley was standing in shocks in the field, having been cut on the 6th of August, while scattered ears of wheat, which I found around the fence, were fully ripe, (August 12th).   Wheat is seldom cultivated in the North-West, owing to the fact that barley is more useful, as the former is only used when boiled with meat, while the latter is fed to horses in the winter.   The barley was sown on the 8th of May and reaped on the 6th of August, having been in the ground just ninety days.   The heads averaged from four to six inches in length, and were full of large grains of a beautiful colour.   In fact, both wheat and barley were the plumpest I ever saw, and must weigh as much as that brought from Fort Chipewyan.   They stood very thick in the ground and were uncommonly stout, and must have yielded very heavily.   Turnips and Early Rose potatoes were quite large, and both gave indications of a heavy crop."[3]

We started for Little Red River at noon on August the 15th, but, owing to the head winds and great breadth of the river (over 1,000 yards) we feared to cross it.   Towards evening, a thunderstorm came up, but passed off on one side of us and the wind fell. We now redoubled our energies and reached Point-aux-Cache before dark.   Wearied out and exhausted, we spread our blankets on the sand and soon fell fast asleep.   At the first streak of dawn, we were up and ready to proceed.

We were now approaching the chutes, or falls as they are called now.   There are two portages at the chutes.   The first chute is only a rapid, but the next one is a fall of at least ten feet. By noon, we had descended to the very brink of the fall and were within two miles of Little Red River.   We never expected to take the canoe over the fall, but intended to cache our baggage and go on to the Fort on foot.   After examining the fall, however, we resolved to try our old experiment of a bow and stern line, and, after dinner, we shoved the canoe off and let her take her chance.

Each did his work well and we had the satisfaction of taking her over the falls in safety. We fastened the canoe, bow and stern, to the ledge of rock about five feet above the water. After some discussion I decided that I was able to drop into the canoe and bail out the water and so I took the risk and dropped from the ledge into the canoe and soon baled out the water.

The next thing was for Mr. King to get into the canoe, and he dropped into the stern while I was able to keep the canoe steady. When starting, we decided that each of us should take his jack-knife and at the word from King I would cut the bow line and the canoe would then swing out and King would cut the stern line and away we would go. We did this and in a couple of minutes were down beside our luggage. We got our supplies and baggage and loaded up the canoe and, in a short time, were at Little Red River.

"August 17th. Believing that the boats were close at hand, nothing would satisfy Mr. King but that we must go on and meet them. I was disinclined to proceed. However, as I had already come so far, I consented.[4] Our flour was now all gone and we only had a little mouldy pemmican, a few dried berries and some tea. We still had two hundred miles of river between us and Fort Chipewyan, but fully expecting to meet the boats, we did not replenish our stock of provisions, and we had no matches. To make matters worse, Mr. King broke his gun, so this last resource failed us. We worked hard all day, constantly looking out for the boats, and at dark camped at the head of Big Island, in a perfect storm of mosquitoes. We were nearly wild before we got a fire lighted, which we accomplished by means of dried grass and gunpowder. On account of starting without matches, we were unable to have a fire at noon except by taking the hunter's plan. Mr. King had a jack-knife and I went along the river side till I found a pebble that seemed to be flinty and we found that by striking the jack-knife on the flint, a spark would fly out. I then gathered a bunch of dried grass and, with the gun-powder, our fire was started. For the next five days, all our fires were lighted in this manner. Some evenings, an hour was spent in groping around in the dark to get it done. The supplies were now so scant and in such bad condition that it was almost impossible for us to either eat or sleep and our work on the river never ceased."

"August 19th. Constantly paddling on we watched for the boats around every turn, but they did not appear. About ten o'clock, the wind sprang up dead ahead, and we were under the necessity of putting ashore and waiting until it went down. Here we slept by turns, one watching for the boats while the other slept. About five p.m., the wind fell, and we immediately started and worked hard until long after dark."[5]

The next day we passed "Rapid Bouille." We decided to camp and watch for the boats which should have arrived before this. Acting on this decision—caused by the head winds we could not face—we carried our things up the steep bank, made a fire, and had a little uncooked mouldy pemmican and tea. The high wind set fire to the grass and, before we caught all the things together, my clothes were more than half burned and our tent was altogether destroyed. Immediately after this, the wind fell and we resolved to proceed. We still had more than 70 miles to make before we could obtain food, and our supplies were all exhausted, except the mouldy pemmican. We worked hard all the evening and camped on the lower end of an island, and built a large fire, so that if the boats came along in the night the men would see the light and at least fire a gun.

"August 21st. Poor food and hard work now began to tell on me. My stomach loathed raw pemmican, and all other food was gone—our gun was useless—and it became painfully evident that from some unaccountable cause the boats had not yet left Fort Chipewyan. Sixty miles lay between us and safety, and we must either hurry on or starve. We had still a few pounds of pemmican, but, with all my efforts, it would not stay on my stomach, so I reluctantly ceased to eat. We toiled on until after midday, when I became so ill that we had to put ashore. I lay down on the sand utterly exhausted and very sick. A review of the situation brought me to myself, and I rose up, determined to struggle on as long as I could hold the paddle. Without a word, we worked on and on, and reached Quatre Fourches River two hours after dark.   Tying the canoe to the bushes, we crawled up the bank and were soon asleep.   I awoke in the morning as day was breaking and, as I opened my eyes, I saw hanging over me an enormous pair of horns and a huge face, which I concluded was the devil himself.   King woke up and saw the beast, but, the gun being useless, he did not trouble it.

King said that sometimes the water from Peace River ran into this river and other times it ran out and we hoped that the Peace River was flowing in, but, to our consternation, it was flowing out so the current was running very swiftly.   We found the water flowing steadily into Peace River and we knew that we had twenty-five miles upstream to go before we could get food.

My stomach had now become so weak that tea would not remain on it, so I drank water and ate a few high-bush cranberries. We discovered that our united energies would not propel the canoe against the current, so, fastening a line to the bow, I went on shore and hauled the canoe for more than sixteen miles, floundering through mud and water, knowing that the goal was drawing nearer every step.   While tramping along the river, when I felt sick and weak, I plucked a few cranberries and, on my recovering, trudged on.   Every half hour, a fainting spell would overcome me, but, by persistent effort, I would overcome it and, at length, wearied and exhausted, we reached the fishery just as it was getting dark.   The last eight miles, I had to take to the canoe, the mud being so soft and I so weak, I could not stand upon it.   (He evidently lost consciousness).   Being unable to stand, I sat in a clump of rushes and was soon the centre of a crowd of Indians. I made signs that I wanted food and rest and would soon be all right and they, misunderstanding, brought me Perry Davis' Pain Killer and other medicines, but I made signs that I wished to eat and a voice in the crowd, speaking good English, wanted to know if I could eat fish and potatoes. I promptly said "Yes" and he took me to his tent and I ate and slept, I believe, most of the night.

In the morning, I felt a new man.   None of the people would believe that we had brought our little canoe from St. John's, seven hundred miles away, as such a thing had never been done before by two men.

The next morning I went down, in a canoe, to Fort Chipewyan, a distance of eight miles and was well received by Mr. Macfarlane, the gentleman in charge of the Athabasca district. On
my arrival, I had an interview with a number of the Hudson's
Bay Company's officers, who were here from all parts of the north
to get their year's supplies. One and all advised me to return
eastward, as it was possible I could reach Fort Garry (Winnipeg)
before winter set in, but I could not get out westward until late
in the spring. I, therefore, much against my inclination, decided
to return eastward. Mr. Macfarlane informed me that he purposed sending a boat up the Athabasca to Methye Portage in
the course of ten days, which would connect with another going
down to Isle-a-la-Crosse, and by these I could get half way to
Carlton. The boats for Peace River started the day after we
arrived.[6]

During the ensuing ten days, I collected all the information
possible regarding the country, its capabilities, resources and
future prospects. One thing struck me very forcibly, that I was
1,300 miles from the Arctic Sea, and 1,200 miles from Winnipeg.
It was only then that I realized the immensity of our Great North
West.[7]

I met many of the chief Hudson's Bay Company's men and
talked with them day after day and got information from them
about the Yukon and the North and down the Mackenzie and
one and all said that the country northward and westward was
exceptionally fine in every respect.

Fort Chipewyan is not well situated for agricultural purposes,
with the exception of the small spot of garden ground near the
fort. Less than two miles from the fort, however, is a French
Mission, where I obtained the samples of wheat and barley which
are in Ottawa, and which later took the Bronze Medal at Philadelphia in 1876.[8]

The reason so little land is cultivated arises from the fact
that most of the inhabitants are flesh eaters and look with con-
tempt upon vegetables and vegetable eaters. Mr. Macfarlane told
me that just as much meat was eaten when flour and potatoes
were served out to the men as when they got none. This state-
9

ment agrees exactly with what we found after we left Fort Mc-
Leod—that our two Indian boys seemed never to be satisfied, no
matter how much bread they ate.

Multitudes of fish are taken in Lake Athabasca of many
kinds and all are fit for food. Geese are killed in prodigious
numbers in the latter part of September, it being no uncommon
occurrence for one man to kill one hundred in a few hours.

On the afternoon of September 2nd, three large boats in
charge of Mr. King, accompanied by myself, as passenger, started
for Methye Portage. I left my kind friends with regret and
started on my homeward trip in the anticipation of reaching Fort
Garry before the setting in of winter. This part of my trip was
so different from that which I had just passed through that I
felt, as I sat in a large boat, that I was almost in Paradise.

Our three boats contained twenty-seven men besides myself
and Mr. King, but, as usual, we were on half rations as we were
now on our way to get the supplies for Chipewyan for the winter.
We rowed for a short distance across the lake and entered the
delta of the Athabasca and when night fell we fastened our boat
to a log and lay down and went to sleep. I, being weary, never
awakened until morning. My slumbers were broken at the first
streak of dawn on the morning of the 3rd by the cries of innumerable geese which seemed to be above, around and beneath me.
On raising my head, I found all our men imitating the cries of the
flock of geese which were rapidly coming towards us and answer-
ing the cries of the men. On they came and, in less than five
minutes, twenty-seven shots had been fired into the flock and large
numbers of them were dead or dying in the water. During the
next two weeks, such scenes were almost of hourly occurrence and
the excitement was pleasing in the extreme.

We had started with less than half rations, calculating to get
a partial supply of food by hunting as we ascended the river and
the men were not slow to take advantage of their opportunity.
Canada geese and large white waveys were the ones we obtained.
It took us a day and a half to pass through the delta.

As we ascended the river, we gradually passed from mud to
sand, but were fully fifty miles up it before we saw anything like

a pebble. The first indications of "tar" were in the form of pebbles composed of sand and tar, formed above and carried down by the ice.   From this time forward, we continued to see deposits of tar wherever we came near the river margin.   We sailed up the river for days, owing to the wind being in our favor, and made no stops.   On the 7th of September, the river valley became narrower and real banks appeared about 50 feet high and the country was apparently level.   Where we breakfasted, on the left bank, I observed a bed of tar conglomerate about thirty inches above the river.   There was sand above and below it and the ooze along the shore, both at this point and many places below, looked like the ooze from petroleum streams.   Fully one-half of the pebbles along the shore, in many localities, are composed of tar conglomerate.   The tar was frequently observed, sometimes forming a bed two feet thick.   Early in the afternoon, we came upon the shale beds which produce the tar and sailed past them all the evening.

We landed at this point and found a light gray sand-stone, partly saturated with the tar, and over this, again, shale largely charged with alkali matter; this was the sequence all the way, although at times there was much more exposed.

Where we landed, the ooze from the bank had flowed down the slide into the water and formed a tarred surface extending along the beach over one hundred yards and as hard as iron. But, in the bright sunshine, the surface is quite soft and the men would, when tracking along the shore, often sink in up to their ankles.   For more than twenty miles this rock was observed, and it was from it I obtained fossils.   At the place where the Hudson's Bay Company got their supply of tar for the boats, I noticed a little stream of water flowing into the pool, which was coated with an oil scum and under the stream was an abundance of tar.

Instead of getting the tar on the beach, as I expected, I took it from this pool, which was about forty feet down the stream. I filled one jar at the spring and another jar on the beach by taking the tar and sand and washing it in the water.   That there must be enormous quantities, I am quite satisfied, on account of having seen the tar along the bank for over one hundred miles.[9]

On the 8th, we reached the forks of the Clearwater and were received by Mr. Moberly, the gentleman in charge of the post. Here, we learned that the food we had expected to get had not reached him so we were placed on short rations again.

Mr. Moberly informed me that he had examined the channel of the Athabasca all the way to the lake, the past season and found water enough in it at its lowest stage to float a steam-boat drawing six feet. I carried his plans to Winnipeg that same fall.

We now entered the Clearwater and had much difficulty in many places in ascending the river as the water was getting low. The last day on the river, our food gave out and the men worked steadily along with the boats, frequently stopping to rest and have a smoke. Later, during one of our stops, I said to one of the men, "How far have we to go now?" He considered solemnly for a few moments and then said, "Five smokes." I construed this to be true information as regards the distance, but soon learned that the men, in making the ascent, stopped at certain points to rest and, of course, smoke.

Late in the afternoon, we reached Methye Portage and volunteers were called for by Mr. King, to see how many men felt able to walk across the portage, which was fourteen miles. Over twenty volunteered and the rest of us pitched our tents and sadly sat down to wait for night, as we knew that we would get no more food until the next morning, and we had been all day without any. I may mention that the half-breeds and Indians showed no signs of discontent because we were starving, but just tightened their belts and walked on.

We were hardly settled in our tents, and I was writing in my note book very dolefully about our condition, when I heard a great uproar and an old squaw arrived with thirteen rabbits strung round her. Early in the day, a runner had been sent ahead of the men to the portage and a squaw had been out setting traps and she brought the thirteen for the starving men.

After breakfast, brought over by one of the men, we all started across the portage. We learned that the boat at the other side of the portage was waiting for me, and we hurried across and I only remained long enough to eat a few mouthfuls at the southern end of the portage before I embarked for Isle-a-la-Crosse. The men were anxious to be off as they had only three days' provisions and it would take a week to get to our destination.   I got five days' provisions from Mr. King, but, as soon as I learned that the men were on short rations, I put mine into the common stock.

My present companions could all speak English, the greater number having been brought up in Manitoba.   After poling down a little river about two miles, we stopped for dinner and here was an old half-breed who fished and raised potatoes.   I bought some potatoes and fish and we went a short distance further and camped under the lee of a point.

On the 15th, it was quite mild and pleasant and felt almost like summer and, shortly after, we passed into the Methye Lake and the outlet of the lake was full of white-fish apparently going up-stream.   We had supper at Buffalo House on Buffalo Lake and, after supper, the wind being fair, we embarked and sailed steadily on until 4 a.m., when, the wind failing, we put ashore.   After sunrise, a head wind sprang up with which we battled all day and reached the "Narrows," that connect Buffalo and Clearwater lakes, before dark.   Chipewyan House is situated at the eastern end of the "Narrows" and at the head of Clearwater Lake.   Here the Chipewyans have built themselves a number of houses.   The evening we arrived there, one old fellow named Edward Big Belly, was making a table and appeared quite an expert with the plane and chisel.

Our supper, that night, was somewhat peculiar.   I sat at the table and ate fish and potatoes with a knife and fork.   The men sat on the floor and ate them with their fingers.   Old Edward Big Belly, with his wife, sat in a corner eating pemmican, while all around on the floor were Indians smoking and staring at the eaters.   The Chipewyan women looked more like men than their husbands.   Of course, the former do all the work, while the latter only eat and smoke.

Sept. 19th.   The head wind of the night before detained us at the House and, in the morning, our prospects were no brighter; the wind being still strong from the same quarter.   Early in the afternoon, we started and, shortly after, were wind-bound again at

the mouth of Deep River which connects La Crosse and Clearwater lakes.   Here we were compelled to remain all day owing
to the gale which blew directly up the river.

To make matters worse, our provisions were exhausted and
we could not set our net owing to the wind.   Forty miles still lay
between us and Isle-a-la-Crosse, but plenty of fish were to be had
if we could only reach their haunts.   One of the men went out to
hunt and shot a partridge and came in and prepared it for the pot.
To add to the flavor of the bouillon, he put the pemmican into the
pot and boiled it with the partridge.   This was the fare for seven
of us.

The wind fell during the night and in the morning we started
for Clearwater Lake, but found the wind still dead ahead so we
were compelled to stop at the entrance to the lake, but ran into
a sheltered bay and set our net.   We set the net safely and in a
short time, we had caught eight fine white fish.   At once they
were made ready for the pot and, Indian fashion, were cut down
the back and thrown in the pot.   After boiling the proper time,
they were not served up but eaten exactly as I had seen Indians
on Lake Superior eat, six years before.   I thought it such a peculiar way of eating fish that I always brought it in in my lectures,
when I was speaking about Lake Superior—we all sat around the
pot and each man, when the bouillon cooled enough, would dip
in his hand and take out the fish, and we all rejoiced.

On Tuesday morning, September 21st, we sailed up the lake
with a steady breeze and, late in the afternoon, when looking forward, saw two points covered with aspen.   They ran out into the
lake on either hand; ahead, the lake extended from these points
and was lost in the distance.   The placid water, the bright sunshine, the rounded outline of the land, the deciduous leaves of
the forest trees touched with the first tints of autumn, interspersed with pyramidal spruce, made a scene seldom seen except
by the wanderer in distant lands.

When I reached the fort, I was heartily welcomed by Mr.
MacMurray, the officer in charge of the establishment, and I
learned from him that the only way I could reach Green Lake
would be by taking passage with Edward Big Belly, who had

followed us from Chipewyan House, who was going to Green Lake to trade. A bargain was soon made and it was agreed to start early the next morning. Edward was accompanied by two boys, a son and a nephew, and had a very nice birch bark canoe which would carry us all in safety.

The distance from Methye Portage to Isle-a-la-Crosse is computed as being one hundred and thirty miles. I was warned by Mr. MacMurray that Edward Big Belly was not a good Indian, and to be careful of my provisions, while I accompanied him in the canoe. I found out later that he was only a bad Indian because he preferred dealing at Green Lake rather than leaving his furs with Mr. MacMurray. The next morning, I started for Green Lake and, as we left the land, the wind increased and, being fair, a blanket was hoisted and our canoe sped like a thing of life across the lake. The wind kept increasing and by the time we reached Beaver River it had risen so much that, had we been in a wooden canoe, we must have been swamped. The wind, still increasing, we rushed up the river at railroad speed and camped in the evening on one of the long, narrow islands with which the river is filled. I quote again from my diary:

"We started with four days' provisions, but hoped to make the distance in three. My companions know nothing of English but are kind and competent. We were early astir on the morning of the 23rd. For the first three hours after starting, there was swift water, alternately with still pools, and at the second forks of the river, which we reached a little before noon, the main stream continued about one hundred yards wide, though the volume of the water was sensibly diminished."[10]

At the first streak of dawn on the 25th, we were off and, after passing two short rapids, all current ceased and the river looked like a stagnant pool and, as we proceeded further up, the current still got less and, in the afternoon, about 2 p.m., we came to the discharge of Green Lake. On reaching Green Lake, Mr. Sinclair, the officer in charge of the post, told me that the lake was raised more than twenty feet every spring by the influx of Beaver River.

Mr. Sinclair received me most kindly and at once took steps to enable me to continue my journey. The only available animals were an old ox and a miserable horse and, with these and a young Cree for guide, who was never over the road before, I was to start the next day, from the southern end of the lake, for Carlton, a distance of 140 miles.

On the afternoon of the 27th, Mr. Sinclair took me up the lake in a birch-bark canoe, so small that I had to stand in the water and hold it while Mr. Sinclair took his seat in the stern. Up till now, I had been in boats which were perfectly safe, but this one was so small that the two of us almost filled it and to sit steady in it, while he paddled, was almost impossible. I certainly was afraid for my life, and asked him if I might be permitted to paddle as well as himself. He said that I might, if I wanted to, and I found that working took my mind off the danger. Long after dark, we reached the head of the lake and I thanked God for His preserving care of me, since I started down McLeod's River on the eventful 3rd of July, and for having kept me safely through nearly 1,600 miles of river navigation.

My guide was a poor childish fellow, but I got along very well with him although I could not understand a word he said nor he one of mine. We did not take the old horse, but a cart and the ox, to carry my stuff. I walked in the rear, while he walked by the ox or sat in the cart. To pass away the time, I would sometimes sit down by the side of the road and read four or five pages of the "Heart of Midlothian," which Mrs. MacMurray had given me at Isle-a-la-Crosse. On the third morning, on our way, I sat down, as usual, to read on the roadside and read a number of pages and rose up and walked on expecting to overtake the cart. When I had walked a mile or more and had not seen it, I became frightened and thought that possibly the man had hidden in the woods and left me to shift for myself. This thought pressed heavily upon me as I had nearly one hundred miles to go before I reached the Mission, where I would get food. After walking a mile, I turned back and went to the place where I had sat down and examined carefully both sides of the road as I went, and found that the Indian had not turned off, and so I concluded that, by some unaccountable means, he had disappeared and that there was no hope for me but to go on to the Mission. About two o'clock, I started, determined to walk on as fast and as far as possible before I gave out.   In going back, I noticed certain things on the roadside, amongst others a dead horse, and I wondered to see it was so like one I had seen in the morning, the only difference being that it was on the left hand side of the road instead of on the right hand, as the one was in the morning.   Proceeding, I came to where there was a broken stone, which I examined, and found it was one that I had myself broken in the morning and here I had been all day going back on the road I had come.   The scales immediately fell from my eyes and I saw that I had been blinded all day and had been completely lost all that time.   I turned back and walked rapidly to where I had sat down in the morning and discovered that instead of sitting on the right side of the road, I had sat down on the left hand, and, when I had risen to my feet, I turned back instead of forward.   I mention this to show that, on a plain road, a man may get lost if he is not attentive to what he is doing.   In all my long life, I never got lost but once and that was on a beaten road.

It was now growing dark and I heard a faint "Hello," which turned out to be that of the Indian who had turned back to see if he could find me. He had stopped at noon and, as I had not come up with him, he waited the afternoon in hopes I would turn up, but, having failed to do so, he came to look for me.   I reached camp at dark and tried to explain to him what had happened, but he could not understand and he told the people at the Mission, when we reached there, that I had been sick when, in reality, I was lost.

In due time, we reached the Mission and found it in charge of an English clergyman, called Hines, and, in all my experience, he seemed to be the most practical missionary I had come across. He told me his aim was to teach the children English and the old men and women how to farm.   This, he was doing, in the most practical manner, and, as I sat in his little school, the Sunday I spent with him, and saw the crowd of attentive children and old men and women scattered all over the floor listening to what he said and the children's answers, I saw for the first time what a wonderful power education of a practical kind would have on the future of the Indians.

On the evening of the 6th of October, I reached Carlton, having been thirty-three days on the road from Fort Chipewyan, the computed distance being 600 miles, so that, including stoppages, I made twenty miles per day.   I experienced no difficulty in passing through the country as the officers of the Hudson's Bay Company had done everything in their power to assist me. The Indians did everything they could to make me comfortable and never touched an article nor did an improper act on the whole trip.

I rested two days at Fort Carlton and, in the meantime, had the pleasure of meeting Capt. Crozier, of the Northwest Mounted Police, who had been a Lieutenant in the company in which I served at Prescott, in 1866.   We were pleased to see each other and Mr. Clark, the gentleman in charge of Carlton, invited us both to dine with him that evening.   Besides the Captain and myself, there were two priests, one of whom was named Père Andreau.   While taking dinner, we were discussing the future of the country and Père Andreau said that he was going to bring a large number of half-breeds from Manitoba to settle on the Saskatchewan and form a new French province.   After dinner, I told the Captain that I would make a note of what the priest had said as it meant trouble in the future and that I would advise him to do the same.   Whether he did so or not I cannot say, but he commanded the Northwest Mounted Police at the battle of Duck Lake, the first engagement in the rebellion of 1885.

On the 8th, I was again on my way and this time in company with a number of half-breeds who had brought goods from Fort Garry to Carlton for the Hudson's Bay Company.   I purchased a light wagon to convey myself and traps across the plains and one of the half-breeds furnished the horse.   He did everything for me and agreed to take me to Winnipeg in twenty-one days, weather permitting, for $45.00.   I may say here that, all the time I have spoken about travelling, I never had a shilling in my pocket as all my expenses were furnished by the Hudson's Bay Company. We now had six hundred miles further to go before I reached Fort Garry.

When we came to the South Saskatchewan, we crossed on

Batoche's ferry and I found him a very fine man.   We got along wonderfully well until we had both oxen and horses in our company and, owing to the cattle being with us, we could not make as much progress as many of the men wished.   Besides myself, we had with us a young fellow who was going from Prince Albert and wished to reach Winnipeg before winter.   We passed along as rapidly as possible and had some uncommon experiences on our way but I will only mention a few.   One, in particular, comes up before me and I will relate it as a novel experience.

One afternoon, we reached a bad place on the road called a slough.   In the middle of it my horse refused, or was unable, to pull the wagon out, so the guide and myself were left sitting in the pool.   He called out to one of the men, who immediately took his horse out of the cart and hitched a rope to the horse's tail well up to the rump, and threw the other end to us in the cart.   My guide fastened the rope to the shafts and the half-breed on shore and the one in the wagon, after a few "sacrés," started both horses on the jump and we were hauled to shore in a few moments.   I expected the horse's tail to be pulled out of the beast, but instead we were brought to dry land.   Since that time, I have learned that it was the common way amongst the half breeds in olden times to pull one out of the mire.

As it was late in the season, we decided to start early in the morning and go on as fast as possible by day and this mode of travel we kept up for quite a number of beautiful days.

One morning, when we were about to start, I decided to remain behind and write up my notes and was busily engaged when I became poetical and had just written: "I think I hear the tramp of the coming millions," and, as I had reached this period, a concert broke out a few yards behind me, and, on looking around, I saw a line of coyotes sitting on a ridge and giving their peculiar howl.   I need scarcely add that I never became poetical again.   When I mentioned it to the men, they said that coyotes always followed a party of half-breeds when on the trail to pick up the refuse of the camp when they had left.

Our fine weather continued until the evening of the 23rd of October, when it began to thicken up and the next morning we were off long before daylight, but, as the day broke, we saw that we were in for a snowstorm.   We halted in a little clump of willows and had a cup of tea.

We had scarcely started again when the storm broke and, in a few minutes, the air was filled with driving snow.   For the next sixteen miles, there was neither bush nor tree, and for the whole of this distance we tramped against a furious gale and driving storm.   Late in the afternoon of the 24th, we reached the timber and, under the direction of our experienced guide, penetrated to a little marsh surrounded by wood, and camped.   We could hear the roar of the gale outside, but not a breath stirred where we were.   There was fine pasture for the horses and cattle in the marsh and we had no difficulty in making ourselves comfortable.   In a short time, we had blazing fires and, after the ice was thawed off our clothes, we sat about the fire making a shelter for the night.   I lay under the wagon with my feet to the fire and was so comfortable that I never wakened until the morning.

Next morning, the snow continued to fall just as heavily as before and a consultation was held as to what was best to be done.   Most of us preferred to remain in camp, but my guide would not hear of it.   He said that our only hope lay in pushing on as fast as possible before the horses and cattle gave out.   We trudged on and at one o'clock reached Boggy Creek.   In this valley, we had dinner, and, as it seemed to be clearing, the young fellow, who was with us, and myself, remained behind intending to overtake the others in a short time.   When we left the creek, we thought the snow was falling less heavily, but, when we reached the ridge, we found it was blowing a blizzard, and exactly in our faces, as we started out on the trail.   We now had twelve miles over an open trail to go before we would reach Pine Creek where we had decided to camp for the night.   The young man and myself decided to trot along with our heads lowered to see if we could escape the force of the wind.   We knew we were on the trail, but were without any tracks as the wind had obliterated the tracks of our party immediately after they had passed.   We wondered why we did not overtake them, as we knew we were going very fast, but we learned later that they all ran for their lives.   By and by the young man said that the storm was breaking, because he could see much better, and I looked across at his face and said: "Why, you fool, your whole face has frozen up and you are looking through ice." We turned our backs to the wind and then cleared our faces. By this time, I was afraid that our trip was going to have a serious ending, as we were on a trackless prairie and had to face a blizzard that filled the whole atmosphere with snow. By good fortune, I knew that the grass on each side of a trail is longer than the grass on the trail and, as I ran along, I kept my eyes on the left-hand side of the road and, by that means, kept the track.

Towards evening, we reached the creek, and found that the men had erected a teepee and had a blazing fire in the center and everything was comfortable. When we reached the camp, we were thirsty, but I was unable to open my mouth and the water was poured down my throat by one of the men, as I wore a long beard at this time. It took me over an hour to get it thawed out.

Next day, we reached McKinnon's and left part of our horses and the oxen, as they were unable to proceed further and, for the next eight days, we trudged through the snow to Winnipeg. We saved our horses and cattle, but some of our party nearly broke down. When one was exhausted, another would take the lead and break the way for the others. We were the only party that escaped without loss, numbers of horses and cattle having perished in this long continued storm.

I reached Winnipeg on the 3rd of November and put up at the Queen's hotel, and, that evening, I was interviewed by a number of the citizens as soon as they heard that I had just come in from the Peace River and could tell them of the wonders of that unknown land. I remember only four of the gentlemen; but one of them is still alive, namely, Rev. Dr. Geo. Bryce, of Winnipeg. The gentlemen were, Consul Taylor, Dr. Bryce, Archdeacon G. . . . and the collector of Inland Revenue. Consul Taylor was the American Consul and was called by the people of Winnipeg, "Saskatchewan Taylor," as he always maintained that the Saskatchewan valley held most of the wheat lands of the north. I had with me the wheat and the barley that I had picked up at

Fort Chipewyan, and I now exhibited them for the benefit of the company. The wheat was finer than any they had ever seen before, many of the ears having five and six grains in the fasicle.[12]

I left Winnipeg on the 5th of November by stage, and, in those days, the stage always had a guard, who rode beside the driver. Our trip to Fargo in Dakota took fifty-seven hours, and we had the usual experiences of travellers at that early time, but only one episode stands out in my mind at present and that is— Somewhere in Dakota, we reached the outskirts of a village, and, owing to the rough condition of the road, the driver took to the side and, as we were approaching the stopping-place, we came to where there had been a house at one time but now just the cellar remained. One of the runners of the sleigh took the edge of the cellar and tipped up and two ladies who were sitting in the rear of the sleigh fell into the cellar and, of course, screamed as loudly as possible and the other passengers were wishing to help the poor things but I advised them to raise the runner and have the horses pull the sleigh on to the road again. I said, what proved to be the truth, that ladies who could scream, like they were doing, could not be badly hurt. We reached Fargo next day in the evening.

The next day, I took the train for St. Paul and reached home on the 13th of November having been gone eight months and having travelled at least eight thousand miles.

CHAPTER IX

1875-1879

Notes on Climate—Recommendations in regard to Route of Canadian Pacific Railway—Offers of Positions—Publication of report on Country between Port Arthur and the Pacific, 1877—Made Emeritus Professor of Albert College, 1879—Exploration of the Prairies, 1879—Up the Assiniboine to Fort Ellice, then to Long Lake—Crossing the Saskatchewan River—Battleford—Red Deer Valley—Calgary—Adventures en Route—Description of the Country—Blackfeet Indians—One of the last Buffalo Hunts—Return to Winnipeg and the East.

I found all well at home and immediately took up my studies at Albert College, and decided to write a slight sketch of my trip. This, I took to Montreal, to show Dr. Selwyn, and to ask him what kind of a report I was to make. From Montreal, I went by the Prescott railroad to Ottawa to lecture to the Literary and Scientific Society, which had asked me to favor them with an account of my trip. The next thing, I remember, is that Mr. James W. Ross, who was Member for Middlesex at that time, invited me to dine with a number of the Liberal Members at the Windsor. As a result of that dinner, I was invited to call on the Hon. David Laird, who was Minister of the Interior, and, in the conversation with him, he said that there was to be a great meeting of the Members that night as (Sir) Richard Cartwright, the Finance Minister, was to announce his budget. He said that he expected a surprise for the opposition. And, sure enough, he did, because (Sir) Charles Tupper was prepared to advocate a low tariff, but he found that the Ministers had decided to leave tariff as it was. The result was that (Sir) Charles could not make the speech and, after a few remarks, adjourned the house until the next day.

Mr. Laird asked me if I would like to see Mr. Mackenzie (the Prime Minister) as he had been enquiring about me. I said that I certainly would, and I found him to be a very pleasant little Scotchman, but very conservative, for he would not believe one word I told him about the Northwest. When I told him you could travel for two hundred miles and not see an acre of bad land he said, "I canna believe it." The reason for this assertion was that, in Ontario, we had good land always intermixed with poor soils.

On my return to Belleville, I at once took up my regular studies and, in the meantime, thought over my report and began to compile the notes I had taken.[1] In doing this, I made many discoveries that had not appeared to me of value before. One was, why should the climate of the lower part of the Peace River be as fine as the climate of Winnipeg, one thousand, two hundred miles from it, and ten degrees further south? This led me to take up the studies that I had almost given up, that is, Blodgett's Climatology[2] and Maurie's Geography of the Sea. These two books I found invaluable. For many years, I had been satisfied that to tell the climate of a country by its annual temperature was altogether out of the question, as the three growing months of any year anywhere were factors that produced the crops. So, in making my tables, I took the three growing months of any part of the world and took their average and I found that, in every case, these were the factors that produced the crop. In fact, heat and moisture are the chief factors in the growth of good crops. In working at my report, I began to realize the immensity of the country I had come through, and its wonderful value for the future of Canada, and, the longer I worked, the more this realization grew. In conversation with the men at Chipewyan, I found they raised wheat as far down the McKenzie as Fort Simpson in latitude 62° and up the Liard to 61° and at Winnipeg, in latitude 50°, conditions were apparently not so good as the conditions I found on the lower Peace River, and the distance between the two points was fully one thousand two hundred miles.

At this time, Mr. Mackenzie was in power and the ideas of the Liberal party, which were then called "Reformers," were exactly opposite to those of Sir John A. Macdonald's party.   Sir John was determined to build the railroad from the Atlantic to the Pacific, and Mr. Mackenzie could not see any wisdom in building a continuous railroad from Port Arthur to Port Moody on the Pacific, and, hence, he favored the plan, which was then called "Water-Stretches," owing to the report that Palliser had made that the southern part of the prairie was all desert and that the northern part, which was wooded, was fertile, and this northern part was now called the "fertile belt", by everybody, hence, all the survey parties sent out by Mr. Mackenzie aimed to proceed through the fertile belt to British Columbia.

At this time, the projected railway west of Winnipeg was to cross Lake Manitoba at the Narrows, proceed up the Swan River, and continue on the water-shed from there to Edmonton and so on to the Pacific.   Horetzky and I, having seen the two passes to the north, were considered fit to give an opinion and he re-commended that the railway be built past Lac La Biche and north of Little Slave Lake and through the Peace River country to Pine Pass or the Peace River Pass itself.   Sandford Fleming still recommended going through the Yellow-Head Pass and his surveys culminated on the country west of the Yellow-Head. This was the condition when I came to him in 1875.

My report opened the eyes of many men throughout the country, but had little effect in Parliament, as the two parties, as usual, were fighting the usual game of ins and outs, and that is the kind of thing that went on.

I was frequently invited to go to cities throughout Ontario to lecture and tell of my travels and what I had seen.   These lectures lifted me out of the rank of teacher and made me a public man.

In the autumn of 1875, I was asked to become Science Master of Ottawa Normal School and my friends saw the Minister of Education of Ontario and he said that he was in favor of my appointment, but the Government always advertised for qualifica-tions.   The present Chief Justice Riddell, of Toronto, was then teaching in the Normal School at Ottawa and offered to take chemistry in which I was deficient and I would take algebra from

10

him. This suited the Minister of Education, but he said he would have to go by the result of the advertisement. My friends thought that there was no chance for me, as I was a Conservative, and the "Globe" advocated one of their own men and he was appointed. This man was the late Dr. Baptie. Next, I was offered the position of teacher at Sheboygen, in the State of Michigan. They offered to double my salary, but I declined as that would take me away from Canada. Next, I was offered the Bursarship at Queen's College, Kingston, but my friends were over-ruled and Mr. Ireland, was appointed in his father's place. (Mr. Ireland, who was appointed, was my eldest son's wife's uncle, which I found out later). I began to consider myself of more importance now than I had before and took my place in the city accordingly. I still retained my work in the College, however.

Time passed and, in 1876, Mr. Mackenzie asked me to write a full report on the whole country between Port Arthur and the Pacific. I did this and it was published in the Railway Report of 1877.[3] It raised my stock above par and opened the eyes of a great many politicians and other people. It was now observed that Mr. Mackenzie himself was awake, as he began to see the value of the western country. My report opposed the fixed idea of cold, barren land in the north, but, as I had never seen the south, I could say nothing about the prairie.[4] The surveys were still going on, in the same old way, and no parties were satisfied, but many people were immigrating to Manitoba and, since I crossed in 1875, they began to go on the prairie itself. Up to that time, no settler had passed from Manitoba on to what was called the "Second Prairie Steppe."

During the summer of 1877, I took my son, James,[5] with me for his first trip, which was to Toronto and Niagara, and he will remember that we met Seton Thompson's father and Dr. Codray. Things were now approaching a crisis and, in 1878, an election was held and Mr. Mackenzie was badly defeated and Sir John A. Macdonald came into power. Immediately on Sir John's accession to power, an effort was made to get some real knowledge about the prairie country both north and south. Sir Charles

Tupper became Minister of Railways and, in the winter of 1878, arrangements were made to send ten parties to the prairie and the country north to Jasper and report on the value of the country. (Sir) Mackenzie Bowell was appointed Minister of Commerce and, in the winter, informed me of what had been decided by the Government for the next summer, and asked me if I would lead one of the parties.   I refused unless they appointed me permanently to a position that I had in view, but I did not mention that to him. After consultation with Sir Charles, Mr. Bowell wrote me to say that Sir Charles would make me permanent as long as they were in power, but he would not promise it any longer. When this was decided, I resigned my position in Albert College and, late in April, 1879, went to Ottawa and met Sir Charles and Mr. Fleming.

The leaders of our ten parties were in Ottawa at this time and we were each called in to make an estimate of what amount we would need in order to carry out our explorations.   None of the surveyors would make an estimate and I, in my innocence, immediately sat down and made out my estimate and, after I made it out, I doubled it and took the doubled estimate in to Mr. Fleming and he looked it over and told me it was excellent. While I was with him, a surveyor called O'Keefe, belonging to Hamilton, came in and was asked to make out his estimate, and he immediately said that he was unable to do so and he was told that he had better look over mine and give in something like it.   Whether he did so or not, I cannot say.   I went back home and was made, by the authorities of Albert College, Emeritus Professor, and I have retained the title ever since.   I shortly afterwards went to Ottawa to receive my instructions and found that I was the only one commissioned to explore on the prairie.[6] All the others were to examine the country which was then called the "Fertile Belt" and northward.

I received my instructions from Sir Sandford Fleming but Col. Dennis, who was Deputy Minister of the Interior, wrote them.   Until many years later, I did not know why this had been done.   I may state here what my instructions were.   I was to proceed to Fort Ellice and take the trail there for Edmonton and, when I reached the 102nd Meridian, I was to travel by compass to the head of Long Lake and from there, by compass again, to the Elbow of the South Saskatchewan, cross it and proceed westward to the Hand Hills which were north of the Blackfeet Reserve, and, from there, if I had time, to proceed to Old Bow Fort, on Bow River, north of Calgary.   In the formation of my party, I engaged my nephew, David Macoun, and John Ogilvie, and the Government appointed, as my assistant, a surveyor named Wilkins, and he took with him a young man named Sidney Savage, who was an old pupil of mine and a fearless young scamp.   I just had the four.

Early in May, 1879, I started for Winnipeg by way of St. Paul and reached there in due time.   The day I arrived at Winnipeg, a boat was preparing to start for Fort Ellice on the Assiniboine, which would take me two hundred miles into the interior without effort.   I immediately saw the Captain and asked him if he would remain one day longer and I would proceed with him and take my outfit and men on the steamer.   He agreed at once and, in one day, I bought my whole outfit and arranged for my horses and hired John Matheson, native of Winnipeg, to whom the horses belonged, for him to take the horses overland to Fort Ellice and I bought the carts and our summer's provisions and all the necessaries for the expedition and placed them on the boat and I was ready to start the next morning after one day in Winnipeg.

The boat was loaded to her utmost capacity and, as there were large numbers of surveyors and their men on board, there was no accommodation for me.   My assistant, as I found him in all cases, looked out for himself, without reference to me, and obtained a very comfortable location.   Mr. W. F. King, the astronomer who lately died, said to me, "Macoun, how is it that you have no berth?"   I told him that there were none left.   "Why," he said, "Your assistant has a fine berth."   And I said that I knew this but that there was not one for me too.   "Oh," he said, "You are one of the gentlemen here and I will inform the Captain that Mr. Wilkins has taken your berth and you will get a hint to go to bed early."   The result was as I have said, Wilkins was shifted and he had to look out for himself the same as the rest.

In getting my supplies, I obtained four iron bound carts, the first that had been used on the prairie. Everyone thought that the wheels would shrink up and come apart when I reached the prairie. But I knew better. I took the four carts and two buckboards and engaged for nine horses, and went forward on a 3,000 mile trip without any fear of the future, because I did not know at that time what doubts and fears were.

On board the boat, I had plenty of time to think the matter out and decided that our trip would be a success whatever our failings were. The trip up the river was pleasant and very interesting. Captain Weller had been up as far as Rapid City Landing, later called the Grand Rapid, the year before, and this year he was determined to go up to Fort Ellice and that was why I wished to go up with him. The company on the boat was very interesting. An Englishman named Harper was one of the passengers with whom I discussed matters at the wheel-house beside the Captain. Our vessel was a stern-wheeler and had much difficulty in navigating some of the short bends of the river and often we had to back and pull to get around a corner. When we reached a rapid we, were able to ascend it by "Warping," then we ascended the rapid without any difficulty and soon passed the site of the future City of Brandon. Above it, we came to a Reserve given to the band of Sioux that I had seen in 1872. When we came up opposite the settlement, we tied up for a few minutes and the whole population turned out to have a look at us, men, women and children. As usual, I was sitting with the Captain and my friend the Englishman, and, as he saw the Indians crowding up, laughing, he yelled to me: "Macoun, by George, they laugh like white men." And, while they laughed, I said to the Captain: "Captain, give them a blast!" And the Captain pulled the lever and gave a tremendous whistle and every man, woman and child fell instantly to the ground and rushed away in the grass on hands and knees, and so we passed on.

When wood was needed for the boat, we stopped where there would be a growth of green ash and got enough to supply our wants. Without accident, we reached Fort Ellice and all our possessions were placed on the bank and we took possession and carried them up to the prairie above. My man was there with the horses and we erected our tents and got our things under cover as soon as possible. We had three tents—one for myself and nephew, another for Mr. Wilkins and his brother-in-law, and another for Matheson and Ogilvie. When we had all our belongings together and our four carts and two buckboards, my assistant, Wilkins, came to me and said: "'Professor, we will never be able to take all this stuff on our conveyances; we simply cannot do it under any circumstances." I knew now was my time to assert myself and I said: "Boys, from what Mr. Wilkins says there is some doubt as to our ability to take all our stuff with us and I wish to tell you that 'can't' is not in my vocabulary and the man who uses it on this trip can consider himself dismissed.[7] The boat has not gone back yet and any man who wishes to return is at liberty to do so at once, but I wish to tell you that, from this time forth, any man who thinks he knows more about his work than I do ceases to be an employee of mine." I gave orders, on retiring that night, that we were to rise at 5 o'clock every morning while on our trip, that the tents were to be pulled down at six and we would be ready to start as individuals at seven. Next morning, my nephew was out at five and called the camp and all the men were on the alert but my friend Wilkins, who was still in his tent at six o'clock. Matheson came to me and said: "Professor, Mr. Wilkins is not out of his tent yet; shall we leave it standing?" I said: "What did I tell you all last night?" He said: "To pull down the tents at six." "Well," I said, "Carry out the order." I may say that he was only too glad to do it, and four of the boys pulled out the pegs and let the tent down with a smash on Wilkins, who might have been standing up at the time but, when the tent fell, he went down with it and came out on his hands and knees swearing at the men. I told him that the men had had my permission and every day that he was late in coming out of his tent the same thing would happen. My next order was to separate all the men's belongings. Mr. Wilkins and myself were to take everything that belonged to us on our buckboards and, to each of the men, I assigned a cart and he packed his share of the stuff in it in his own way with the understanding that whatever was in the cart could be got at at the shortest notice.   In other words, our men must know where each article that he had in his cart was placed.   My reason for doing this was that I had a spade, an axe, a shearing-hook and many other small articles that might be wanted for instant use, and I desired each man to be aware of what he carried.   When we began to tie up our stuff and fix it all, we found that we had room enough for all we had.

I may mention here that I had agreed, at Winnipeg, with Captain Moore, who had started a grist mill at Prince Albert, that I would take a certain number of bags of flour from him and he would deliver them at Battleford before the middle of July. By this means, I left part of our heavy material to be taken up in the middle of the summer.

We packed up our stuff and experienced a thunder-storm and heavy rain.   The next morning, we started on our westward trip. During the day, before we started, I went to Fort Ellice and had a talk with Mr. Macdonald, the chief factor in charge, and he said to me: "Where are you going on your trip?"   I said that I had a hard road before me, but that I had two surveyors who ought to be able to give me a direction and he said: "You cannot go through this country without a guide as there is no one who knows anything about it except our men."   "Well," I said, "My first objective is the head of Long Lake and would you bring out a guide so that I can have a talk with him?"   So he brought out a half-breed and I told him that I was going to the Elbow of the South Saskatchewan, also that I was going by the head of Long Lake and he immediately said: "You cannot go that way for there is no trail."   I said: "I am not going to travel on trails, but am going to travel by compass."   He shook his head and said that I could not possibly do it, nobody travelled that way.   I now turned to Mr. Macdonald and I said: "Mr. Macdonald, it is this man's brains or mine; if I take him, I go the way he says; if I take no guide with me, we go the way I say; I am going to take no guide."

The next day, we started, and for a few days travelled on the road leading from Fort Ellice to Carlton, the chief highway of the

North West at that time. My instructions were to go by this road to the 102nd Meridian and from there I was to travel by compass to the head of Long Lake. The 102nd Meridian was marked on this road so that there was no possible chance of my missing it. This was the initial point of my expedition and I learned, a few years after, that the reason I started at the 102nd Meridian was that Captain Palliser had said in his report that the "Desert" commenced there.

Our mode of procedure, from this time forward, was for Mr. Wilkins, in his buckboard, to lead and give the direction, while the carts followed him, and I brought up the rear in my buckboard. This was the way we travelled for two months. Our direction was a little north of west and we aimed to travel at least eight hours a day and make about sixteen miles. We had an odometer on one of the carts and knew how far we travelled each day. Mr. Wilkins, at night, in his tent, made a map of our trip at two miles to an inch so that we could see where we were and how many miles we made each day. I noticed that the cart in charge of certain of the men was often in difficulty and sometimes overturned and at last I had to pass a law that any man who allowed anything in his cart to be injured, the value of it would be stopped out of his pay. From this time forward we had no more mishaps, each man walked beside his horse and saw that he got into no difficulty.

Days passed, and we saw no travellers nor roads and had few difficulties, but a most wonderful country full of flowers and copse-wood and small streams and, altogether it was a most delightful place. Everywhere we looked, it was the same. One day, when we were crossing the open prairie, two policemen suddenly came up with us and wanted to know our business. They had noticed our ironbound carts and knew that they were a different kind of vehicle from any they had seen in the country before. One of the policemen was Inspector Griesbach.

We were now about due west of Qu'Appelle Station, where the policemen had their quarters. Of course, we had no means of knowing where we were as our map was very poor. We found no difficulty in crossing the country. There was plenty of water, open meadows and copses of poplar, and over the whole country was an immensity of flowers. We had never seen or thought of such a country as the one we were passing through. My company were in the finest spirits, and I discovered that the four boys were first class men and capable and willing to do anything that was required of them. We soon passed Last Mountain on our left and, after a number of days, we reached Long Lake, our first objective.

At Long Lake, we found ourselves eight miles out of our reckoning, as the head of the Lake was still eight miles off. The country we had passed through may be summed up in a few words taken from my note-book:

"To the east of the head of the Lake lay rich country which produced enormous mushrooms and various flowers and this caused me to call this region "The Flower Garden of the North West." While crossing the plain, before we reached the Lake, we found mushrooms by the cartload and used them every day while travelling at least two hundred miles in a westerly direction. From the reports of other travellers and my own observations, I am led to believe that, on the whole prairie, an abundance of mushrooms will be obtained after a rainfall during the summer. One species of *Lycoperdion* (puff-ball) was seen that grew to a very large size and numerous others were noticed during the whole season, scattered over the plain in great profusion."[8]

The following notes from my journal will illustrate the flora in the vicinity of Long Lake as seen in the first week of July, 1879. "Flowers are a most conspicuous feature of the prairie. *Hedysarum* and various *Astragali* vieing with the lily and vetch in loveliness and luxuriance. Often, whole acres would be red and purple with beautiful flowers and the air laden with the perfume of roses. Sometimes, lilies (*Lilium philadelphicum*)[9] are so abundant that they cover an acre of ground, bright red. At others, they are mixed with other liliaceous plants, such as *Zygadenus glaucus*, and form a ring around the thickets which we passed. Another time, we come upon a pool of fine, pure water and in it grows *Carex aristata*, which the horses love so well. Around it, where the water is nearly gone, are *Carex marcida* and *lanuginosa;*

outside of these a ring of white anemones and, growing where it is slightly drier, another flower, *Potentilla gracilis*, and, as the ground becomes still drier, *Penstemon confertus* would appear and, lastly, the lilies would surround the whole."[10]

Mushrooms were extremely abundant and attained a fabulous size. They grew in regular "fairy rings," often more than forty feet in diameter. Some rings we found to contain so many that, taking all, good and bad, from one ring, we could almost load a cart. Other rings were devoted exclusively to the giant puff-ball which was extremely numerous on almost every part of the plains. Amongst many others, I measured one speciman of mushroom which was 33 1-3" in circumference, 2 3-4" through the cap, with stem over 2" in diameter, and weighed over three pounds.

When we reached the head of Long Lake, we found the first creek at the eastern corner was bad water and, about a mile further west, along the north end of the Lake, we came upon another creek that flowed in, that contained a large quantity of pure water and, further west, still another creek, so that three creeks were found to flow into the Lake. Hitherto, we had found water to be plentiful, and had had no occasion to trouble ourselves about where we would stop for either fuel or water. Rising out of the depression in which the Lake lay, we reached the summit of a slight rise and we were struck almost speechless by the sight that lay before our eyes. We were now on the verge of the real prairie and we now knew that we had never seen a real one before. Looking west, north, or south, a level expanse of green meadow lay stretching out before us to the horizon, without a break and without anything resembling a live animal or shrub. We passed on about two hundred yards to the prairie and came upon a pool of water and I thought it was wise to camp, although early in the afternoon. As soon as we camped, my nephew and another man got on a couple of horses and rode back to where we had passed through a little burnt wood and pulled down enough of the dead trees to keep us in fuel for a week. That was cut up and the next morning placed in the cart. We had a ten gallon keg with us for the purpose of carrying water where it was scarce, but hitherto we had not used it. We now filled our keg with water

ONE OF THE GRAIN FIELDS IN SASKATCHEWAN.
THE AUTHOR'S PROPHECY FULFILLED.

and, for the next four months, we never travelled without its being full. John Matheson, who owned the horses, had been a buffalo hunter and he regaled the boys and myself with stories of buffalo hunting and, if all his experiences were recorded, they would fill a volume. He earned from us a nickname of "Lying Jack Matheson," as we were never able to tell the difference between what was a true story and what was a fabrication. However, he knew many things that were of great value to us and, amongst others, how to obtain fuel when our wood would be gone.

He asked me what I thought we would do and I instantly said to him: "If necessary, we can burn dry grass." He laughed at me and said: "We can do better than that. When we were hunting on the paririe, we used buffalo chips." I learned that the chips were not wood, but droppings of the buffalo that were perfectly dry, and for months, this was the fuel we used. As soon as I learned this, I had a bag attached to the rear cart and ordered each man to put any droppings that he saw in the bag and, in this way, we carried with us every day, a supply of fuel.

Another thing that we discovered was that our horses preferred brackish water to pure so that, if we arrived at a pool that contained brackish water, we could camp and use the water we carried while the horses drank from the pool.

As there was no regular cook attached to the party, each man took on part of the work and, at any rate, it was always accomplished in good time and suited all hands. Our bread constantly consisted all summer of bannocks, baked in a spider.

I do not remember how many days we were in crossing to the Elbow of the South Saskatchewan, but we reached it in due time, although we found ourselves, as usual, eight miles to the east of it, showing that our map was not correct. When we reached the Saskatchewan, I had another work to do besides the crossing of the river. I had been instructed at Ottawa, before I left, that when I reached the Elbow of the South Saskatchewan, I was to see if it were possible to make a canal that would carry water from the Saskatchewan into the Qu' Appelle. This was one of Mr. Mackenzie's pet schemes of "water stretches." Mr. Wilkins and the young men worked on that job and Matheson and I remained at the Saskatchewan. The results of the levelling were that the head of the Qu' Appelle was eighty-seven feet higher than the Saskatchewan, so that question was settled. The distance across was found to be eleven miles.

On the 13th of July, 1879, we reached the Elbow of the South Saskatchewan, at the head of the Qu'Appelle Valley. At this point, the river was 770 yards wide and flowing with a steady current. Sixty miles to the north, there was a ferry and, forty miles to the south, Palliser had crossed twenty-three years before, but with the loss of a wagon. After examining the river carefully both above and below the Elbow, I decided to cross at this point. The means was the next consideration. There was no timber to construct a raft, so we decided to build a boat. We had no boards, but we had a large tent, waterproof blankets and cart covers.

John Matheson, of Winnipeg, who had charge of the horses and outfit generally, made a wooden frame about nine feet long and four and half feet wide at the stern, shaped like the letter "A" and interlaced with willows; over this we put the tent and over all, we nailed the waterproof blankets. By means of this frail boat, we purposed taking across a river, nearly half a mile wide, four month's provisions, all our camp equipage, four carts and two buckboards, besides risking our own lives.

The night before we undertook to cross was an anxious one and, shortly after sunrise, we were ready to make the attempt. Our boat was found to leak considerably, but one man baled to keep it afloat. I called for volunteers and my nephew, David Macoun, and Sidney Savage, volunteered. They were both good swimmers and courageous. A small load was put on board and with one man pulling two small oars and another baling, they started. After crossing a small branch close to us, they drew the boat for a long distance up the river by walking on a sand-bar. When they thought they had ascended far enough, they attempted to cross the main channel, but the width (over 250 yards) being much greater than they had expected, they were unable to make the shore and landed on an island near the further side. In coming back, they were carried half a mile below our camp and had to haul the boat up. They were in good spirits, however, as the boat was quite safe and, by going further up the bar, they were sure they could make the land the next try. Another load was soon on board and hauled far up the sand-bar and was easily taken across. All working with a will, the greater part of the provisions and baggage were across before night, but much time was lost in getting the horses across, as they frequently turned back when almost half way across. One or two were very nearly drowned, being unable to stem the current for five hundred yards at a stretch. These, after resting awhile on the bar, some distance below us, finally reached the shore. The next forenoon, we brought over the remainder of our outfit and, by sundown, camped on the crest of the valley with the mighty river sweeping in graceful curves at our feet, while behind us lay the river and, in front, those illimitable plains which, on our maps, were shown as a waterless and treeless desert. On the morrow, we entered on the great plain, which we eventually traversed in every direction and lifted the veil which had enshrouded it for many years.

Having accomplished two of my objectives, we now turned our faces to the great prairie and took a course for the next, which was the Hand Hills, over two hundred miles to the west. We expected to suffer from the want of water and fuel. In a few days, we discovered that this was true in fact as well as theory. One afternoon, when water was getting scarce and could not be found, we had a thunder-storm and it filled a small pool by which we camped, and this made us sure of our water for one night at any rate. At this point, I decided to leave the party and, with Matheson, my buckboard, one cart and two horses, to start for Battleford, where I was to get the balance of my provisions for the summer. Mr. Wilkins calculated our distance to Battleford to be one hundred and twenty-five miles, and our direction was twenty degrees west of north. Mr. Wilkins was to go due west to the Hand Hills and remain there until I reached him in course of time. All he had to do was to go, by slow marches, to the Hand Hills and camp. That was my instruction.

After breakfast, Matheson and I started on our journey and travelled steadily in our given direction, twenty degrees west of north. We had a compass, an axe and a little food. We travelled until late in the afternoon without finding any water, but then we reached a fine creek flowing in a deep channel through the plain. We suspected that this was Eagle Creek and began to have an idea of our whereabouts. The horses could scramble through by sliding down the bank, but they would be unable to pull the cart, so Matheson and I took off our boots and carried the stuff across and drew the cart and buckboard across also. By the time we had done this, we discovered that our legs and feet were literally covered with leeches. Of course, I was badly frightened, but Matheson only laughed at me for my fears and asked me if I had a jack-knife. Of course I had, and he told me that all that had to be done was to scrape them off. We always did that when we passed through places where there were leeches.

Next morning, we were on our way again and passed through the Bear Hills and found some water, but no wood. At length, we reached a trail which was well beaten and Matheson, when he looked at it, said that it was the main trail to Edmonton and therefore, it would take us to Battleford. This trail extends south of the Eagle Hills, whereas there is no trail going to Battleford which goes along the base of the Eagle Hills. After reaching the trail, we had no difficulty and finally arrived at Battleford, where I found my flour and oatmeal in the store.

At this time, the Hon. David Laird was Governor of the North West Territories and lived at Battleford.[11] Inspector Walker, of the North West Mounted Police, was then building the fort in the forks between the Saskatchewan and the Battle Rivers, as he expected an outbreak amongst the Indians at that time. When I told Gov. Laird that I was going to go south from Battleford to the Red Deer, he told me that it was very unwise as White Bear, the Indian Chief (who afterwards caused the rebellion in 1885)[12] was at Sounding Lake, with a large number of Indians and, as this lake was on my way to the south, he said that it would be very dangerous for me. They were on the watch at Battleford all the time, and the women were very much afraid. I told him that I was under orders and I was bound to carry them out no matter what happened, so Matheson and I started south on a trail that the Blackfeet used when they came south.   We travelled rapidly, but, after one hundred miles or more, we came into broken country[13] and had a great deal of difficulty in getting along as we left the trail and guided ourselves by compass.   I remember, one afternoon, we reached a creek and had to unload our cart, carry everything across, load up again, and, in half an hour reached the same creek and had to cross it again in the same manner.   Eventually, we reached what we thought were the Hand Hills, but saw no sign of my assistant.

Shortly after we arrived, an English half-breed, called Phillips, came to the camp and, in conversation with him, he told us a party had been there for a number of days before and had left a couple of days ago and headed for Battleford.   I asked him how he knew that they might be my party and he said: "They had iron-bound carts and I see that you have one also." We arranged with him at once for him to follow these men up and bring them back.   This was on a Tuesday and that night there came on a great thunder-storm and, for the next five days, Matheson and I lived on oatmeal porridge without salt, and this, I consider, the greatest privation any man can undergo except actual starvation.

On Sunday morning, Matheson and I determined to head for Battleford ourselves, as we could not exist without something more than oatmeal and flour.   We felt that the half-breed had been killed in the thunder-storm and, as he took our gun with him, we were finding out that we could not exist as we had nothing but the articles mentioned.   Matheson and I packed up on the Sunday morning and started on the trail, that we saw in the grass, of the half-breed that had deserted us.   We had proceeded about an hour when, in the distance, I saw a man on horse-back riding at a furious rate from the direction in which we were going. We waited until he came up and we found him to be Phillips, who told us that he had gone eighty-seven miles before he overtook the party and that they were now coming back and would reach camp in the afternoon.   We returned to our old camp at once.

While waiting for the return of the party that had run away, I made quite an examination of the vicinity and saw a great many evidences of what had taken place in the past. ◼We were apparently camping where a great battle had taken place between the Crees and the Blackfeet. Skulls and leg-bones were seen in many places in large quantities although the smaller bones had been eaten up by the animals. Great circles of stone were found and in one place we found where the chief's tent had been pitched surrounded with the tents of his warriors. This was the order in which I found the Blackfeet encampment a few days later, when we reached there.

In the absence of the other party, Matheson and I had come to the conclusion that, as my work for the season was now done, I would have ample time to go to Calgary and up to Old Bow Fort and get back to Battleford in time to go east. On the return of the party, I broached the subject to them and gave Mr. Wilkins provisions for fifty days for himself and two men, while Ogilvie decided to go with Matheson and myself. The Wilkins party was to proceed by slow marches up along the Red Deer River for a certain distance and then turn north and west and not attempt to reach Battleford before the 10th of October. The next day, they started on the proposed route and Phillips, the English half-breed, told me that he could show me a way down to the Red Deer valley, where there was a ford and a way up on the opposite side, to the prairie beyond. On examination, I found that this was really where the Blackfeet crossed the Red Deer when they were meaning to attack the Crees. We found little difficulty in descending the five hundred feet that formed the bank of the Red Deer about a mile below where we had camped. We found the valley by the Red Deer to be but a few hundred yards wide and the river a beautiful stream of clear water, flowing through its centre. Ascending on the opposite side was more difficult than descending, but it gave me an opportunity to see the rocks on both sides. The strata was exposed so that I could see layers of coal and remains of extinct animals and shale and solid rock. I had never seen such an exposure before.

When we reached the summit, we entered what was called Crowfoot Coulee, and, in this, I discovered my first coal exposure, from which we took fuel to burn.   We knew that to the south of us was the Blackfeet encampment, and, before we reached it, we expected to find a trail that would take us to Calgary.   As we approached the trail, we found that every small hill was occupied by a man and a horse, the man standing at the horse's head.   Matheson said: "Why, those are Blackfeet pickets and we are surely surrounded by the Blackfeet."   I took in the situation at once and said: "We will go into the Blackfeet encampment and not risk ourselves and our horses on the exposed prairies after dark."

When we reached the trail, we crossed it and went on south and came to the Blackfeet encampment a little before dark. There were about one hundred and twenty-five beautiful tents, most of them being made of tanned buffalo hide.   We were unable of course, to talk to the people, but a number of women came around the camp while we were eating and I gave them pieces of biscuits and, by signs, they asked us if they could wash the plates. We said yes and, before they washed the plates, they actually licked them clean.   We were wondering why no men were to be seen when an Irishman, Father Scallen, who was the missionary attached to the tribe, came to see us and asked me what in the world made us come there.   I said at once: "I came here for safety because out on the prairie we felt that we were surrounded by the Indians."   He said: "Do you know that the people here are dying of starvation?"   I said: "Certainly not, we have come from the north and have had no word that anything was the matter here."   He said: "There are two lying dead in their tents now who have died of starvation."   When I heard this I said: "You tell the Chief that I am going up to Calgary and that to-morrow I will give him all the provisions I have except what we will need to take with us up to the fort."   We retired and left all of our provisions in the cart and had our doubts as to whether we would see any of them in the morning.   We were agreeably surprised, therefore, that not one particle of our food had been touched.   Father Scallen came to see me again in the morning and I told him that I was going to remain for the day and to tell the Chief, who was Crowfoot, since so celebrated, that I would have dinner for himself and all his Chiefs at noon.

11

At noon, Father Scallen and six or seven distinguished looking Indians came to dinner. When we were about through, a
young man in great excitement came to the tent door and said
something in Blackfeet and, immediately, Father Scallen jumped
to his feet and ran out of the tent, followed by all my guests except
Crowfoot and his brother, who was the War Chief. Afterwards,
Ogilvie and I went out to the prairie to look around and we found
that all the people seemed to be going towards the Bow River.
We walked down towards the river and, on the way, Father
Scallen came up to us again, riding on his fine horse. I said:
"Father, what in the world is up, that you all should run away?"
"Oh," he said, "I did not tell you. That young fellow came and
told us that the Buffalo were close up on the other side of the
river and I and the others ran to the hills to get our horses and,
in a few moments, you will see quite a procession." And, sure
enough, we did. He gave up his horse to the War Chief, who
immediately mounted and proceeded to the river and plunged in,
and then came a stream of young braves on horseback, armed
with guns and without any clothes except the usual breech-clout.
Nearly every horse had an Indian hanging on to his tail as they
went across. As soon as they reached the far side, they disappeared over the sand hills, and Ogilvie and I were left to do as
we thought fit.

Late in the afternoon, the men returned and the War Chief,
who had Father Scallen's horse, had killed no less than six cows
and the others had killed numbers also. The Priest's horse, of
course, was the best buffalo runner and that was why the Chief
was so successful. The next morning, I visited the War Chief.

When I called on him, that morning, he was sitting in
his tent like a lord and, in front of him, was a large heap of bloody
meat, cut up into pieces of possibly 20 pounds weight. Every
once in a while, a squaw would come into the tent and say some
words in their language, and he would nod his head and she would
take a large chunk and leave. This went on all the time I was
with him. The advent of the buffalo relieved me of giving my
provisions, so we packed up and left their camp for Calgary in
the afternoon.

We had now ceased to travel by compass and had the beaten trail which we followed clearly. On our arrival at Calgary, we camped under Nose Hill, where there was a ford, and visited the the fort, which was a stockade placed on the north side of the Elbow River where it entered the "Bow." At this time, there was only one house on the site of the present Calgary and it was I. J. Baker's store and the clerk, from whom I bought some necessaries, was Mr. King, who is now Postmaster of Calgary. After spending a short time at Calgary, we went up to Morley, and from Morley to Old Bow Fort, at the entrance to the Rocky Mountains. We went up the Bow as far as the Point of Rocks and looked up the valley, down which Cascade Creek comes, and which I believed to have been the valley of the Bow. While at this point, we caught many large trout in the Bow, and saw the Stony Indians hunting goats on the mountain to the north. From this point, we returned to Morley and were soon on our way to Edmonton. Matheson, Ogilvie, and myself were now satisfied that we had done our work and my object was to reach Battleford by the 11th of October. Shortly after we crossed the Red Deer River, Matheson rode on to Edmonton to see his father, who then resided at that place. I instructed him to be at Battleford on or before the 10th and, the day he arrived, he was to start Wilkins on his way East. Ogilvie and I were now alone and, for four hundred miles, we saw no person except when we reached Hay Lakes, thirty miles from Edmonton, where there was a telegraph station. It happened that the day before I reached there, Dr. George Dawson[14] and the Rev. Mr. Gordon had been there and sent a long telegram regarding their work at the Peace River. I may mention here that Dr. Dawson was sent to see whether he would agree with my report of 1875 on the Peace River and the other parties that I spoke of were sent to examine the "Fertile Belt" and north of it, and see if they confirmed my reports.[15] I found later that I had been sent to see if Palliser's report was of any value. After seeing Dr. Dawson's report, I sent a long one also and told that I had seen no bad country at all.

Ogilvie and I took the trail for Battleford and, as it was now getting late in the season, we hurried on—but three hundred miles is a long distance to travel at a slow pace and it was on the 15th of October when we found, by observation, that we were nearing Battleford.   For a number of days, we had been passing over ground without any trees or shrubs and our fuel had given out.   Our thermometer showed, on our last morning on the prairie, to have fallen to 16 degrees and, as it was the last day we expected to sleep in the tent, we cut up the poles and made a good fire and warmed ourselves.   On this last day, we travelled fast and almost at sun-down we saw Battleford about eight miles off and, after some delay and taking a wrong trail, at the foot of the hill, we at last reached Battleford by guess.   I had seen the Evening Star while on the trail, rising to the left of Battleford, and so we steered for the Star allowing a little for its increase in altitude, and reached Battleford late in the night and camped right in the road.

In the morning, we reached the town and found Matheson there.   He told me that Savage was in jail and had been there for a month.   On making inquiries, I found that he and Wilkins had had a quarrel on the prairie and, by the efforts of David Macoun, there was no blood shed, but Wilkins swore that Savage was going to take his life and, besides, he had mutinied.   I saw the Magistrate and talked the matter over with him and, at my request, he allowed Savage to be set free.   I offered to take him with me, but he said he preferred staying at Battleford.   He remained there all winter and came next year to Winnipeg, but I never saw him again.

After leaving Battleford,[16] we took the lower road, which was along the Saskatchewan and found it a worse trail than the one that Matheson and I had followed in the summer, south of the Eagle Hills.   We hurried on and, in a few days, overtook Wilkins and found that he was making very little progress.   After a couple of days, I decided that Ogilvie and I would leave the party and proceed as quickly as possible to Winnipeg, so that I could make out my accounts and have everything properly arranged when the others reached the city.   After a number of adventures and some difficulties, Ogilvie and I reached Winnipeg.   On the same evening that I arrived, an engineer named Barclay reached

Winnipeg with his party and, before many hours, his whole party, besides Ogilvie, were as drunk as men could possibly be and Barclay and myself were the only sober men. It was ten days after this before my party arrived and, in that time, Ogilvie had been no use to me as he was drunk the most of the time and, worse for himself, had used up all his wages.

I found that, since spring, there had been great changes in Winnipeg and a large number of influential men were then in the city and I told numerous people about what I had seen on my travels and it was not long before I was asked to lecture and I had to refuse because it was understood that no explorer could make statements for publication until he had reported to the Government. My friends told me that Sir Charles Tupper was then on the way to Winnipeg and, if I had permission from him to lecture, would I do so. I told them that I would like to very much, and they wired to Sir Charles and, I suppose, told him that my report of the country would be in accord with his views, so he gave permission. It was soon arranged that I would give a lecture in the Court House and Chief Justice Wood of Manitoba was in the chair. The audience was the finest one I have ever had to listen to me. Apparently, there were over one thousand men, all full of enthusiasm. I was just in the condition to fill them full, because I was in a state of more than common excitement. In announcing the discoveries I had made, I fearlessly announced that the so-called arid country was one of unsurpassed fertility and that it was literally the "Garden" of the whole country. I also called attention to the Qu'Appelle country and showed that at least 12,000,000 acres were in one solid block on both sides of the river. I told them so many things that they were filled with amazement and, to wind up, I declared that these lands lay at their very doors and were without inhabitant. My lecture was published verbatim and the "Winnipeg Free Press" devoted more than a page to it.[17]

In passing through, on the railroad, from Winnipeg to Fargo, North Dakota, I was reminded of the time when I went in the stage coach with a number of shivering passengers, as we passed over the bleak prairies of Dakota. The winter stage coach ride of fifty-eight consecutive hours from Winnipeg to Fargo, which I took in 1875, made a most lasting impression upon my mind. Night and day we kept on and enjoying a nap, in a stage coach with the temperature at zero, was the greatest luxury we had. Our waking moments were filled with torture, but sleep, such as it was, made us oblivious to suffering to the very marrow in our bones, which seemed to be freezing and, as I think of it, I shudder at the recollection. We had a very pleasant trip on the present journey to Belleville and reached there in due season, and I found my family all well.

On my arrival home, I very soon saw that my life, as hitherto, would advance a stage and I would take a more prominent place in the eyes of the public. On this account, I will write a short summary of the causes that produced those changes that took place in Canada, after 1850. I wish more particularly to state my connection with the North West as I soon saw that my life was now passing from that of a teacher to that of a public man.

CHAPTER X

1879-1880

REVIEW OF CONDITIONS IN CANADA IN REGARD TO POLITICS AND
THE CONSTRUCTION OF THE CANADIAN PACIFIC RAILWAY—
CONFEDERATION—PURCHASE OF LAND FROM THE HUDSON'S
BAY COMPANY—FIRST RIEL REBELLION—EXPLORATION FOR
ROUTE OF C.P.R.—CONTRADICTORY STATEMENTS IN REGARD
TO VALUE OF PRAIRIES FOR AGRICULTURE—FOURTH EXPLOR-
ATION OF THE CANADIAN NORTH-WEST, 1880—QU'APPELLE
VALLEY, MOOSE JAW, OLD WIVES LAKES, SWIFT CURRENT,
CYPRESS HILLS, FORT WALSH, HUMBOLDT, ETC.—MEETINGS
WITH INDIANS—MANY INTERESTING EPISODES AND INCI-
DENTS..

WHEN we reached Canada in the year 1850, Ontario was then called Upper Canada and Quebec was known as Lower Canada. These two provinces were united and held Parliaments alternately in Quebec and Ontario. After a certain amount of discussion, it was decided to have a Capital for these two provinces, and Queen Victoria was asked to make a selection. She did so and selected Ottawa, which was then called Bytown. Immediately, a commencement was made to erect Parliament Buildings that would be permanent and, in 1867, the buildings were completed and occupied. Before this time, nego-tiations had been carried on with the Maritime Provinces, that is, Prince Edward Island, Nova Scotia and New Brunswick. Con-federation was carried and John A. Macdonald and George Brown buried the hatchet and united, to perfect the Confederation. It took some little time to cause George Brown to leave the Govern-ment, and the two parties, called Tories and Reformers, were organized again. John A. Macdonald, as soon as he got in power, resolved to carry on what he had advocated years before; that is, the purchase of the Hudson's Bay Territories from the Company. This was carried into effect in 1869, the year I was on Lake

Superior.   In 1870, Riel revolted and was quelled by General
Wolseley, who took a large number of Canadians across from Port
Arthur to Winnipeg.   The next move of John A. was to unite
the Eastern Provinces with British Columbia, and this was accomplished in 1871.   In making the bargain, he agreed with
British Columbia to build a railroad from Ontario to the Pacific
so as to connect the whole country.   This bargain was strenuously
opposed by the so-called Liberals, or, as they were called then,
the "Grits."   This opposition continued for over fifteen years.

I will now try to explain the cause of the delay and difficulty
that occured in connection with the building of the road.   Captain Palliser had been instructed by the British Government to
see if it were possible to overcome the difficulties of connection
between the Canadas and the country west of Lake Superior and
north of the 49th Parallel.   Palliser was sent out in the year 1857
with a party of engineers and scientific men to see if there were
any practicable passes in the Rocky Mountains by which horses
could cross to British Columbia.   After spending the summers of
1857, 1858 and 1859 in exploring the country, he returned and
reported on his mission.   His conclusions regarding the passes
through the mountains were *as accurate* as his conclusions regarding the lands.[1]   On page sixteen of his report is this revelation
"The connection, therefore, of the Saskatchewan plains east of
the Rocky Mountains, with a known route through British Columbia, has been effected by the expedition under my command
without our having been under a necessity of passing through
any portion of the United States' territory.   Still, the knowledge
of the country, on the whole, would never lead me to advocate a
line of communication from Canada, across the continent to the
Pacific, exclusively through British territory.   The time has now
forever gone by for effecting such an object.   The unfortunate
choice of an astronomical boundary line has completely isolated
the Central American possession of Great Britain from Canada,
in the east, and almost debarred them from eligible access from
the Pacific, on the coast of the west."[2]

Years came and went; Canada acquired control of the interior, united with British Columbia, and, as a part of the con-

tract, agreed to build a road through the mountain barrier, declared by Palliser to be impossible. Parties were organized in the month of June, 1871, for the purpose of making an instrumental survey and gathering knowledge of that little known country extending from Ottawa to the Pacific, that would enable our engineers to locate a railway line with an easy grade from west to east. Mr. Sandford Fleming was appointed the Chief Engineer and, with characteristic energy, he set to work. Parties were at once organized and the first detachment left by the River Ottawa for the interior on the 10th of June. On the west coast, a party of the staff left Victoria for the mountains the very day that British Columbia entered the union, July 20th, 1871. Besides examining the country generally, two of the Rocky Mountain passes were to be carefully explored; the Yellowhead Pass, entering the mountains by the Athabasca River, and Howe's Pass, which is the source of the North Saskatchewan. The year 1871 closed with the knowledge that no insuperable barrier prevented the union of British Columbia with the east by an iron road. The magnitude of the undertaking now became apparent and the necessity of building a road over 2,730 miles through an almost wholly unknown region was laughed at in the United States and the project was looked upon as chimerical by the people of the Mother Country and opposed by the "Grits" of our own country.

Early in the summer of 1872, the Chief Engineer decided on crossing the country himself and, by a mere chance, as described elsewhere, I went with him. On our arrival at Edmonton, the party separated and Mr. Horetzky and myself started for the country bordering on the great Peace River, to examine this Pass and reach the Pacific by the best means in our power. Two months of hardship, found us west of the Rocky Mountains and, instead of one Pass, we found two; the Peace River and the Pine River Pass. On his return, the Rev. G. M. Grant published his work, "Ocean to Ocean" and at once the ideas of the reading public were turned to this wonderful country which he described in such glowing terms. My report of what I saw was published in 1874, and, as I frequently stated what I believed, my report was much criticised, my statements and conclusions being at variance with the popular opinion. Two more years passed away, line after line had been surveyed, and knowledge had spread regarding the country. I had been in British Columbia, had seen the Peace River country in summer and had gone down the mighty stream to Lake Athabasca. Again, I reported on the country and this time stronger than before, showing at the same time the products of the soil in testimony of my statements.

In the spring of 1876, I was before the Committee of the Dominion Parliament to give evidence as to the character of the country to Winnipeg and the Pacific[3] and, although held up to ridicule by some of the members, Mr. James Trow, Chairman of the Committee of Colonization, became interested and believed the greater part of my apparent extravagances and, next year, crossed the country to the Saskatchewan and saw for himself.[4]

By the year 1877, the surveys were apparently drawing to a close, and this year I was invited to write a report on the whole country for the information of Mr. Mackenzie, who was Minister of Public Works, and cautioned, in plain words, not to draw on my imagination. In response to this, I wrote as much truth about the country as I dared, for I saw that even yet my best friends believed me rather wild on the "illimitable possibilities" of the country. When summing up various areas, I reached the enormous figures of 200,000,000 acres and recoiled from making public this number on the ground that the very immensity would deny that amount of credence I desired so, as a salve to my conscience, I kept to the large number of 200,000,000 but said that there were 79,920,400 acres of arable land and 120,400,000 acres of pasture, swamps and lakes.[5] At this time, there was so much to engross the minds of the people; the surveys seemed endless; the expense was enormous, that many Members of the House, and at least one Leader, (Mr. Blake) became so conservative that he considered British Columbia was bought at too high a price. My statements appeared as those of an honest but cracked-brained enthusiast and little attention was paid to them. The country was declared to be largely an irreclaimable waste which was too arid for the growth of grain, where there would be extreme danger from frost and the severity of the winter, and periodical visits of the grass-hoppers. These statements were brought in to do duty in aid of the speaker who might oppose me.

I will now make some remarks about the commencement of the railway construction to bring the matter up to date. In 1867, patriots established the Dominion of Canada and at once the cry was raised for our rights in the West. A determined stand was now made and most extraordinary stories were told in England before the committee of the House of Commons showing that the country was little better than an iceberg. This was done by men who knew the country well but they wished to continue their ill-gotten gains. In 1868, Bishop Taché published his sketch of the Northwest and he, too, like the Hudson's Bay Company, looked upon the country as scarcely suited for civilized men. Its rivers were supposed to be unsuited for navigation, and its climate hyperborean. One section, however, is spoken of as being suited to a farming community, indeed, on page 63, when discussing the probabilities as to who the future owners of the country would be, he says: "For my own part, as there are extremely great advantages in the way of colonizing the few points in this vast territory capable of cultivation, I acknowledge frequently that I would as soon (perhaps preferably) see the country remain as it is as to see it changed, if the changes are to be such as it appears to me they would inevitably be."[6]

It will be remembered that, in the early stages of the settlement, French half-breeds lived entirely by hunting and had their headquarters at Pembina. Our people commenced to survey the very lands these claimed as their own, without making any arrangements with the half-breeds. This was the cause of the half-breed outbreak in the winter of 1869. On the 11th of October, a survey party under Mr. Webb was stopped by a party of French half-breeds under Louis Riel. They were very peaceable and did nothing worse than to step on the chain. Mr. Webb ceased work and retired. Mr. Webb, through Col. Dennis, applied to the Hudson's Bay Company, but they paid no attention to the application. The murder of Scott followed later on and the expedition by Gen. Wolseley in 1870 brought the rebellion to a close.

The construction of a transcontinental railway formed part of the basis of union between the Dominion of Canada and British Columbia. The admission of that province took place in 1871. Steps were at once taken to make a survey of the proposed line. Part of the arrangement was to build a line from Winnipeg to Emerson to meet the railways coming up from St. Paul. The reason of this was to enable the Mackenzie Government to bring supplies from the United States as the road from Port Arthur to Winnipeg was going to take a very long time to build. This branch-line was completed in the spring of 1879 and, about this time, a syndicate of Canadian and American capitalists obtained control of the St. Paul, Minneapolis and Manitoba Railway and all its connections. No time was lost by them in completing their line, to make connections with the Canadian road at St. Vincent (Pembina). Many things were transpiring now in a short time, and history was being made. Winnipeg, by this time, had caught a strong hold on the country and had begun to see a great future. Winnipeg wished a railway-bridge to be built across the Red River at Winnipeg, to connect with the Government road coming from Lake Superior. Many battles took place at Ottawa around the building of this bridge, and Mr. Fleming, who was Chief Engineer, refused to build the bridge and use it as a connection with the railway. He intended to cross the Red River at Selkirk and build direct to Portage La Prairie, and, in fact, had the road surveyed. I was at Ottawa at this time and I agreed with Mr. Fleming that it was dangerous to build the railway bridge on account of the great floods that had taken place there for months in 1825 and other years. My later knowledge showed that Mr. Fleming had not taken into account that the Red River was perhaps four times as wide in 1879 as it was in 1825. I make the following statement of a Mr. McDermot, one of the early settlers: "The Red River channel at Winnipeg is very different now to what it was when the first settlers came in. The soil is alluvial and the continual action of the water on the banks is having the effect of increasing the width of the waterway." It is said that Mr. McDermot first crossed the stream on a small oak tree that had fallen into the channel. Today, several trees would be necessary to span the river, for the width is about three hundred yards on an average.

In order that the magnitude of the undertaking in building the Transcontinental Railway may be properly estimated, I will give a review of what had been done during the eight years of the surveys from their inception to the close of 1879.   In June, 1871, the country was still in the state it had been for ages.   Annual fires crossed the prairies; periodical quarrels took place amongst the Indian tribes; the buffalo came and went; and the long, cold winters passed away and were succeeded by the genial warmth of spring.   In 1873, the Boundary Commission commenced operations at the Lake of the Woods and, in the two succeeding years, continued their work west to the Rocky Mountains.   Early in 1874, the Mounted Police were organized and sent out and at once law and order reigned on the plains.

The first money provided for the survey of the Canadian Pacific Railway was in the session of 1871.   Callander, close to Lake Nipissing was the first point pitched upon.   From this point, the line was projected to go north of Lake Superior and, from thence, passing the Lake of the Woods, reach the Red River at Selkirk, near Winnipeg, on the prairie.   From this point, the line was projected to cross the narrows of Lake Manitoba, pass through the low country lying at the base of Duck Mountain, up the valley of Swan River and westward from Livingstone (Swan River) Barracks to the Elbow of the North Saskatchewan and thence west to Battleford, Hay Lakes (Edmonton) and so on to the Rocky Mountains at Jasper House.

In the spring of 1879, other surveys were made of the country south of Lake Manitoba for the purpose of running the line south of the Riding and Duck Settlement.   Two summers were spent on these surveys, and the line definitely located for two hundred miles and one hundred of these placed under construction.[7]

In the early winter of 1879, I was summoned to Ottawa to make my report and the authorities were so pleased with my work that they asked me to remain in Mr. Fleming's office all winter and revise the reports of the other parties as well as completing my own.   Mr. Rideout was the editor of the "Railway Report for

1879-80'' and I was his assistant.[8] That winter, there were a
great many discussions in Parliament and I was constantly correcting mistakes made by the Opposition and lecturing in various
places when called upon by the people.   On this account, I had
the whole question at my finger ends and had no difficulty in overcoming opposition from every quarter.   The debates in the House
were very acrimonious and brought out the animus of the speakers
so plainly that you could see that the statements of the Opposition
were for opposition only, not having any regard for the facts.

Like all new countries, many conflicting accounts were given
of Manitoba and the North West.   Travellers and others, whose
names, out of deference to their standing in society, I will not
mention, wrote *strong stories* about the country.   Manitoba was
declared to be little else than a bog or marsh.   The great plain
was shown conclusively to be a desert.   The sandy, barren waste
declared by those men to be useless, but still rich by nature.
Others, passing hurriedly over its trails and seeing sand or gravel
in the ruts or around the badger holes wrote: ''The whole region
passed over today possesses the sandy or gravelly soil and an arid
climate and is worthless for agricultural purposes.''   In the hands
of practical farmers, the latter has so changed its appearance that
another class of writers see and write of its unequalled qualities
for farming purposes in the North West.

My work, now passed, has been to refute false statements
regarding the country, its climate, soil, capabilities and resources.
By whomsoever misleading statements were made, I met it with
prompt denial and have always given my reasons for doing so.
There is one class of speakers, however, to whom I have made no
answer.   This class comprise the representatives of the people
and, if they make statements at variance with known facts, it is
not my province to dispute them

As I have said, I remained in Ottawa during the winter of
1879 and '80.   I worked in the office of Mr. Fleming and was
acquainted with all the discussions and squabbles that were going
on in the House and country.   My reports of previous years had
caused quite a ferment amongst the people and the Members
naturally took sides with Sir John or Mr. Mackenzie.   I attended

the discussions in the House and, at one of these, when Sir John
brought in the bill to build the road from Ocean to Ocean, Mr.
Mackenzie, who, I think, opened the debate in opposition to Sir
John, stated that the country was of very little value and held to
the opinions of Palliser[9] and others who deprecated the whole
country.   In his desk at this time, he had my report written in
1877 for himself and, instead of using it, he ignored it altogether
and quoted Bishop Taché and Palliser.   I became so excited that
I called out that he had my report in his desk and why not read
it also.   In a minute, I felt a hand on my shoulder and, on looking
up, I saw one of the ushers, who invited me to keep still or else
leave the building.   Either on this occasion or another one, Mr.
Blake, who, apparently, was leading the House, said that the
railway, when built, would not earn enough to pay for the grease
for its wheels.   His idea of building the road was to build it as
fast as the settlers went in.   He was utterly opposed to British
Columbia and objected strongly to the road being built west of
the   mountains.   He brought up the question of the absence of
maps of British Columbia and he asked Sir John to have one made
that would give them some idea of the country.   I was asked to
see that a map was prepared, and did so.   All the arable land
that I knew of was to be left in white and all the rest was to be
colored brown.   To my horror, when it was produced, it was
almost all brown.   Mr. Blake, when he received the map, looked
over it and very calmly held it up and shook it at De Cosmos,
who was then Member for Victoria, and said to him, "Macoun,
who is your champion, has done you brown."[10] Before this, I had
stated in conversation with Mr. Blake, that there was very little
agricultural land in British Columbia but it contained immense
forests of the finest of timbers, unknown quantities of minerals
and more edible fishes than any other part of the Dominion.   Sir
Charles Tupper, as Minister of Railways, formally acknowledged
his belief in my statements and, in his great speech on the Pacific
Railway, in the spring of 1880, accepted my figures as the basis
of his calculations,[11] but not before he had satisfied himself that my
statements were not the guesses of an ill-informed enthusiast.   A
number of gentlemen had taken up the railway route by Pine

Pass in preference to that of the Yellowhead Pass and considered it their duty to belittle my statements and, in one or two instances, to make counter ones. The first route was advocated by the Liberals, or Grits, and the second by the Government. In my report of this year, I classified the lands on the basis of all the knowledge hitherto obtained and showed that there were 150,000,-000 acres suitable for pastures and wheat culture.[12]

Before Sir Charles made his speech, he came into the room where I was working and he said, "Macoun, Fleming and myself are prepared to swear by you, but, for God's sake, do not draw on your imagination." Sir John, himself, had his doubts of me and was far less enthusiastic of the country than Sir Charles Tupper. As a proof of this, I may state that, in an interview I had with the Premier in May, 1880, he said: "Mr. Macoun, I think you are very enthusiastic regarding the country." I said: "It may be so, Sir John, but my enthusiasm is bred of belief." Before this, Mr. Mackenzie and Mr. Blake had shown, in their speeches, during the session just closed, that the country was of little value. Sir John, I could see, scarcely allowed himself to accept as a fact that which he so ardently desired, but Sir Charles Tupper entertained no doubts and encouraged me to do my duty and stick to what I considered to be the truth.[13]

While not at work at Ottawa, I was called to various cities in Ontario to lecture. I can remember especially being at Kingston, two days at Toronto, and also two at Hamilton and, in every case, the hall or church was filled with an applauding, enthusiastic crowd.

During the summer of 1880, I was sent to the field, but this time I received a map of the country with a blue line placed in zig-zag fashion upon it and was asked to travel on this line during the summer. The line itself was intended for me to go through all the worst places mentioned in previous reports. My party, this year, consisted of my nephew, David Macoun, George Moore, of Winnipeg, and Mr. Woods, of Madoc. My Government assistant was Mr. Jukes, of Niagara District, and, from Captain Therket, a nephew of Col. Dennis, I received my instructions. My previous exploration had caused the surveys to be conducted that year more to the south and Marcus Smith and a large party examined the country around Fort Ellice and westward.   The survey was carried past Portage La Prairie and in the direction of where Brandon now stands and before I left Ottawa, it was decided that the city of Brandon should be laid out as a city and that the road, in any case, was to pass that way.   This cut out Odanah and Minnedosa, where the people expected the line would pass if it went north.   It was much easier reaching Winnipeg in the spring of 1880 than it had been the other seasons, when I came out and, as I was going south from Brandon this year, I went up to the Grand Rapids by boat as I did in the preceding year.   Marcus Smith, with his large party and myself and my party, almost filled the boat, although there were many Englishmen on board who were going to take up land in the vicinity of the Grand Rapids.

When we landed, my stuff was all to be put on the south side of the river while Marcus Smith and his men camped on the north side.   The only incident I remember of importance as taking place at that time was one that was characteristic of exploration parties.   Marcus and myself had each taken a keg of lime-juice, containing five gallons, but, when Marcus wished for his lime-juice in the evening, behold, it was gone.   He immediately sent his assistant to me, expecting that I had it amongst my stuff and, behold, my keg was gone also.   The only difference between us was that mine was really lime-juice and Marcus' was whiskey.

This summer, Sir John went to England and he was able to form a syndicate and men ready to furnish the means to build the railroad.   In the winter, the surveys had been extended to this Grand Valley, where I was camped, and Mr. Smith was now getting ready to extend them further.

While in camp at the Grand Valley, I had ample opportunity of studying the peculiarities of the people, Camped by themselves were a number of English families, the members of which kept themselves apart from all others and seemed to court seclusion.   No attempt was made to gain information and, as a usual result, no one was profited.   One day, two young men with
12

their outfit started off for Rapid City.   Owing to the heavy rain
which had been falling for some days, the trail was very bad in
many places.   Lacking experience and being accustomed neither
to ask nor take advice, they made little progress and camped less
than a mile from the Landing, after having loaded and unloaded
their wagon four times.   Scarcely any progress was made the
next day and the second night they camped at a water-hole in a
little hollow.   A Canadian, passing by, told them to pitch their
tent on an adjoining hill as the mosquitoes would be bad that
night.   In response, he was informed that they knew their own
business.   How they passed the night is not known, but, early
the next forenoon, they reached the Landing again, sold their
outfit for what they could get and were off for more congenial
companionship in Winnipeg.   On the same boat which took them
back were a number of others who, like themselves, through ignorance, self-will, or cowardice, had given up in disgust.

     I was camped on the south side of the river and, late one
evening, three young Englishmen crossed the river with two heavy
loads of goods and two prairie carts.   While we were remarking
on their foolishness for starting so late, they passed us without a
word and proceeded on their way towards the Brandon Hills, to
which they were bound.   They had not gone two hundred yards
when an axle broke and their load fell to the ground.   We went
up to see what was the matter and, as soon as I learned the nature
of the accident, I offered to loan them a cart and had my men
assist them in loading it up, but I advised them then to stop all
night where they were, or leave part of their load.   The leader of
the party now asked me my charge for the cart and assistance
and, as I only laughed at him, he said they had been told before
they left England to hold no communication with Canadians as
they would charge an exorbitant price for everything they sold,
and do nothing for you without pay.

     We became more confidential and I told them what we
thought of them and how we looked on their proceedings. As I
advised him to leave potatoes and flour and a large trunk in his
broken cart during the next day, he asked would it not be stolen?
I informed him that only white men stole and that Indians and

half-breeds, no matter what was said to the contrary, were strictly honest and, as a matter of principle, did not appropriate anything found on the prairie.

My instructions were to proceed from the Grand Valley to Moose Mountain and I was waiting for the remainder of my outfit on the next boat so that, when I received it, we started on our line of travel. As I have already stated, I had a map given to me by Col. Dennis upon which he had marked with a blue line the track I was to take for my summer trip. On this line, I proceeded for the whole summer and the first "leg" was to Moose Mountain. In the evening of our second day out, a thunder-storm arose in the west and, when close upon us, two of our horses ran away in front of the storm. These horses were my own and were very fine Canadian horses. The other horses had all been hobbled and, as soon as mine ran away, I ran out of my tent bareheaded and followed them. Davie Macoun immediately caught a horse, took off the hobbles, jumped on his back and, carrying two spare halters, galloped after me. It was almost dark and the lightning and thunder were awful. Davie galloped past me and headed the horses and, half a mile from camp, we rounded them up. Another man came rushing up and we put a halter on each of them, and the storm was about over by this time. Each flash of lightning made me feel as though it was to be our last and I ordered each man to take a halter and I took another and kept away from the horse so that if the horses were struck we might be saved. The next ten minutes were awful. The strain was dreadful on all of us, but the storm passed and at once darkness came on and we had no idea which was the direction or way to find the camp.

When darkness came on, Mr. Jukes ordered lights to be put up and, by good luck, we saw the glow and made our way to camp which we found in good order and the tents standing as we had left them.

In 1879, I had learned from Matheson how to pitch a camp and, as we always practiced it, it came into order for this storm. When seeking a camping place for the night, any time during the summer, an elevated spot, near a hill and water, should be chosen so that comparative freedom from mosquitoes may be secured, if there should be a little wind.   Feed and shelter for the horses are absolutely necessary, as both may be needed by night.   All the conveniences should be placed west of the tent, and each tent securely tied to a cart by the guy rope, passing over the end of the ridge pole.   The rear of the tents should be next to the carts, so that, should a storm arise in the night, there would be no danger of the tents being blown down.   By taking these precautions, no storm can do much damage and men fall into the habit of doing this as a matter of routine.

In the latter part of June, 1879, I encamped on the trail, just west of Qu'Appelle, but on a plateau above the river valley. About three hundred yards distant, another exploring party stopped for the night.   We arranged our camp in our usual manner, and retired to rest.   About two o'clock, a.m., a terrific storm, rain, thunder and wind, broke over us, and for five hours we lay and listened to the terrific uproar.   After the rain had ceased, we attempted to make a fire, but could not succeed for some time owing to the force of the wind and wetness of the wood. · Our tents had withstood the tempest's strength and kept us perfectly dry.   Not so with our friends in the other camp.   Their tent had been blown down at the commencement of the storm and there was not a man in the camp that had a dry rag.   Of course, in letters to their friends, they made out that their wretchedness was not due to their own carelessness.   I visited their camp and found that the storm was altogether unexpected and had caught them unprepared, and their tents tumbled about their ears in a few moments.

I soon found that my party this year was far inferior to the party I had last year when Matheson knew the prairie and modes of travel, and Ogilvie also, and they were first class men.   In our present case, Davie and myself were the only men who were of any use, the others were inexperienced and, in some cases, inefficient.   Of course, crossing the prairies without a road was .a serious matter, and we had to cross a number of creeks with steep sides or coolies in which they ran, and our difficulties were enhanced by the ignorance of the men.   We reached Moose Mountain in safety, however, and found it just as it had been reported, a series of hills surrounded by water and the hills protected from fires by the water, but there were no signs of a mountain. Here we had our first view of an elk, and, I am sorry to say, my last view. As we were going along the trail, a few yards from us, an immense elk jumped to his feet, apparently with a spread of horns six feet wide and a splendid looking animal. We gazed at him and he at us and then turned about and, as far as the eye could see, he galloped without a stop until he was lost in the distance. This was the first and last deer that we saw on the prairie.

My next objective was Old Wives Lakes, and Mr. Jukes laid our course for the centre of the Lakes. We now entered upon a section of the prairie that was extremely rugged, although almost level; we called it "The Great Clay Plain," and Regina is situated on the northern end of it. The ground was so rough on account of the great cracks that were in it, that the horses' shoulders got sore with the jarring of the carts and water became so scarce that we could only obtain it by digging into the clay in a hollow. One Saturday evening, we reached a beautiful pool of water and camped and decided to remain over Sunday. Sunday evening, a thunder-storm came up and, after it was over, there was a clear sky to the west and we saw a lake quite distinctly and decided that this was Old Wives Lake for a certainty. Mr. Jukes immediately took its bearings and Davie and I decided to go to the lake the next day.

Getting the right direction from Mr. Jukes, Davie and I, with my buckboard, started in the morning to see if we could reach the lake. We travelled twenty miles and came up against the Dirt Hills, which are the outliers of the Coteau. We found no lake and saw no sign of one and very little water, excepting at a small creek that we crossed on our way to the hills. On Tuesday evening, we reached camp and next morning were about to start for the day's trip when I asked Mr. Jukes if our water keg was filled and he said "No; but we will fill it at the first waterhole we reach." I laughed and told him that likely this one was the last we would see for some days. Davie asked to fill it and I said: "No; they must bear the penalty of their own misdeeds." We travelled all that day and neither horse nor man saw a drop of water and, late in the evening, we had to camp and I decided to start due north in the morning in an attempt to reach Moose Jaw Creek, which I knew must be to the north. By this time the men began to realize their foolishness in not doing what they always had done, both this year and last year.

"Travellers should always have a five or ten gallon keg with them and see that this is filled with good water at least once a day. When travelling, without a guide, this is absolutely necessary, as water may be extremely scarce in the district where a person may chance to be and great suffering may result. In July, 1880, my party and I were thirty hours without water owing to the carelessness of the man whose job it was to see that a supply was on hand. We were never without water again, and I gave no instructions regarding it. The above incident happened on the western part of the Great Souris Plain. The plain, for sixty miles east of the Canadian Pacific Railway crossing at Moose Jaw Creek, is waterless and great caution is necessary when traversing it. Many other localities where water is scarce might be cited, but it is unnecessary to mention them as wise men will be prepared for all such, while fools will run to their own destruction, or, like my party, suffer for their neglect of known duty. Water suitable for horses is generally obtainable at least once a day, but that for culinary purposes is much scarcer than many may imagine. I speak of surface water."[14]

I make the above quotation from my book on the "Great North West" for the purpose of showing that many mishaps that take place on the prairie are caused by carelessness, or something worse. My men were instructed to keep our keg full of fresh water and, although idle for two days, had made no attempt to fill it. I was learning that inefficient men were the cause of many breakdowns in exploring parties as well as with travellers generally. Before going into my tent, I told them that I would never ask them to put water in the barrel again, but I had no doubt but that they would do it. It seems that after I retired to rest there were signs of a thunder-storm and they took their flannel shirts and spread them out on the grass to catch the rain, but none came. Davie was very sorry for me, but I told him that the men were just as shortsighted as he was, because we had plenty of moisture with us if we only had sense to use it. I asked him to bring in a tin of tomatoes and he opened it and we had as much food and drink as we required. I deliberately kept this from the men as a punishment for their folly.

We turned north at four in the morning and, about noon, reached a trail that was running at right angles to our path. On examining the map, we saw that it was the trail leading from Qu' Appelle to Moose Jaw and, shortly after, a party came along and we learned that Moose Jaw lay to the west of us and that the hills we saw in front of us were on the opposite side of Moose Jaw Creek. We at once headed for the creek and had great difficulty in getting the horses out of the carts before they ran down the hill into the creek and it was laughable to see them drinking until they were tired and then roll over in the stream, they were so pleased with themselves. We had learned our lesson, but we were none the worse for our want of water.

Next morning we followed the trail to Moose Jaw, or rather to where Moose Jaw stands today. Our next object being Old Wives Lakes, we proceeded westward up the trail that went in that direction. The trail led us to the north end of Old Wives Lakes and my next point was to reach the eastern end of the Cypress Hills. We now took a line for this point and, on Saturday evening, reached a large lake called at this time Bullrush Lake. Here we camped over Sunday and, the lake being deep, we considered it held fish and we got out our lines and, in the morning, found that each line had a lizard attached to it, but no fish. Some of the men later bathed in the lake and, after they came on shore, they had to be scraped to get rid of the leeches.

After crossing Swift Current Creek, we headed for the east end of the Cypress Hills. When we reached there, we found that they rose in front to over four hundred feet and, as the face of the Hills was not too steep, we were able to reach the summit with the horses and carts. The view from the summit was a very wide one as there was nothing to obstruct our view to the east, north and south. We travelled for a number of days along the summit of the hills, which always rose higher as we proceeded until we reached a trail that was crossing the hills at right angles to our line of travel. An examination of our map showed that this was the Police trail from Maple Creek to Fort Walsh. As our next point was Fort Walsh, I decided to follow the trail to that point and, in a short time, we were off the hills and proceeding to the south-west on a very good trail. In due time, we reached Fort Walsh and rested there some time from our tiresome journey.[15]

When we reached Fort Walsh, I was warned that the Indians were stealing horses in the neighborhood and to be careful or I would lose mine as all the trappers' horses had been taken the night before I reached there. By the advice of Col. Irwin, who commanded at the Fort, I put my horses with those belonging to the Police and they were quite safe. After remaining with the Police for a number of days, we started on the 15th of August on the last part of our trip. I was instructed, when I left Fort Walsh, to go north to the sand hills that lay to the south of the Saskatchewan and proceed from that point in a straight line by compass to Humboldt in the north, on the trail leading from Carlton. When we left Fort Walsh, we climbed up on to the hills and came to a camp of the Assiniboines, who were then holding a sun dance. It was a very large camp in a beautiful valley surrounded by hills. Many of the young braves were being initiated into the status of "Braves," and we enjoyed the sport very much. Amongst other things that were going on, was that of small boys shooting at marks with bows and arrows and my men and a number of the young Indians gathered at one point and I put up some tobacco and gave a plug to each one who could hit the mark. The shooting was the worst I had ever seen, both by the Indians and the white men. The head Chief was named "The man who stole a boat," and he was about the poorest shot of the lot.

After we left the Indians, we began to descend into the plain to the north and, at the foot of the hills, we pitched our camp for the night. I may mention here that, owing to the fact that the plains at this time were unsafe, owing to Sitting Bull and his Sioux being at Wood Mountain,[16] I took the precaution to carry the Union Jack on a stick in my front cart so that, when we camped at night or travelled in the day, the Union Jack showed that we were not a trader.   After we had all retired to sleep, we heard a great confusion amongst the horses and Davie and I rushed out to see what was wrong, but saw no one.   In the morning we were afraid that our horses would have been stolen but found them where we had left them the night before.

Next day, being Saturday, we travelled north and, late in the afternoon, found that there was no sign of water, although there were numbers of dry creeks on each line of travel.   I sent Davie on horseback to ride around and he rode a long time before he signalled that he had found water.   Our mode of signalling was very simple.   If we were looking for water and found it, we simply lay down and rose again and lay down the second time, or just dismounted and did the same.   It being Saturday, we camped on the margin of a creek and found water in a deep hole.   On Sunday, we examined the country around there and found that it was literally "bad lands."   The hills were all clay and the creeks were all with sand in the bottoms.   Sunday night, there came up a great thunder-storm and an immense rainfall took place, which lasted until late in the afternoon of Monday.   We were now surrounded by water; the creeks were overflowing their banks and the ground was just liquid mud as far as there was no sward.   Later in the day, we reached a creek that had to be crossed and Davie, as usual, tried it and immediately he sank down as it was a quicksand.   However, he managed to cross it on his hands and knees.   As I mentioned before, I carried a hatchet and a spade always with me and, as there were a large number of tall, slim, willow bushes on the borders of the creek, we cut them down and made a first class bridge over the sand and in less time than an hour we were across and all our carts as well.   The following extract is from my work, "The Great North West."

"In August, 1880, we reached the dry bed of a creek on the north side of the Cypress Hills and, after examining it for miles, found it partly impassable.   The banks of the creek were perpendicular and the bed a quicksand.   So soft was the sand that the man who tried it had to cross on his hands and knees.   A brief consultation was held and, while one party cut down the willows to bridge the quicksand, another dug down the banks.   In an hour, we were across and ready for our next difficulty, which soon came.

"The next day was extremely warm, men and horses were thirsty, and, as it drew on towards noon, I climbed a hill and saw, scarcely a mile away, a beautiful lake, glistening in the sun. With joyful hearts, we hurried on and unhitched close to the lake. The horses, naturally, went to the water, but to our astonishment, would not take any. An examination showed that our beautiful lake was liquid mud, with scarcely an inch of water on the surface. We had our dinner, as we carried our own supplies, but it was sundown before our utmost endeavours could find any water for the horses."[17]

"While travelling on the prairie, in September and October, no fire should be lit during the day, unless two or three persons are standing ready to extinguish the fire in the grass, when sufficient ground is burnt over for saftey. No fire should be left uncovered when the party moves away, and it is the duty of the leader to see personally that all fire is either extinguished or covered up. There is a fine of $200.00 for the starting of a prairie fire and, as the informer gets half the fine, Indians and half-breeds are constantly on the alert, during the dangerous season, to pounce on any delinquent. Many people blame the Indians for setting the prairie on fire, but my experience leads me to lay the blame on the white men, especially the young bloods who go shooting in the fall. A stump of a cigar dropped on the prairie is much more dangerous than an Indian fire.

"Travelling, on the prairie, is an easy matter, with or without a road. Experience, combined with intelligence, however, is necessary to insure success. My plan is never to combat a difficulty without seeing my way to overcoming it. Most people, when travelling, take a guide or a man who has been over the country before and who knows or professes to know where the water holes are. As a rule, these men are not of a high order of intelligence, and dare not venture off the beaten track. They know nothing of the use of the compass and laugh at any person essaying to cross the country by the aid of one. Should these persons get into a region not visited by them before, they are perfectly helpless, and will do more harm than good.

"When the Canadian Mounted Police first entered the country, they always took a guide when moving from point to point.
On one occasion, when Colonel Irwin and party were passing from
Fort Walsh to the Saskatchewan in the direction of Battleford,
they camped on the open plain. In the morning, when they
started off, the atmosphere was cloudy and the sun obscured.
After travelling steadily all day, they reached their old camping
place in the evening, although they thought they were forty miles
away from it. When questioned, their guide explained that he
had travelled with the wind on his right hand all day and could
not be blamed if it changed. Numerous incidents of a like nature
could be related, each instance showing that guides are mere in-
cumbrances when in an unknown district."[18]

After leaving the lake with the bad water, we travelled a
couple of miles to the west and got round the end of it and then
turned north-east and, in a short time, struck another lake, which
was excellent water. Shortly after, we came upon a series of
sand hills, which, to our surprise, contained no less than thirty-
two large trees (*Populus balsamifera*). We had been told, years
before, by Dr. G. M. Dawson, that there never had been forest
on these plains,[19] but it became quite evident, when we saw these
trees, that all they required was safety from fires and they would
grow as well on the prairie as anywhere else. The hills were composed of loose sand and the hollows in nearly every case had pools
of water and near these the trees were standing. At present, the
lake mentioned is called Big Stake Lake on account of these trees.

We now proceeded on our course to the north, as I was
ordered, and, after passing the sand hills, took a straight course
for Humboldt, on the Carlton trail. As we were proceeding along
the road in the forenoon, we observed an Indian and a horse on
every hill that we could see, and I knew at once that these were
Indian pickets. As we were liable to fall in with Piegans, Sitting
Bull, or Sioux of Sitting Bull, I deemed it prudent to interview the
nearest scout. I told the party to keep on their regular road and,
when they came to water, to stop for dinner and I would go to
the hill where the scout was. I took my gun and went in his
direction and, before I reached him, he mounted his horse and

came to meet me. I was now elevated a good deal above the valley in which the men were travelling and I saw, to my surprise, about a mile off, in the direction of the sand hills, a large party of Indians driving horses into the hills. I found the Indian did not understand English but I showed him by signs that if he came with me to where the men were now stopping, I would give him his dinner. As I remarked before, we had the Union Jack displayed on one of our carts and I showed him many of the articles that we had that showed we were not traders and had him observe the flag. After dinner, he mounted his horse and rode away.

In the autumn, when I reached Fort Ellice, I saw Colonel McDonald, and he informed me that the party I saw at the sand hills had just come from the northern side of the Cypress Hills and had stolen all the horses belonging to the Assiniboines. They were Piegans and the same horse thieves that had been so busy at Fort Walsh when I was there.

We were now on the last leg of our journey and were not limited for time as I had arranged with my wife that I would telegraph her from Humboldt on the 20th of September. For nearly a month after this, we travelled steadily on the prairie and our only difficulty was crossing creeks and getting fuel, as in this region there were few buffalo chips and no wood of any kind. We passed close to the Elbow of the Saskatchewan where I had been the preceding year and then on to the north and came into a tract of very difficult country. The following extract will show one of the great difficulties in passing through a country where white mud-flats were a feature.

"White mud-swamps are the terror of both Indians and half-breeds. To a person, incautiously attempting to cross one, or having led a horse to the margin to drink, he will find it a difficult matter to get on firm ground again. In the south, where the rain-fall is slight, these swamps, in the dry season, are hard-baked clay flats, covered with a sprinkling of saline plants. Proceeding northward, these greatly change their character, and pass into the much dreaded swamp. One of the worst kind has a dry surface which will not bear the weight of a horse, and into which he sinks deeper at every step, until he lies down from sheer exhaustion.

"The much dreaded salt plain, west of the Touchwood Hills, contains a number of swamps and all of the very worst description. Southwest of the hills, we became entangled in a series of these, in the autumn of 1880, and it was only by hard work and much ingenuity that we saved our horses. When we entered on the clay flat it seemed quite hard, but first one horse went down and then another, until nine were lying panting on the yielding surface. By the time we got across, both men and horses were almost worn out, as all the carts had to be taken over by hand, and the men had to assist the poor horses when they sank down completely exhausted. Nearly all the "sloughs" spoken of by travellers are embryo mud-swamps. In every case, they are merely saturated Cretaceous clay, and pass from liquid "white" mud in the north to hard-baked clay flats in the south. These constitute the "bad lands" of the south and the saline swamps and "sloughs" of the north."[20]

We were now approaching the Carlton road, because we found a few willows near the ponds and, as we proceeded further north, remnants of burnt forest and Mr. Jukes, by his observations, decided that we must be near Humboldt. It was decided that Mr. Jukes and Davie should ride two of the horses to Humboldt and send my telegrams to my wife and the Government and wait for a reply. This was done and, after riding eight miles, they found they were close to the village. On their return, we made ready to start on our way to Fort Ellice, which would be the end of our journey.

On reaching Fort Ellice, we found great excitement prevailing. Mr. Marcus Smith, who had charge of the surveys in that vicinity for the last two years, found his party in open mutiny and, under his assistant, they had deserted and started for Winnipeg. At dinner that evening, Mr. Smith, myself and Mr. McDonnell and another gentleman, whose name I forget, were taking dinner together and discussing the situation pro and con. I knew little about the trouble but listened with attention when Mr. McDonnell asked me: "By the way, Macoun, did you reach Leach Lake the past week?" I told him that we had camped there two days ago. Immediately, Mr. Smith exclaimed, with an expletive, that the lake had no existence for he had men looking for it the whole summer and no one of them had found it.   I calmly said that they did not know how to look and then he turned his attention to me.   At this point, Mr. McDonnell took me aside and told me that the gentleman who had dined with us was the Police Inspector from Shoal Lake, who had come up to make an examination of the facts as Mr. Smith had sent a courier to him at Shoal Lake to take the men prisoners who were now on their way to Winnipeg.

As my trip for the year was nearly over, I may as well say a few words in regard to the surveys and railway questions that had been considered up to this time.   My earlier reports on the value of the prairie country had been causing considerable discussion between the Liberal party and the Conservatives for some years.   The Liberals, of course, held with Mr. Mackenzie, whose idea was to build the road in parts and have water connections in other parts.   This idea of his led to the first survey being made across the narrows of Lake Manitoba, and the extension of the railway to the northwest by Livingstone and onwards in the "fertile belt" to Edmonton.   About 1874, Mr. Horetzky began to talk of a road through the pass that he and I found in 1872 (the Pine Pass).   His idea was to run north and across the Saskatchewan at Fort-a-la-Corne and on by way of Lac La Biche, then cross the Athabasca and take the north shore of Little Slave Lake, and so cross to the Pine Pass.   Marcus Smith also advocated this route, but Mr. Fleming decided, in 1872, for the Yellowhead Pass and all his efforts in succeeding years were to carry out that idea.

My early reports had influenced many people, but the politicians were still in opposition to each other and my report of 1877 seemed to have caused some doubt even in the mind of Mr. Mackenzie because certain modifications were made in 1878 that were carried out later.

In the spring of 1879, Mr. Fleming gave notice to the people at Portage la Prairie that the railway would certainly go to that point, showing that Mr. Mackenzie's plans, made the year before, were thrown aside.   When I was going west in 1879 most of the men on the steamboat were going to go up the Assiniboine on their way to survey a route from the Grand Rapids to Fort Ellice.

The formation of the, "Syndicate" in the autumn of 1880, and the transference of the Canada Pacific Railway to it in the spring, upset speculations of many site seekers, and turned their attention to the more southern district. The announcement, that the "Syndicate" was about to take the southern route was soon followed by the selection of Brandon as the site for a future city. Mr. Sandford Fleming, in his Railway Report for 1880, advised the Government to adopt this route, and to found a city at this very point. The following extract is taken from page 248 of the Report:

"I have carefully examined all the data at hand, and I think that a modification of the latter line points to a scheme worth the consideration of the Government. If the railway is carried to a point in the valley of the Assiniboine, near the mouth of the Little Saskatchewan, where the land remains unsurveyed and ungranted, there might here be established the site of a city which would shortly become important."[21]

After giving various reasons in favor of this scheme, he says, on page 240:

"The adoption of the lines to the point I have indicated in the valley of the Assiniboine, near the mouth of the Little Saskatchewan, would provide 150 miles of excellent trunk line leading from Winnipeg and Selkirk to the coal deposits, and would, to that extent, make provision for the supply of fuel, where no timber exists, and thus supply one sorely felt need in many countries. The laying out of a city at the point mentioned, and the location of stations at regular intervals on other ungranted lands, along the line, would secure to the Government all the benefit arising from the enhanced value which would be given to the land, to assist in meeting the cost of the railway."[22]

It will be seen by the foregoing extracts that both the Government and its officials were aware of the importance of Brandon as a railway centre, and, had the Government held control of the route, they would most undoubtedly, have carried out the above suggestions. It will be seen, then, that Brandon is not a speculative point, but one where, naturally, a large city would spring up. I place the above extract here because it brings the matter of railways up to date and shows that my work was appreciated more fully than I realized at the time.

We reached Portage La Prairie in due course and found that the railway had reached Poplar Point, eight miles out, so I left my party to go out to the railway and reached Winnipeg without difficulty. My men arrived shortly after in good shape, but the horses were nearly dead, as there had been a frost and a thaw and the wheels took up the clay and, every few hundred yards, the men had to stop and clear out the wheels to enable the horses to draw the empty carts. This was the condition of Portage Avenue, the great street of Winnipeg in the autumn of the year 1880.

CHAPTER XI

1880-1881

EXCITEMENT IN THE NORTH-WEST—LECTURES ON THE WEST—
NEGOTIATIONS WITH THE "SYNDICATE" FOR THE CONSTRUC-
TION OF THE C.P.R.—FIFTH EXPLORATION OF THE NORTH-
WEST—INTERVIEW WITH JIM HILL, RAILWAY MAGNATE, RE
ROUTE OF C.P.R.—DECISION TO SEND RAILWAY VIA BOW
RIVER PASS—EXPLORATIONS ALONG LAKES MANITOBA AND
WINNIPEGOSIS AND RIVERS ENTERING THESE LAKES—AD-
VENTURES, MISHAPS AND AMUSING INCIDENTS—DIFFICULTIES
OF RIVER NAVIGATION—UP THE RED DEER AND DOWN THE
SWAN RIVER AND THE ASSINIBOINE TO FORT ELLICE—TAKES
TRAIN FROM BRANDON TO WINNIPEG—INTERVIEW WITH
LORD LORNE AND DONALD A. SMITH—PERMANENTLY AP-
POINTED IN THE GOVERNMENT SERVICE—WRITES A BOOK
CALLED "MANITOBA AND THE GREAT NORTH WEST."

THIS ended my second prairie exploration and, in a few days, I was on my way to Belleville and arrived safely at home and found the family all well and evidently glad to see me, as I myself was to see them. I was not long home until I commenced work on my report and, during the winter, between writing and lecturing, I was constantly busy.[1] The country was in a wonderful state of excitement, owing to the facts I had made public and the reports of others. At this time, politicians were out of the question as the Opposition was completely smothered by the facts that were brought forward. I lectured during the winter in many cities of Ontario and, in the latter part of the winter, I was asked by the Secretary of the Governor-General if I would deliver my lecture before the Governor at Ottawa and I sent a reply that I would be happy to do so at any time set for it by His Excellency. The night of the lecture in Ottawa, I had a packed house and many of the leading men of the Government and the city were there. The Governor sat on the front seat

13

almost under the platform from which I lectured and he, apparently, was engaged in writing during the early part of the lecture and
I thought that he was not interested in what I was saying. Instead of that, he was taking notes and I was greatly cheered when
I discovered that this was so. I had been asked to give my
lecture on the North West. I never gave the same lecture twice
because I was so full of the question that I could talk for a week
without stopping, so that my discourse was along the lines that
the Aide-de-Camp told me that His Excellency would like to get
information on. At the close of the lecture, I always gave an
opportunity to anyone interested to ask questions and one prominent civil servant asked how I knew certain statements I had
made to be facts. I immediately unbuttoned my coat and produced my note-book and opened it and read out the remarks from
it and told my interlocutor that my statements were convincing
to an intelligent man and that, if they did not convince him, I
was sorry for his intelligence. I may say that this remark brought
down the house and the Marquis of Lorne clapped his hands and
cheered with the rest. I was worried no more and my friend was
silent.

Besides lecturing and writing, I was now interested in birds
as, during the preceding summer, when we shot a bird on the
prairie, I described it in a note book and, in the case of the Mallard,
I made out no less than three species as the young bird, the male
and the female were all so different. At any rate, I took an
interest in birds after that and this winter I commenced their
study.

There were great changes going on in Ottawa at this time, and
the publicity given to my lectures caused much excitement
amongst the adventurous people throughout the country and
largely increased the immigration from Ontario to Manitoba.

While I was in the west in the summer (of 1880), Sir John A.
Macdonald went to the Old Country and opened up negotiations
for the purpose of forming a company. The following extract is
taken from my work on the "Great North West."

"In the meantime, negotiations had been opened with the
'Syndicate' for the construction of the road, and the parties

entered into the arrangement with every element in favour of the 'Syndicate' making a good bargain. Our own people had done their best to show that the road would never pay running expenses when built, and that the country through which it would pass was, in many places, a howling wilderness and would remain so. With these weapons in their hands and, in addition, with a know- ledge of the country, which would carry everything before them, (one section of our people had persistently rejected and refused to build), the 'Syndicate' entered the fight.

"The bargain with the 'Syndicate' was scarcely concluded when they showed their determination to carry the road still further south. Acting on my report of the preceding year, they sent engineers south of the Assiniboine and examined the country westward. The City of Brandon was located and their examina- tion of the country was so satisfactory that they sent engineers into the Rocky Mountains to examine the Bow River Pass, or, as it is called in the reports, the Kicking Horse Pass. These en- gineers have reported, and it is believed that the road may be carried through the mountains at that point. At present, the road is located from Winnipeg to Moose Jaw Creek; a distance of four hundred miles. From this point they can go west to Calgary or turn to the northwest in the direction of Battleford."[2]

At this time, I had an interview with Colonel Dennis and was told that I might prepare myself for another expedition the coming summer; this year they were not going to send me to the prairie but I would be asked to spend the summer on Lakes Manitoba and Winnipegosis, and the rivers entering those lakes and the Assiniboine River. I learned later that the Marquis of of Lorne was intending to make a tour through the North West the coming summer and he asked me to lecture so that he could gain information regarding his trip. Colonel Dennis informed me that the Marquis wished to have me with him as guide, but he also told me that the Government had decided that I must be used this summer in the exploration I have mentioned above. My next surprise was an invitation from Jim Hill, the railway magnate, to go to St. Paul to meet the "Syndicate" in his office, when I was on my way to the West.

I now began to refuse offers from various incompetent men to be attached to my party during the summer. As it was, I chose three boys and took my nephew, David, as my man. The three boys were, J. M. Macoun, my own son, George Moore, of Winnipeg and Henry Williams, of Belleville. These three boys were hardly twenty years of age and the exploration I was to make, I learned later on, had been tried by three parties, all of whom had failed and I was asked as a last resource. I have given the composition of my party and, when I look back on what I was expected to do, it was a wild adventure, and yet, the boys came through it like men and did the best they could, but, oh! when I think of their poling the boat up stream and their want of success and chiefly failure, I feel that I was a very ill prepared man for what I was expected to do.

In due course, I reached St. Paul and met the "Syndicate," with their engineer, who had charge of the railroad end. We sat in Mr. Hill's office at a round table with maps spread out and, amongst others, there were two gentlemen from Montreal, members of the "Syndicate." The maps that were spread on the table showed me that, at this time, the surveys had been extended beyond Moose Jaw and they had already located the road to that point, which was four hundred and four miles from Winnipeg. At this time, there was no decision made by them as to what pass the railroad should take. They were prepared to go to the northwest to the Yellow Head, or west, to the Bow River, as the "Syndicate" would decide. The engineer showed them that he had been stopped by the South Saskatchewan, because its banks were very high and they were of such nature that they were liable to crumble and wash away at any time. As we talked, I told them my experiences of the year before and told them of the easy road that could be made from Moose Jaw, west to Seven Persons Coulee (near Medicine Hat), and I told them of looking up the Bow River Pass two years before and seeing a wide open valley. I told them, also, that there were at least four hundred miles from Moose Jaw, where there were no trees and scarcely a shrub, and I was asked by the engineer where they could get the ties. I told him at once that was not my business, it was his. After some more discussion,

Hill raised his hands and struck the table with great force and said: "Gentlemen, we will cross the prairie and go by the Bow Pass, if we can get that way." He immediately gave his reasons for his assertion; he said: "I am engaged in the forwarding business and I find that there is money in it for all those who realize its value. If we build this road across the prairie, we will carry every pound of supplies that the settlers want and we will carry every pound of produce that the settlers wish to sell, so that we will have freight both ways." (Years after this, Mr. Fleming told me that for good or for evil, I had sent the road into the Bow River Pass.)[3]

After my interview with Hill, we went to Winnipeg and I was delighted to find that I could carry my supplies from Winnipeg to Portage La Prairie on the train, which we did. I found my nephew, David Macoun, was baggage-man on the freight when we reached there. While in Winnipeg, I made enquiries as to how I could get along after leaving Portage La Prairie and found that I could get a sail boat going up Lake Manitoba and, by good luck, I came across a gentleman at the hotel who was going to take the census on Lake Winnipegosis and he agreed to take me and my party from Manitoba House to Swan Lake House in his sail boat while he was taking the census on his way; I found that that was my best plan of procedure and agreed to go with him.

Our start from Portage La Prairie was made after a heavy rainstorm and, as the wagon that held all of our supplies could not carry all the party, the most of us walked while the wagon proceeded over the prairie, There were many puddles and hills on the road and our young men paddled through the former and came out besmirched with mud and some of them were wearing city socks! We reached Totogon a little before sunset and, as we approached it, the mosquitoes were in such numbers that they actually obscured the sunset. When we reached our destination, the place where the hotel was, we found that the water of the lake had risen so high that the floor of the hotel was flooded and we had to walk up to our knees in water for a quarter of a mile to reach it. This was the first day for my young men and they stood it well.

Next day, I arranged with a man to take my party and provisions to Manitoba House on the upper part of Lake Manitoba, in his sail boat.   Early in the morning, we started and had dinner somewhere on the shore of the lake.   After we started from our dining place, the wind arose and the boat went through the water so fast that the canvas canoe, that I had brought all of the way with me from Belleville, was swamped and everything was lost that was in it excepting our bedding, which floated.   We gathered up things and righted the canoe and were soon on our way again. Some time after, a thunder-storm struck us, when the man told me there was no harbor along that shore for the next ten miles. We worked in towards the shore, however, and I saw by the condition of the atmosphere that an awful storm was approaching. After some talk with the owner of the boat and my promise to make good if we were wrecked, he agreed to make for the shore. The roar of the storm overhead was so great that we could hardly hear, but, before it descended to the water, we were almost on shore and, when the first wave struck the boat, I was sitting in the stern and it came on my back and I broke its force.   By the time the next wave came, the boat struck the shore, head on, and the boys jumped out and, two on each side, grasped the gunwale and, when the third wave struck, it lifted us with great force and sent the men and the boat straight over the sand bank that lined the shore and we found ourselves actually in a lagoon of the lake while the lake itself was in an awful turmoil just a few yards from us.   The storm soon passed and we found ourselves in perfect security.   We camped there and, in the morning, we had to dig down three or four feet of the sand bar to get out to the lake, and we sailed up to Manitoba House without further mishap.

We spent some time at Manitoba House and obtained all the information possible regarding matters pertaining to Manitoba Lake.   After a few days, the gentleman with whom I had made a bargain to take us to Swan Lake House put in an appearance and we started off with him.

Our experiences after this were on the sail boat and were very pleasant and not very exciting as we had plenty of time and my young men collected many birds' eggs and enjoyed the eating of them. Some of them ate more than was good for them and had trouble, though they made light of it. In going up Deep River, which is the discharge of the Lake Winnipegosis, we kept close to the shore as the river was deep and not rapid. My nephew, Davie, got tired sitting in the boat and said he would go on shore and stepped out of the boat on to what he thought was the bank and immediately disappeared and, in a few moments, rose again and, without saying a word, crawled back into the boat. I remember asking him where he came from, as he looked more like a drowned mouse than a man. This was the only episode, that I can remember in going up the lake, that is worth recording. In due time, we arrived at the mouth of Swan River and stopped over Sunday. The river was in flood and the water very high and the boys, being good swimmers, nothing would do but they would do stunts. My son, Jim, showed himself to be the one most willing to take risks and he swam up the river for a long distance and, from where we were on the shore, he looked as if he were standing up, but he yelled for the boys to come to his assistance as he was going to drown. The men who owned the sail boat realized what was the matter and started in our canvas boat and reached Jim when he was almost exhausted. It seems that all the time we thought him standing up he was treading water to keep himself afloat. He was none the worse for his exertions and I passed a law then that there was to be no more swimming in the stunt line.

Some time after this, we reached Swan Lake House and there my agreement terminated with the Census taker. I now arranged with the authorities at Swan Lake House to have a skiff built that would carry two of the party and the greater part of our provisions. The skiff was flatbottomed and clinker built and it was the boat that I steered for the remainder of the season. After leaving Swan Lake House, we headed for the Red Deer River, which enters Lake Winnipegosis at its head.[4] Here, we camped by some salt springs, and we found that the river was in full flood, that even the banks were covered and the water, in many places, right in amongst the trees. The boys volunteered to take the canvas boat up the river and see what the prospects would be for us to make the ascent. At their return, they reported that it was going to be very difficult to ascend, but they thought that they could track up the skiff with the provisions by my steering and they pulling on the shore.

I may say that now I began to realize that we had started out on a very dangerous trip without preparation or experience. I was totally ignorant of river navigation and the boys knew nothing at all. Not one of the young men could use a pole or ever had seen it used and I was unable to teach them. One morning, they took the canoe up the river for some miles and carried part of the provisions and cached them, and came back in safety. They said that, if I would risk it, they would tow my boat up stream and all I would have to do was to steer and keep her from running in towards shore. As it was the best we could do, I decided to take their advice and we broke up camp, loaded the boat with flour and bacon, and I sat down in the stern to steer. All went well for a mile or more, and then we came to a slight bend in the river and their hauling on the boat caused her to swing in-shore and I shoved her off and shoved too strong and, before you could say, "Jack Robinson," I was in the middle of the river and they hauling for all they were worth to bring me in again. This caused the bow of the boat to almost take water and, as there was every appearance of the boat going to capsize, I walked over the top of the flour and sat down on the outer gunwale of the boat from the bow and I then called for them to slack up, which they did, and the boat came up on an even balance and they brought her gently to the shore. When I reached the shore, I found one of the young men was nearly undressed as he thought the boat was going to capsize and I would be drowned. He had thought he would jump in and save me if possible. I mention this as it was the most serious mishap we had for the season.

After a good deal of hard work, we reached Red Deer Lake and camped at the lake and, as it was Saturday, we pitched our tents and prepared to stay over Sunday. In the night, an awful thunderstorm arose and a very strong wind with it. The boats were in an unsafe position, so we all got up and went down to the shore and placed them in safety and returned and went to sleep again.

Early in the morning, a storm of wind arose and, as we were in a grove of poplars, and some of them dead, we heard them crashing on all sides of us. The men were camped a short distance from me and we got up and stood by our tents and watched the storm. Almost in front of us, a large poplar broke off and, as it fell across, it struck two trees standing almost together and broke both off. From where I stood, I saw one falling straight for me and had just time to move one step to the left till it crashed down and broke to pieces my tin case, which was lying beside the tent. By taking only one step, I saved my life for, just then, the second tree fell on my left and actually brushed my shirt sleeve as it fell. The men saw both trees fall and thought that I would be killed, but, with God's blessing, I was saved for the time.

Our troubles, however, were only commencing. We had a large river to ascend that had been attempted three times before us and the surveying parties failed each time. I, with four boys who knew nothing about poling up river, were to ascend this river that was reported to have thirty miles of rapids. When we entered the Red Deer River, before it entered the lake, we found it was still in flood but not so high as it was lower down. I am not sure how many days we worked in making the ascent to a tributary coming in from our left. This river was likewise in flood and we saw no way to cross it as we were unable to paddle the canoe or row the boat, so my son decided that he would swim across to the other side, carrying a rope, and he would haul the boat across when he reached the land. He boldly struck out for the other shore and, when he reached the middle, the current became too strong for him and he was carried down. I called for him to hold on to the rope and we would haul him in, which we eventually did, and he was none the worse for his swim. How we eventually crossed I fail to remember, but that we did so is certain. When we reached the rapids, we attempted to pole but we were all unfitted for it and so had to give it up. Our mode of procedure from this on was for the men to track up in the shallows along the river margin while I steered the flatbottomed boat in the stream. This is such slow work that we made very little progress, but finally reached the upper part of the river, where there was little water, but still we made headway by rolling the boulders out of the way of the boat.

One day, we came to a barren that was covered with blueberries, so we landed and went up and had a beautiful time amongst the berries.   I may mention here that we always carried a double-barreled shot gun for the purpose of killing ducks and, this time, I took it on shore with me and laid it against the bank. Shortly after, we started up the river again and met a party of Indians, and to show them that we were friends, as the Hudson's Bay Officers do, I fired off the gun and blew off four inches of the muzzle of the right hand barrel.   Evidently, dirt had got into it when I left it against the bank.   Days passed and our only trouble was little progress and the abundance of leeches, which troubled the men when they were wading, as they had to clean out their toes and scrape their legs every time we landed.

Of course, we had a map with us, showing us which branch of the river we were to take that would lead us to the lake out of which Swan River ran.   When we reached this branch, we turned up to the left (to the east) and, after travelling for a number of days, we reached a small stream going to the left and entered it. This was the stream shown on the map that flowed from the lake we were wanting to find.   We had been a longer time on the river than I had expected and our flour was getting scarce so I had to limit the party of five to three bannocks a day.   The rule was, that I cut the bannock into five equal parts and each man chose one and I gave him the part bearing his number and I received the fifth part myself.   We lived this way for fully a month.   Every opportunity I got, I shot ducks, and supplied the men with plenty of fresh meat and our bacon still held out.

When we entered the small stream, we found it encumbered every few hundred yards by a beaver dam and we, without exception, dug them away and hauled the boat over.   Later, it narrowed so much that the alders along its banks closed it in to such a degree that they had to be cut away with our axes, of which, by good luck, we had two.   At last, it became so narrow and so shallow that we had to give up.   We were all wet and shivering with cold, so I opened my bottle of brandy that I had taken for just such an occasion as the men being exhausted and cold.   We camped and discussed our position that night.   I decided that, in the morning, Davie and one of the men with a gun would go and, if possible, find the lake and then see if it had an outlet to the east, if so, we were in the right position and, he was to fire his gun. A few hours after, we heard the gun at a distance, and I answered and he understood that he was to try, on his way back, to find a road over which we could haul our flatbottomed boat and canvas boat.   He found a way by which we could haul them across, as there was much moss and some swamp on the way.

The following day, I went across when they took the canvas boat and, while they were gone for the larger one, I made a wharf of the branches by which we could walk over the mud to where the water was deep enough to float the boats.   I believe that it took us only a day to bring all our stuff across and the next day we entered on the lake and it was little better, for some distance, than liquid mud which made it difficult for us to get through. We passed out of the lake into a nice creek and our hearts rose to know that from this time on we had no more ascending of streams but that, to Winnipeg, our course would be down stream.

After some time, our little stream got larger and we, most unexpectedly, reached Swan River through a clump of bushes. Our difficulties now were all over, as we knew that no matter what happened, we could float down to Livingstone (the Police Headquarters).   By this time, our flour was almost exhausted and the men's clothes were in an awful state, but our spirits were high and we were afraid of nothing.

Late one afternoon, we reached Livingstone, and I was the only one of the party that could make an appearance without having something done to his clothes.   Inspector Griesbach, who was in charge, was very kind to us, and, one afternoon, I went out shooting with him and, while he shot a great number of prairie fowl, I obtained nothing.   Late in the afternoon, he asked me if I would like to see some snakes, and I told him that I would, very much,   He took me some distance to a little hollow where there were a few rocks and a number of stumps and small trees and he said: "Do not be afraid, but follow me."   I followed him and we both stopped on a little mound and we found ourselves surrounded by thousands of snakes, which were twined around the trees and stumps and each other and about a foot of the body of each protruded, and so it was all heads, with the mouths open, which showed, and they were all hissing at the same time. I need scarcely say that it was almost too much for me and I never saw such a sight before nor since. They were all garter snakes. They were going into winter quarters.

After being at Livingstone for a few days and examining the country, I made arrangements to cross the fourteen miles that lay between Livingstone and Fort Pelly. I hired a wagon which took over the two boats and the men walked. At Fort Pelly, we were now on the Assiniboine and, from it, we intended to go down to Winnipeg. After a few days at Pelly, we made our arrangements and obtained some provisions and started on our way to Fort Ellice, three hundred miles to the east. We found the Assiniboine exceedingly crooked, but, as we were going down stream, we cared little for our slow passage. Once in a while we would enter a small rapid and the boys used to cheer and try to go faster than the rapid would carry them. They seemed to think of the rapids they had been ascending all summer.

One afternoon, the canoe was ahead of my boat and they passed around the bend and, after that, I heard a shot and, as I came around the bend, behold, my nephew, Davie, was up to his neck in the river. We asked what had happened and he said that they were hunting for his gun. He said there was a number of pigeons in a tree on the bank and he shot at them. He was sitting on a box in the canoe, and fired at the pigeons in the tree, and the recoil of the gun caused him to lose his balance and he tumbled headlong into the river, taking his gun with him. By good luck, the river only took him up to his neck and, when we saw him, he was using his feet on the bottom to locate the gun, which he found and then dived and brought it up. I mentioned that the river was very crooked and quite narrow and, as we came down, we found two fair sized trees had fallen across and blocked the way for the boats. While the men were cutting the trees, I walked down the bank for a few yards and, through a clump of willows on the bank, I saw quite a number of ducks in the stream and, having a gun with me, as usual, I thought I would have a shot at them   I had both barrels cocked and, in pressing down the muzzle to get on a line with the birds, I evidently pulled the trigger of the right hand barrel; this was the one that had burst some weeks before, and the charge struck my thumb and carried the whole face of the thumb away, except a slight nob of flesh at the point.   I called the men and told them that I had shot myself and they came down at once and tied a rag around the wound, and then a handkerchief, and, although it was painful, I could bear it.   After they cut the trees, and the boat came down, I took my place at the stern of the flatbottomed boat and began to steer as usual.   However, in a short time, I fell forward in a faint and frightened the life nearly out of the boys.   We immediately put to shore and held a consultation.   We were now on a part of the river that was full of bends.   They made us often run a mile down stream and a mile back again without making more than a few yards of headway.   We knew, that, below this, there was an Indian farm and it was decided that I should walk down on a trail that ran some distance from the shore and get the wound dressed and they would follow the river and, perhaps, reach there as soon as I would.   I found no difficulty in walking down and told of my mishap and had the Indian farmer and his daughter to look at the wound.   He told me that it was a very serious wound in a bad place and it was possible that I would take lock-jaw, and the daughter upbraided him for frightening me.   I told them that I was not afraid, I had arranged with my son before I left the boat and the young men would be there in the afternoon.

Late in the afternoon, the young men came with the boats and said they had been going up and down the river valley all day, as there were at least four or five bends at the same place. I can remember little about the next ten days except that I suffered greatly with my thumb.   I may mention that we had no soap and that it was impossible to wash it and, therefore, I kept it tied up and, as the evenings and nights were cool, I carried my right hand under my left arm when I was sleeping or steering.

When we reached Fort Ellice, I found Dr. Otto Klotz at the

Fort, and I immediately asked him to give me a cake of soap as I wished to wash a wound in my hand. As soon as I uncovered it, the whole face of the thumb was seen to be covered with a purple flesh and the soap given me being carbolic soap it caused such excrutiating pain that Mrs. MacDonnell, the wife of the officer in charge of the Fort, came into the room and saw my condition and she immediately said: "Oh, dear me! Mr. Macoun, how did that take place?" 'I simply said that I shot it off, and she then asked what I was going to do and I said I wanted to find out and she asked if it were painful and I said: "Yes, it is awful." "Well," she said, "I can soon stop the pain." And she went out and got a basin of hot water and stirred into it a handful of baking soda and stirred it well. Then she had me put my hand into it and the change was so great that it was like passing from Hell to Heaven. It took away the pain at once. She then told us that one of the men had shot himself through the hand a year before and that the only thing that was done to his hand was to keep it covered with a rag wet with water in which baking soda was dissolved. As soon as I had my hand dressed, I found I was all right again and my anxiety now was to get to Winnipeg as as soon as possible as my work was over.

My party now broke up and Davie Macoun and young Williams remained behind and took up land later. My son and young Moore decided to come on with me and I hired a half-breed with a horse and cart to take our stuff to Brandon, where I took the train. The distance there was said to be one hundred and twenty miles, and the half-breed promised to take us there in three days. The young men had been on the water all summer and were aching for a walk on land so we started on foot. I gave the young men the privilege of riding in the cart at any time they saw fit. Every hour or two we stopped and I bathed my thumb. We plodded on and, late the first day, struck the railroad, where the men were working. As we were walking along, an Irishman, who was also walking, said: "Are you leaving the country?" I said: "Yes; as fast as we can get out of it." He said: "I am doing the same myself. Just think of it, the frost in the winter sinks down forty feet and the men say that neither themselves nor I could stand it for a year and they told me it is wise for me to get out. Forty feet!"

At the end of our second day, the half-breed pointed out a bend about two hundred yards away, where he intended staying all night. Both of the boys sat down and moved no further for the next half hour. Our third day was uneventful and we reached the vicinity of Brandon before dark, and, as soon as the boys saw it, they sat down again. We did not reach the city until after dark. I never saw the boys so tired in my life.

The next day, we took the train for Winnipeg and I may say we all enjoyed the ride. I was only a few hours in the city until John McTavish, the Commissioner of the Hudson's Bay Company, called upon me and said that His Excellency, the Marquis of Lorne, had left an invitation for me to go up to Silver Heights for breakfast the next morning. Silver Heights was the residence of Donald A. Smith (Lord Strathcona). Early the next morning, Mr. McTavish called for me with his carriage and took me up, fourteen miles, to Silver Heights.

At breakfast, there were the Marquis, Mr. Smith and myself, and we, of course, enjoyed the talk very much. The Marquis wished to thank me for the information I had given him the preceding winter and stated that he had followed the route that I had given him, the whole of the past season and found I was right in every particular. When Mr. Smith heard him say this, he turned with great unction and said: "Your Excellency, Mr. Macoun and myself are the only two men that have the right opinion about this country." I was almost prompted to say: "You old rascal, six years ago you wrote that the statements I had made about the growth of the wheat at Fort Chipewyan were all lies, and that I was untrustworthy in the statement I had made about it to the Government." In 1875 he was head of the Hudson's Bay Company and now, in 1881, he was acting the patriot for the Government in power.

It was fortunate that I kept my temper and now I related to the Marquis why it was that I had my right hand bound up and told him the circumstances by which I was eased of my pain. He was so pleased with my story that he wrote the whole matter in his note book for future reference.   Shortly after this, my son and I were on our way home, which we reached in due time and found all well.   My wife was now so accustomed to running the establishment alone that I was never in doubt of her want of success.

I remember little about my work this winter except to say that I was busier than ever.   I commenced to write my report at once and, before it was finished, I was asked to go to Ottawa and report verbally on the country I had seen and the results of my expedition.[5]   They were greatly pleased, as I had succeeded, in my three trips, in settling so many questions that they were very enthusiastic about me at this time and the Deputy Minister, Lindsay Russell, said that he thought it was time that that permanent position they had promised be given me at once. He said: "Sir John is here and I will go in and speak to him now." He went in and came out almost immediately and said that Sir John said "certainly, Macoun must have a permanent position." Russell said to me: "Now is your time to go in and see Sir John and get it in writing because he is very liable to forget what he says."   I went in and told Sir John and he laughed and said: "Russell does not give me as much credit as I deserve."   He gave me the writing and made some very pleasant remarks and I left him very well satisfied.   My appointment was to take effect on the first of January, 1882.

When I went home, I found a request from a publisher asking me if I would write a book on the North West and he came to see me and we talked the matter over and I decided, as I was full of the subject, and could now have everything made public by the Government, to write the book and, in the course of the winter, with the assistance of my two daughters, Clara and Minnie, I wrote the book "Manitoba and the Great North West." (an octavo volume of 687 pages).   I included in it almost everything I knew and thought about the country.   The compilations were made by the girls and I wrote most of the chapters from my notes. Other chapters were written by men who were acquainted with the subject and the book was published in the spring.[6]

PROF. JOHN MACOUN IN THE PRIME OF LIFE.

CHAPTER XII

M Y early studies, while on the farm, and when teaching, were largely influenced by studying Humboldt's "Cosmos" and Lyell's "Principles of Geology." These two books enlightened me a great deal, and, later, when I began to lecture in Albert College, I had to lecture on physical geography, meteorology, geology and botany. These four studies took the most of my time and thought, and, having no teachers, I formed my own opinions and enunciated them with great force. My mind began to open as I taught and I constantly asked myself the question as to why such statements were made by the authors, and, later, I asked my pupils in both school and college the very same thing; in fact, at this stage of my life, I asked proof for every statement made in books and lectures, and, I believe, that is the cause of my want of belief in many of the statements made to-day.

In 1863, I had read a paper on Bog Plants and showed they wanted coolness for their roots. At that time, it was generally thought that heat was the great necessity, but, in studying the life of Linnaeus, the great botanist, I found that he came into notice while he was an assistant in a botanical garden, I believe, in Holland. He saw an alpine plant drooping and almost dying and he immediately got some ice and put around it and, at once, the plant began to grow. The gardener thought he was going to kill it by putting the ice around it, whereas it wanted the condition in which it desired to live. In my plant studies, I discovered that certain plants required heat at the roots and moisture above,

14

while others wanted coolness below and heat above, and others, again, dry soil and little heat. But our weeds seem to care nothing for conditions—all they want is a chance to grow, which they do whether the farmer desires them to do so or not.

These things may seem simple, but they are worth reflecting on for one can start from a premise like this and reach many a happy conclusion. I made applications and said that heat by day and cold at night seemed the two factors needed and made other observations. I had read a paper at the Botanical Society in Kingston and the Kingston "Whig," next day, in criticising the paper, said that my application was the first time that they had seen Tyndall's Heat as a Mode of Motion explained.

When I went to Lake Superior in 1869, I saw many things that opened my eyes regarding botany and, amongst others, I found that the flora within 100 yards of the water was quite distinct from that three hundred yards away. The one was semi-arctic and the other the usual flora of a cool, damp, country. I deduced from this that heat and moisture were the two factors that produced any climate in any place. I discovered this when at the Lake and, in my later report in 1877, I stated it distinctly and said that all that was needed was to drain the land and the result would be more heat and less frost. Today, the region above Lake Superior and a little west is noted for being in places excellent farming land while, in my day, it was all swamp and muskeg.

It will be seen that I was fully prepared for my trip with Mr. Fleming in 1872 and also with Dr. Selwyn in 1875. I could talk with confidence on what I saw and, in my book "The Great North West," published in 1882, I wrote in my own ideas and those of others. Following are quotations from it.

"The general conclusions which I arrived at from my explorations of 1872 and 1875 were:

1st. That, as there was but one flora common to the region extending from 8 to 12 degrees of latitude, or as far north as 60° and, as that flora required a high summer temperature for its existence, the thermometer would be found to show a corresponding temperature of heat throughout the whole district.

2nd. That exceptional or special conditions must exist to

produce that high and even distribution of heat discovered as ranging over so great an area."

These conclusions have since been established as facts by the recorded observations sent in from the meteorological stations at Winnipeg, Fort McLeod and Fort Calgary in the south and Fort Rae and Fort Simpson in the north.   (See Meteorological Report for 1878).

"In 1879, my attention was mainly directed to an investigation of the causes of the supposed aridity of the district lying to the south. I found a parched surface, dried and withered grass, and in short, every appearance of the existence of such aridity; but closer examination showed that these indications were illusory. At the point, "Blackfoot Crossing," latitude 50° 43', where the consequence of aridity appeared the strongest, I came upon ground broken up in the spring, bearing excellent crops of all kinds—oats being four feet high, while, on the land outside the fence, the grass was burnt up and all other vegetation withered.   From this I argued that the rainfall in the district was evidently ample for the requirements of vegetation, but that, until the baked crust was broken, it could not penetrate the ground as rapidly as it fell and so a great portion was evaporated by the dry atmosphere and lost.   Thus, the apparent aridity vanished before the first efforts of husbandry.   Next to the question of aridity was that of the high and even temperature of the climate.   On this point, I simply accumulated data bearing on the observations of former years, all of which served to prove that the great plain to the northwest, and north of latitude 49° extending along the Saskatchewan and other rivers between the 100th and 115th Meridians and the narrow strip of coast north of Monterey, California, present decided features of difference from other districts of the American continent.   These differences and peculiarities I shall now deal with seriatum.

TEMPERATURE.   "It was long ago asserted as a principle by geologists that land in quantity, situated to the southward of latitude 40° north, very materially raises the temperature of land lying to the north of such parallel."   (Sir C. Lyell).   To the expression, "Land in quantity," I would add—when this character is that of a desert or arid nature. Another maxim is thus laid down by the well-known writer on American Climatology (Blodgett): "That high arid plains are indicative of great summer heat, of an arid atmosphere, and of little rainfall or snowfall." Now, the condition required to test the accuracy of both these propositions are presented in the position occupied by the North West Territory. South of our boundary, within the United States, lies a vast tract of land, generally arid or desert, of which at least 500,000 square miles are embraced in a plateau which has a general level of 6,000 feet. At Laramie City in latitude 24° it is about 7,000 feet above sea level, thence northward it rapidly falls off so that when it reaches our boundary in latitude 49°, at Pembina, it is considerably under 1,000 feet. At the base of the Rocky Mountains, it is under 4,000 feet. From the boundary, the plain extends far to the north and only terminates at the Arctic Sea. In such a wide range of latitude it might well be expected that a considerable difference of temperature would be found. The following Table, however, shows the temperature as being wonderfully uniform. (Meteorological Report, 1878.)

PLACE	LAT.	JUNE	JULY	AUG.	MEAN OF SUM. MOS.
Winnipeg...............	49.53	59.2	65.8	63.3	62.8
Fort McLeod...........	49.39	60.6	63.3	57.0	60.3
Norway House..........	54.00	54.9	63.5	61.2	59.9
Fort Simpson...........	61.52	58.8	63.4	63.2	61.8

In the same parallel of latitude in Europe the temperature is recorded as follows: (See Boldgett):

PLACE	LAT.	JUNE	JULY	AUG.	MEAN OF SUM. MOS.
Penzance, S.W. England..	50.08	59.5	62.1	61.1	60.9
Cracow, Poland..........	50.04	60.0	65.8	64.9	64.9
Koeningsberg, Russia.....	54.42	57.4	62.6	61.7	60.6
St. Petersburg, Russia....	59.56	58.2	62.7	60.8	60.6

"We see that the summer temperature in the North West Territories is exceptional. Believing, however, that, in addition to the quoted causes, there are others which contribute to this result of exceptional temperature, I propose for the present to reserve the fact for further comment, and pass on to the subject of isothermals. The recorded lines of equal temperature show that the various lines of heat, as they make westing from the eastern coast of the continent, change in summer to curve upwards from the Gulf of Mexico in a northwesterly direction to a point in latitude 50, longitude 110 west. At this point, the mean summer temperature is 70° F., while at Winnipeg, on the same parallel of latitude, 150° further east, the temperature is but 65°. Tracing these isothermals still further north, the line of greatest heat passes near Fort Vermilion in latitude 58° 24' and longitude 116° 30 west. I may mention that, at this point, I found barley cut on August 6th, 1875, and wheat almost ripe. Still further north and west, the table shows that Fort Simpson has a mean summer temperature of 61° 8' F. Turning to the west coast, the isothermal lines commence to turn northward from the Gulf of California and, for a time, skirt the western side of the Rocky Mountains. On reaching the low point of the chain, between latitude 41° and 45°, they turn to the east, cross the mountains, and strike the Dominion boundary of the 115th Meridian. These westerly currents, named the "Chinooks," have been known to cause a rise in the temperature of 60 degrees in a few hours. When in that country, I enquired from a half-breed, about their effect on the snow. His reply was: "Chinooks lick up snow, water, and all."

"After crossing the Rocky Mountains, the thermometric current of the west meets that of the east at or about the Hand Hills in Latitude 51° 20', Longitude 112°. There, in 1879, I found that, for days together, during August, the thermometer in the shade, registered from 87° to 92° F. From the Hand Hills, the united currents, following their resultant direction, carry the temperature of latitudes, extending almost to New Orleans, over the North West and confer on it the blessings of a climate, not only exceptional as regards character, but productive of results to the agriculturist, which, I believe, are unsurpassed in any other part of the world.

"Returning to the course taken by the east and west currents, before their union at the Hand Hills, it is a matter for consideration why that from the east departs from the natural law which would give to it an eastward, in place of a western bend, while the western current follows the natural law and bends to the eastward.

"The answer to this question is the key to almost every climatological peculiarity of the North West.

"The data which we have for the investigation of the question: "Why does the eastern current of heat, proceeding northwestward from the Gulf of Mexico, bend to the west?" are:

1st. Recorded observations, which show that land of a desert character, is heated to a greater degree than the land or water adjoining.

2nd. Recorded observations which show that currents of air are constantly on the move to where the land is most heated.

3rd. The fact that, to the westward of the tract running northward from the Gulf of Mexico, lies the "Great American Desert."

To my mind, no argument is needed to show that the cause of the divergence of the eastern thermometric current to the westward is solely due to the position and effect produced by the American Desert. A confirmation of this inference is offered in the eastern hemisphere, where the south east trade winds are drawn out of their course by the heated atmosphere of the Western Indies, and result in the south west "Monsoon," and, further, by the northeastern trend of the isothermals in Northern Asia. In the transition from summer to winter, we find the desert losing its temperature (terrestrial and atmospheric) and consequent attractive influence on air currents warmer than its own. The first effect of this is that the isothermals pass away from their northern latitude and sink southward; next, when freed from the desert influences, they no longer trend to the westward, but to the eastward. On the withdrawal of the southern warm currents, other currents from the north and from the west follow them up, particularly on the shady side of the Rockies, and establish the prevailing northwest winter winds which, being affected by the temperature of the arctic regions on the one hand, and by the mountains on the other, bring the minimum line of cold far to the south. Were the American Desert an inland sea, the summers of our plains would lose their exceptional character, and our winters would be like those of eastern Europe.

"In a book, like the present, however, it would be out of place to discuss the climate of the eastern hemisphere; but it could be shown that precisely similar causes to those which I have specified, exist there and are productive of the same results.

"Having stated what the recorded facts as to rainfall are, I will give my reasons for asserting that these facts are the necessary consequences of the physical conditions existing in the west of the North American continent.

"In the beginning of this chapter, I referred to the position of the Great American Desert, and pointed out one of its effects upon the air-currents rising northward from the Gulf of Mexico— viz, its power to direct and draw them to itself, and to the westward of their natural course. Another fact arises from the heat given off by radiation, during the summer months. The Gulf air currents, laden with moisture, when drawn over the desert, are met by the rarified and heated air ascending from its surface and the rain which, in the original course, they would pour down, being prevented from falling, passes on and is wafted by the prevailing winds in the direction of our North West. There, their land borne and priceless load is given forth in the form of our summer rains. As the rainfall increases northward, the bunch grass is succeeded by sward after which there is copsewood and then aspen forest and spruce on the water-shed.

"Having shown cause for the summer rains, I may now state that the simple suspension of those desert effects which gave the summer rains, is the cause of the almost total absence of rain in the autumn and winter periods.

"It was shown, when writing of the winter temperature, that, as the desert cooled, the main air-currents from the Gulf of Mexico no longer pursued their westward course, but passed to the eastward. This change of direction takes them over the region of the "Canadian Lakes, where they deposit an abundant rainfall."

For many years, this vast extent of prairie territory north of latitude 49° lay as a blank upon the maps, almost unknown to Englishmen and Canadians, and counted valueless except as a fur-bearing country; though long ago, in 1821, Lord Selkirk had said that the valley of the Red River alone would maintain a population of 30,000,000. The Americans were always alive to its true value, but, like true patriots, extolled their own country in preference to the land of the stranger. Over twenty years ago, their writers called attention to it, and Wheelock spoke glowingly of it in his work on Minnesota. In 1872, I first had the good fortune to spend a number of months in the territory, and travelled over its whole extend from east to west and, being impressed with its importance as a field for immigration, I have since then taken every opportunity to make myself acquainted with its climate and capabilities.

"In conclusion, after much study of all valuable material and constant observation, I can but report that our peculiar climate is caused by the "Great American Desert," which commences at the 100th Meridian, exactly south of our prairies and extends with little interruption to the boundary of California. The winds, passing over it, descend on our interior plain, especially northward, giving it heat and moisture in the summer and in the winter wrapping the whole country in a mantle of dry air, which moderates the climate so much that, without the aid of a thermometer, no one would believe the cold was so intense. We have then, a dry, clear, cold winter, a dry spring with bright sunshine; a warm summer with an abundance of rain, but not necessarily a cloudy atmosphere, and a dry, serene autumn, with possibly a snow-storm about the equinox.

"An atmosphere like this, with a soil of abounding fertility extending over a region of almost boundless extent, causes me to feel the words of Lord Beaconsfield were those of a far seeing statesman and that our great North-West is truly a land of "il-limitable possibilities." (Manitoba and the Great Northwest, 1882).[1]

CHAPTER XIII

1882-1884

REMOVAL TO OTTAWA—COLLECTING IN WESTERN ONTARIO AND ON GASPE PENINSULA—BEGINS WORK AT THE GEOLOGICAL AND NATURAL HISTORY SURVEY, OTTAWA—DIFFICULTIES OF THE POSITION—BECOMES ONE OF THE CHARTER MEMBERS OF THE ROYAL SOCIETY OF CANADA—VISITS NOVA SCOTIA AND THE ISLAND OF ANTICOSTI, WHERE EXTENSIVE COLLECTIONS OF NATURAL HISTORY SPECIMENS WERE MADE—INCIDENTS DURING THE SUMMER—BEGINS TO WRITE THE CATALOGUE OF CANADIAN PLANTS—EXAMINATION OF THE COUNTRY ALONG THE NIPIGON RIVER AND LAKE NIPIGON, AND FROM NIPIGON EAST ALONG THE C.P.R., THEN BEING CONSTRUCTED—REVIEWS LIFE—COLLECTIONS MADE FOR THE MUSEUM.

MY transfer to Ottawa was to take place in the autumn of 1882, and I now made terms with the Government to take over my herbarium, which, at this time, had increased wonderfully, as had all the collections I had been making for the last three years while on Government work. I had some difficulty about the terms but it was agreed that the Government would take over the herbarium, but only the flowering plants.[1] The mosses and other material were not to be paid for, and I retained these, as, for many years, I had been selling sets of them. This winter, in my hours of leisure, I had begun to shoot small birds and get a knowledge of ornithology. A young man named Woods cured the skins after I had shot the birds and he eventually became the Natural History editor of the Toronto Globe and died one of the leading writers on a paper in Calgary.

Early in the spring, my son, James, and I started out for a trip to Western Ontario and were in London, St. Thomas and on Pelee Point. The reason of my going was that Sir William Hooker wrote me in 1861 that they had less information in England about the flowers that grew at Lake Erie than they did about those that grew beyond the Arctic Circle.[2] A pleasant trip was made to Point Pelee with Dr. Burgess and Mr. William Saunders of London, Ont. After some time, I left for home and, when I reached there, I got word that I was expected to go with Dr. Ells along the Gaspé Coast, after the end of June.

After my return from Western Ontario, my son James, and I went down to Gaspé for the purpose of making an examination of the coast of the St. Lawrence from Gaspé to Little Metis. At Gaspé, we found that there was a road along the coast all the way up that was fit for carts and Dr. Ells and myself arranged to each take a cart to carry our baggage and the specimens obtained on the way, while each member of the party walked and did the work required of him. Dr. Ells and his party, of course, did the geology, and myself and son attended to the botany. We both made extensive collections and had the usual difficulties and experiences on the way. I remember one instance where we saw an enormous number of herring in a pile and I obtained all we could carry for less than a dollar. I remember another house we passed where the children came out to look at us and, out of one house, seventeen children emerged, all from the toddling baby to the young woman who seemed to be in charge. Later in the season, when near Little Metis, we stopped in one house where there were twenty-four living children in the family and all at home. (It is not my purpose to speak of the botany or anything pertaining to my general work when writing of the travels of this and the coming years. The botanical part is in my note books and they are all at Ottawa.)[3]

When we reached the river Ste. Anne des Monts, the parties separated and Dr. Ells and his party went up the coast with the exception of Mr. A. P. Low and myself. We went up the river in two canoes, with French boatmen for the purpose of climbing the Shick-Shock mountains. We went up the river for over thirty miles and then climbed from the river up to the summit of the mountain which overlooked the St. Lawrence and all the country for a long distance. My purpose in going up was to study the flora at the summit as I had never seen a species growing which we called Arctic. Hitherto I had never climbed a mountain, except one in 1875, and knew nothing of the plants to be collected. On reaching the summit, we found an extensive plateau and came on fine specimens of cariboo which gazed at us for a time and then ran off. We spent three days on the summit and I collected a large number of Arctic plants which formed the basis, in later years, for the excursions made in Quebec by Dr. Fernald of Harvard University. While on the summit, I was attacked by black flies and I was semi-delirious on account of the pain for almost all the time I was there. Mr. Low and I rejoined the party at Little Metis and all of us returned to Campbellton by the railway and went down the bay of Chaleur to Gaspé. The remainder of the season, I collected around Gaspé and there I obtained many sea-weeds that were afterwards named by Dr. Farlow of Harvard Univeristy.[4] My reason for going to Lake Erie in the spring was, as already stated, on account of Sir William Hooker who said that at Kew they knew more about the flora of the Arctic regions than they did that of Lake Erie. My reasons for going to Gaspé and the Shick-Shock mountains were because they would give me an opportunity of studying the northern flora of Canada as we then understood it. It will be remembered that, at this time, there were no railways by which I could travel into unexplored parts of the country.

As I mentioned before, I was required by the Government to take up my residence in Ottawa in the autumn of this year, and, as soon as I returned to Belleville, I made arrangements to dispose of my property and pack up my goods for conveyance to Ottawa. Early in November of that year, my two daughters and I went to Ottawa and the remainder of the family followed us in a few days when we received the furniture which we had dispatched from Belleville by railway. The furniture took more time to come than I had expected and the young ladies and their mother had to live at a boarding-house. After getting settled at Ottawa, I took up my work in the museum of the Geological Survey.[5] I found that I was far from being a welcome guest to most of the members of the staff. I soon found out that they resented the appointment of a man over them.

Before I was attached to the survey, I had aspired to be Botanist and I thought that, possibly, I would be attached to the Agricultural Department, but, instead of that, I was attached to the Geological and Natural History Survey, as it was called at that time.[6] I found that my powers were very circumscribed and my position one that gave me a great deal of trouble. Dr. Selwyn restricted me to mounting only one specimen of each species of plant from each Province, no matter how many I might collect, and the specimens that were not used were tied up.[7]

During this winter, the Marquis of Lorne decided to form a society of all the leading scientists and scholars in Canada, which was called the Royal Society of Canada. The appointments were all made by his own selection and the whole society was to consist of eighty members divided into four sections. His secretary sent me a note asking me if I would allow the Marquis to place my name in the fourth section, which was called the Geological and Natural History section. Of course, I *graciously* accepted the position and was appointed by His Excellency as one of the first twenty of the Royal Society. At present, the members that I know of our section, that remain alive, are: Sir James Grant (Sir James died a few months before the author) and myself. The reason of so many deaths was because they were nearly all old men that were appointed. At the meeting of the Society in May, we were all invited to Rideau Hall and took dinner with the Marquis, who was at the head of the table. I think that it was at this dinner that Mark Twain sat at the Marquis' right, as I know it was at one of the dinners we had that I saw him.

I was now settled at Ottawa and began to put in shape the formation of a complete collection of all the plants of the Dominion (as, up to this time, only a few lists had been published) to take the form of an annotated catalogue of the plants, and mention in it that we had, in our herbarium, specimens of all those plants given under those names. At the time I joined the Survey, very little had been done towards forming a museum there, other than the purchasing of a collection of shells from Mr. Whiteaves[8] when he joined the survey and a few that he had added to it since. Dr. Dawson was the only one on the staff, except myself, that seemed to have any desire to get specimens for the Museum, and he brought home a few of the larger mammals every year, so that, when I joined, there were no birds, excepting a few large ones, and a few small mammals and these were mostly collected or bought by Dr. Dawson.   I had some difficulty in getting cases made for the specimens that I brought to Ottawa and even places for the cases.   Still, I persevered with my plants and kept on at the work I had laid out and, when spring came, I had decided to go to Nova Scotia and Cape Breton.   In the spring of 1883, my son William[9]and myself went to Nova Scotia and we botanized in the Annapolis Valley and I ascended Cape Blomidan and went to Yarmouth, and other places, and Halifax and then went to Cape Breton and hired a rig and went by road all the way to Louisburg, the old French city at the extreme east.   After spending the early summer there, we returned to Ottawa and, later, went down to Gaspé, where I had made arrangements with the owner of a schooner to take us over to Anticosti.

When we reached Gaspé, we found our schooner ready to take us across to Anticosti and, as they were going to fish on the banks, they arranged to call for us at North West Point, about the last of August.   My party consisted of my son and myself and two fishermen with a large fishing boat and a light skiff.   We started from Gaspé in the morning and ran down the bay to get the schooner.

As I look back now, I cannot understand why, in my trips, I made so little preparation, when so much is taken to-day for less hazardous journeys.   My son, Willie, and I did not seem to have anything with us but blankets and a tent; I remember nothing else.   Before we left Gaspé, the men said to me: "We will have to take a mixture of castor oil and Stockholm tar, as the flies on Anticosti are very bad."   Of course, I laughed at them, as I had had experience on the prairie and thought nothing of flies.

After we landed on the beach at Salt Lake and had our things put on the shore, the men pitched the tent and we prepared to camp there for a few days.   The land seemed to be a peat-bog, though it was dry, close to the shore, and a few hundred yards farther in. My son and I immediately commenced work to gather the plants that were in great numbers there. In a short time, I was surprised to find my son desirous to go back to camp because the flies had bitten him up so that, when I looked at him, his face was all covered with blood. Of course, I excused him and told him to go to camp. Later, I discovered that my own face was bloody instead of sweaty, and I returned to camp also and found the men and Willie had anointed themselves with tar and castor oil and they looked to me like three unwashed Indians. I resisted and put no tar on my face for a long time, but, eventually, had to come to it. I may say that this tar, with additions, remained on our faces for ten days or more, as there was no sense in washing. The flies that troubled us were black flies, not mosquitoes. On some of the points in the bog, we found flocks of young Canada Geese that had been hatched in that quarter. Some days after, we went up to S'West Point, where a Mr. Pope was light-house-keeper, and took our boat into the Jupiter River, over a small bar that was at the mouth. We settled down for work at the point and made quite large collections. My intention, when I reached there, was to make an excursion up Jupiter River in the small boat and see what the interior of the Island was like. We started up the river and went for a number of miles until the river got so shallow that we could proceed no further and there we camped.

From the camp, I went a half day's journey up the river, and found no change in the appearance of the country except that it became drier the further we went in from shore. Where we camped, there was a large pool of fresh water filled with trout, and my son and the men made such good use of their time that my share of the fish that they caught was half-a-barrel, and the men took a great quantity themselves. I may say, that I brought these fish to Ottawa, and they were not considered good eating because they were extremely salty, owing to the fishermen having cured them the way that they did the herring on the coast.

After being our full time on S'West Point, we determined to go up the coast further, but a storm at S'West Point came up and was so strong that it closed the bar at the mouth of Jupiter

River and shut us up so that it was impossible to get the boat out except by cutting the bar at low water.

Ellis Bay was the next point where we intended to stop and the people at the light-house warned us that the man who lived there kept Newfoundland dogs that were a terror to all travellers and warned Willie and myself that, if we were attacked by them, they would eat us up. I had decided that my son and I should walk along the shore and through the woods up to Ellis Bay, and that was the reason of the warning. The men intended to cut the channel when the tide went out and follow us up when the tide turned, which would be in the afternoon. My son and I started and everything went well until we approached the man's house, when we heard a tremendous barking and uproar generally. I warned my son to keep behind me and I would walk up to the door and knock. I did this, knocking at the door. As soon as I knocked, the uproar became greater, and I heard someone unlock the door and a great racket was going on inside. The owner opened the door and, as he did so, two tremendously big dogs jumped to the threshold and made a terrible barking, but I was quite satisfied, when I saw them, that their bark was worse than their bite, and, while the man was beating them back, I gave a yell myself and I saw that my yell did far more good than his hammering and the end was that the dogs were quiet and my son and I paid our visit and proceeded on our way. Later, the men came up the bay and we pitched our camp to the north of the house.

After inspecting the country round there, we proceeded to Betsie River, where there was a telegraph station, and we pitched our camp on the bank of the river, a little distance from the house. While there, I met with a mishap. Besides collecting plants, I was making a collection of fossils and, in breaking a rock, a small atom flew up and struck me on the eye-ball and I was unable to do much for a few days, but was cured by a simple remedy produced by the lady of the house. She told me that, if my eye-ball was scraped by a gold ring, taken off a lady's finger, it would enable me to see, as she knew it had been done on the coast before. I agreed to have her husband try and see what could be done. He scraped my eye-ball and, the next morning, behold, I was perfectly well. My son will remember that, when going along the shore, we would come to little creeks and pools of water and that I carried him across so that he would not get his feet wet. Another thing he may remember is what happened at this camp. He, while there, complained that something was biting his legs, and that he thought spiders were doing it. I examined his legs and found that our blankets were infested with fleas and it was they that had caused the trouble. I believe it took him a day, and perhaps more, to clear the blankets.

We had many other experiences during our trip, but these are the principal items I can remember. We eventually reached North West Point and camped close to the light-house until our schooner came around and we were taken back to Gaspé and thence home to Ottawa.[10]

I had decided, as stated before, that I would commence a catalogue of the plants of Canada as far as we knew them at that time and decided to write the *Polypetalae* as the First Part. I had made a catalogue before this of the plants mentioned in the various printed lists that had been hitherto made and, at the Library of Parliament, had obtained Hooker's "Flora," which was the only book at that time that gave the flora of the Arctic regions which I intended to include in my work. I intended that all North America, north of Latitude 49°, should be included and, from that to this time, I have never changed my plan and I am glad to say that my son James followed on my lines.

In the winter of 1883, besides other work, I wrote Part One of my catalogue and, when I had it written, I showed it to Mr. Whiteaves and he said: "If you take my advice, you will put this in your drawer and keep it there for seven years and bring it out then and see what you think of it." I thanked him for his invitation and told him that I intended to publish it and say distinctly that that was all we knew about this section of the plants of Canada and ask my readers to supply other information, if they had it, which would be gratefully received. This I did in all the years in which I have been publishing the remaining parts.

Incidentally, I may say that the first meeting of the Royal

Society took place in the spring of 1884, and I took my place with the savants of the Dominion.[12]

The Marquis of Lansdowne arrived in the fall and took the place of Lord Lorne and he carried on the same sports that winter at Government House that Lord Lorne had established. There were two large toboggan slides in the grounds and the skating rink under cover. It was a great rendezvous for the young ladies and gentlemen of Ottawa, every Saturday afternoon; that is, if their parents were on the visiting list at Rideau Hall.

This fall, when Lord Lansdowne came, he encouraged the sports, as he had a number of children, and was at that time a fairly young man himself. He was very democratic in his ways and always walked with a couple of aides when he came into the city and, if he met anyone whom he knew, he often entered into conversation, standing on the sidewalk like a common citizen. At the same time, he was a nobleman in every sense and showed no condescension when anyone was speaking to him, but talked like a common civilian. This winter, his entertainments were largely attended and the young people, both male and female, were busy at the slides, in the afternoon, and on special evenings when the moon was bright. On these evenings, there would be special invitations for the sports and then there was much enthusiasm and foolhardiness amongst the young people. On one of these occasions, when the temperature was below zero and the moon was very bright, the young people were so exhilarated it became dangerous to go down the slides as they followed each other so quickly. My eldest daughter, Clara, and a young man, went down the slide and were followed immediately by another toboggan. Owing to some cause, they were slow in getting out of the way at the bottom and the other toboggan ran into them and my daughter's cheek was cut open by the impact and she was badly hurt and they had to take her to the Hall and be attended to by Lady Lansdowne and Sir James Grant, who was on hand and who sewed up the wound.

During this time, I was busy with my report and, like all enthusiasts, had no time for anything but the work in hand.

Owing to the work that was being done on the Canadian Pacific Railway, I decided to go to Port Arthur and from there take the train to Nipigon and explore Lake Nipigon. In June, 1884, my son Willie and I started for Port Arthur and, when we arrived there, I went up to the hotel and asked the proprietor the rates per day. He stared me up and down, straightened himself and said: "This is a first class hotel, and the rates are $3.00 per day." The hotel was called the Pacific Hotel and I think another stands on the same site today. As it was a $3.00 house, I did what we always did in a city and put my boots outside in the hall for the purpose of being cleaned during the night. When I got up in the morning, I was surprised to find, though the boots were still there, that they had never been touched. I immediately complained to the proprietor about their not being cleaned and he looked up at me with curiosity and said: "Did you find them at your door?" I said that I had. "Well," he said, "You are very lucky to have got them because they might have been taken in the night and then you would have had none."

In a short time, the train started for Nipigon and we reached there, in due course, and camped near the big eddy pool where the railway bridge was going to be built. It was a good place for collecting and, as I at that time took up the study of almost everything, I had a butterfly net and bottles for beetles, so that we made a collection of insects and, in a lane running back from our tent, we collected specimens of the butterfly which Dr. James Fletcher and a Boston professor described as a new species, and the life history of the insect is framed on the wall behind me as I write. At this point, I engaged an Indian with a fine birch bark canoe to take Willie and me up the Nipigon River to Lake Nipigon, which I wished to explore. We had the usual incidents that take place in ascending a river and, where we camped the first night, the current was running quite swiftly and my son observed a great number of fish in the river and told me that there were many red-finned suckers in the stream and that he would like to fish. I told him he could, but said that the fish were not suckers but that they must be trout and he got a line and a little salt pork and, in a couple of minutes, he had a fine large trout, over six pounds in weight, on the bank and, in a few minutes, he had quite enough to last us for some time.   At this time, trout-fishing on the Nipigon River was an established fact and many fishermen from Toronto came there and camped on the river, near where we had camped.   In due course, we reached the lake and kept up the right hand shore.   I soon saw that it was an immense body of water, far beyond anything I had imagined, so I gave up the thought of going around it and we headed for islands we saw in the distance.   We reached there safely and camped, and, in the morning, a storm commenced which lasted two days and nights and we were unable to leave.   The wind, when it did fall, was so strong that the Indian was afraid to start back as the wind was in our face, but advised me to go from island to island in the direction of Nipigon House, which was an establishment of the Hudson's Bay Company.   This trip, in crossing the wide stretch of water, was the worst I ever experienced in a birch bark canoe.   The waves were high, with the usual white caps, and we had much difficulty in making a crossing, but, by good luck, we reached the Barns and, from there, the next day, we reached the Hudson's Bay Post.

On our return from there, we came down the lake on the Hudson's Bay boat and were quite comfortable as it was a large yacht. While crossing the lake in the Hudson's Bay boat, my son was at his fishing again and caught a fine salmon trout, which was lost by the man who tried to gaff it.   When we reached Nipigon, on our return, we found a boat ready to sail for Ross Bay on the north shore of Lake Superior.   At this time, Ross Bay was the headquarters of the contractor for the railway, Mr. James Ross, and I got permission from him to walk down the line from there to Missinabie.   At this time, most of the road for the C.P.R. was under contract and the men were working every few miles except one longer stretch where it was just a blazed path.   I engaged a man called Fred to carry our blankets and, like heroes, my son and I started off on foot with him to travel over one hundred miles.   I remember, in crossing the bridge at the Pic, we had a good deal of difficulty but managed to keep out of the water and, about a quarter of a mile beyond, we came on a camp where I got the copper utensil that I described at the meeting of the Royal Society in Montreal that summer.

Our journey down the railway is indescribable, as we were tormented by flies, and our path was not strewn with roses. My son will remember that, at one cutting we came to, the men were just leaving it on account of a blast that was to go off at once and they ran to a shanty prepared for the occasion. My son made it, but I was caught on the plank crossing the little stream to get to it. I happened to see the explosion and there were a great many stones thrown into the air and I watched to see if they came my way, but, by good luck, none came near me. The shanty, however, received a few knocks, but they had a double row of ties on it, so that nobody would be harmed. We had a number of adventures, but I will pass on till we reached the camp where the "tote" road went down to Michipicoten.

I sat in the camp of Mr. Kilpatrick and he complained to me that the whisky pedlars were so bad that they had disorganized the whole work on the line. I instantly said that I was a Magistrate myself, but that I had been appointed by Mr. Mowat for the County of Hastings. Of course, I knew I had no jurisdiction there, but being a good temperance advocate, I was easily pressed and swore in two special constables who immediately went to work and confiscated all the whisky in the camp and around it, and took the owners prisoners. The next day, my son and I started for Michipicoten, which was fifty miles distant. We went down the "tote" road and, late in the afternoon, came upon what was called the Mormon Camp. This camp was an outfit who were working on the Canadian Pacific Railway. My son was a tall lanky lad and had a leather belt around him and sheath-knife hanging in it and a half drunk teamster began to chaff him about his appearance and I said: "Let the boy alone, and if you have anything to say, say it to me." The man immediately pulled out a pistol and swore he would blow my brains out and I certainly thought he was about to do so, but I said that it was a shame for him to be talking to the boy as he did and that I had no fears of his doing anything to me. After some more talk, my son and I walked on and that evening reached Michipicoten.

When we arrived there, we found that my reputation had reached there before me and they were prepared to have me do the same there as I had done on the line.   There was no help for it, so I swore in two more constables and, that night, they took all the whisky around the village and took the owners prisoners and I saw them in the cage the next morning.   By this time, I was getting frightened, but worse was to come.   I was told that they expected a Stipendiary Magistrate and a constable from Port Arthur on the next boat and the people thought that I was the magistrate.   An hour or two after this, a boat was seen in the distance heading from the western part of the lake and we all decided that it held the magistrate.   By good luck, however, the magistrate was not on board and the whisky that was on board was not allowed to be landed.   Willie and I wisely took passage for Sault Ste. Marie and I kept to the boat until we reached Collingwood and then made my way to Mr. Mowat's office in Toronto and told him what I had done.   He said: "Mr. Macoun, I have heard about what you did and, in view of the good that was effected, I will say nothing about it, but I wish you to understand that you must never do the like again."

Going back, for a little, to the days when I first taught school, I was standing one afternoon in the school when I saw my future wife drive by in her father's carriage.   She was, at that time, only a young girl of sixteen.   This woke me up and, from that time forward, I really began to learn, my mind having focused on her and, on my studies, as an accessory to the acquisition of her as a wife. Between four and five years after this, after many discussions, we were married, and, immediately after, now having a home, I could commence to form a collection, which I had desired for some years.

When I first taught school, I began to describe the plants that were collected and name them.   Why did I describe the plants?   It was because I had no books with the descriptions in. Twenty years after that, I did the same with birds on the prairies. I wrote out their descriptions and then hunted them up in books afterwards.   In 1860, I taught school at Castleton and collected a great number of species and must have dried some of my specimens as I remember giving a few of them to Professor Hincks, of Toronto University, for identification that year. In 1861, I moved to 'Belleville and made large collections there and, that year, I commenced to form a herbarium. The next year, I married.

Up to this time, I was merely a collector of insects, of minerals and of fossils and, like other young people, considered myself quite an authority on things I knew very little about. This year, the Murchason Club was established, at Belleville, and I at once became a member. There was a great variety of subjects taken up, as no two members studied the same subject, so that I became Botanist of the club and, as I look back, I have no remembrance of giving time to any other subject. Curiously enough, Mr. William Smith, of Norwich, England, one of the members, is still living and I correspond with him after all these years. The meetings of the club added a great deal to my knowledge but my whole mind was given to my school and botany. The year I was married, I began to put together ideas that I had formed before this time. In that year, I commenced to write my catalogue of Canadian Plants and I think that the note-books, or some of them, in which I wrote the names, are still in existence amongst my books and pamphlets. The plan I adopted was actually the way in which I carried out the catalogue afterwards published of the whole of the plants of the Dominion. At this time, every list of plants that was published, I copied into my notes and could see at a glance where any species had been found. I remember getting Borgeaus' list of the species that he collected on the prairie and in the Rocky Mountains while he was Botanist to Palliser's Expedition. This list I got from Dr. Gray. Judge Logie of Hamilton published a list and I incorporated it and Dr. Fowler of New Brunswick, published a list and I incorporated it also. At this time, Mr. Barnston, of Montreal, and Dr. Lawson, Professor of Botany at Queen's University, Kingston, became my intimate friends and assisted me in many ways. Dr. Lawson established the Botanical Society of Canada at Queen's and I became a member. There I met Dr. Robert Bell, Dr. John Bell, and Mr. A. T. Drummond, who is still living. They were then young men in the University and students of botany.   Later, Dr. Schultz made a collection of plants between St. Cloud and Fort Garry and submitted them to me and Dr. George Dawson submitted all his collections made on the boundary, while it was being surveyed,[13] These opened up my trip to Lake Superior in 1869, because Mr. Watt was then planning a Botany of Canada and wished to have a better knowledge of the plants around Lake Superior.

I was now considered the chief botanist in Canada and all collections that were made were sent to me for identification. My trip to Lake Superior, in 1872, culminated in my going to the Pacific that same year, as previously described, and, in 1875, Dr. Selwyn wished me to be sent with him, and the Government granted his request and Mr. Mackenzie, the premier, appointed me botanist to his expedition.   In the meantime, my ambition had increased to such an extent that I began to look forward to being made Botanist to the Dominion and devote all my time to botany.[14]

My three years as explorer on the prairie and elsewhere gave me an opportunity to place my claims and, on the first of January, 1881, I was appointed Botanist to the Geological and Natural History Survey of Canada by Sir John A. Macdonald.   The appointment carried with it a first class clerk-ship and $1,500 a year.

In 1880, while on the prairie, I decided to take up the study of birds and adopted the plan I had followed when I started teaching school; I described the birds as they were shot and, when I found the books, I compared my descriptions with them and so learned the rudiments of ornithology.   In the springs of 1881 and 1882, I collected many species of birds at Belleville and had them skinned by young Mr. Wood, and gave him a York shilling a skin for doing the work.   This was how matters stood when I was ordered to report at Ottawa to be a resident there in the autumn of 1882.

The skins of birds, that I brought, were spread out by me on a table in the Long Room, where the draughting group was, and, after a time, were placed in long drawers that were in the old

Museum and, in course of time, with Dr. Bell's specimens of birds, collected on Hudson's Bay, were destroyed almost wholly by insects, and the remainder burned.

———

CHAPTER XIV

1884-1885

AFTER my younger son and I came back from Nipigon in the autumn of 1884, the British Association was about to start on a trip over the Canadian Pacific Railway to see the country as far west as the line had been built. Dr. Selwyn was to go with the party and intended Dr. Bell or some other officer to go with him as well. At this juncture, Mr. Van Horne, who was later President of the C.P.R., asked Dr. Selwyn to permit me to go out with the Association and talk to them about the prairies. Of course, this was agreed to, as Van Horne at this time was a power in the country. I was informed by Dr. Selwyn that I would be expected to go with the party when they left Toronto, and I prepared myself accordingly and overtook them at Owen Sound. The S.S. "Algoma" was set apart for the party and I met them and obtained passage on the vessel and we were about ninety-eight in the company when we started on our long journey. I remember little of the trip on the lower lakes except that, the first evening, a large party of us went into the hold and there saw the dynamo at work which supplied the steamship with electricity. This was the first vessel on the Lakes that was lit up at night by this means. I knew none of the party and was not introduced, so that I was usually alone until after we passed Sault Ste. Marie. We sailed from there in the evening and the day had been quite warm and, as we passed up along the American shore, the light-houses all seemed elevated above their bases and caused a great deal of wonderment amongst the Englishmen. I was with the party, where they were assembled, and a gentleman went up to the Captain and asked him the cause of the mirage. The Captain said that he was unable to tell them but the pilot, who was, by the way, a half-breed, would likely be able to do so. He was unable to explain it to us. I had been accustomed to putting in my remarks whenever I got the opportunity and, in this case, I did the same by immediately saying that I knew the reason. At once, all eyes were turned upon me and I told them that the light-houses were apparently hoisted up in the air when the air over the land was warmer than the air over the lake. The pilot immediately answered: "How about the matter when the ship is turned up side down as we often see it on the lake?" I told him at once that that was when the water was warmer than the air and the cause was very simple. At this stage a gentleman came up to me and pulled out his tablets and said to the assembly "I am Professor of Optics in London University and will soon tell you whether this gentleman is correct or not." He turned to me and said: "Sir, repeat what you have just said in regard to the light-houses being thrown higher than the land they stood on." I said: "It was because the air over the land was heated in the afternoon and the water was cold as it always was." He immediately made a figure on the paper and applied my statements and turned to me and said: "You are quite correct, Sir. Now let me have your other statements." So I told him the cause of the mirage that turned a vessel upside down and he immediately made a figure and, in a short time, he turned and said: "You are right again, Sir." Then he addressed the company and told them: "Gentlemen, the elevation of the light-houses is caused simply by refraction and the latter case is caused by double refraction." He then passed his drawings to the company and I was at once an object of as great an interest as the light-houses themselves.

Shortly afterwards, we saw a large hawk flying towards the land and some one said it was a falcon and I, of course, butted in again and said that he was in the wrong and that it was a buzzard.

Then another gentleman came up who said he was the President of the Ornithological Association in London and asked me how I knew. Of course I knew, by my familiarity with Canadian birds; I said that falcons fly swiftly because they take their prey chiefly on the wing and the buzzards soar and catch their food mainly on the earth. I now obtained a double standing amongst the men and I required no introduction, as every man that had any troubles about the birds applied to me and, when we reached the land, it was still more apparent, for I was at home there as well. When we reached Port Arthur, we were located in eight pullman carriages and started for our trip across the prairies to the Rocky Mountains. There, by chance or previous arrangement, I am not sure which, Mr. Bennett of Kew Gardens, and Mr. Mennell, of Croydon, and Professor Traill, Trinity College, Dublin, were placed in the car that I was in and from that day to the end of the journey, our two compartments were the scene of constant talk and explanation about the botany and all the flowers that were collected by other parties on the way.

It would take too long to tell of what happened in crossing the prairies, but I can say this much, at any rate. The excursionists made a point of asking me everything that came up and I found that, like Englishmen generally, they took my sayings for all they were worth, and I learned the value of their opinions later in my life. Suffice it to say, that we eventually reached Laggan and, after remaining there all night, we went on as far as Hector where we formed parties to explore or to walk around. Dr. Selwyn led the geologists down to the tunnel and was nearly killed by hammering on the rock at the mouth of the tunnel, which caused a fall of rock which blocked up the exit, and no further progress in that direction could be made. In the meantime, Mr. Mennell and myself had climbed up the flank of Cathedral Mountain and, after we had ascended as far as my shoes would allow me to go, we made some observations. Standing where we were and looking north, we saw a beautiful lake embosomed in the hills, which Mr. Mennell said was like a Swiss tarn and another object we saw was in the distance to the north west. A large glacier with a creek apparently running down it, and falling for a long distance into the valley beneath. I may say that the tarn we saw was named years afterwards and called Sherbrooke Lake and, after twenty years, I discovered that the glacier we had looked down upon with the stream flowing from it was the great glacier at the head of the Yoho Valley.

On the return trip, we had, by this time, become more than chance acquaintances and we had many talks about various subjects and, amongst others, I made the acquaintance of Dr. Chedle[1] and an artist of the "Graphic" and Lord Ross, who, with Professor Ball, were the astronomers of the party. I had a wonderful time and made many friends who aided me in the years to come. That winter, I wrote part two of my plant catalogue and planned and prepared other work, that I intended to perform the next year, which was no less than an exploration of the Rocky Mountains.

I was home only a short time when rumors of trouble in the North West commenced to be talked about and, late that winter, the fight took place at Duck Lake between the half-breeds and the North West Mounted Police, and the rebellion broke out. This caused quite a sensation at Ottawa and Captain Causton, with whom I was well acquainted, told Lord Lansdowne that I was familiar with the country around Batoche. On the invitation of His Excellency, I went down to Rideau Hall and met a large number of gentlemen who were discussing the matter. I was asked if I would not go out to the west and act as advisor for General Middleton, who was going to be the general commanding the forces who were sent out to suppress the rebellion. On the advice of Captain Causton, I refused to go as Middleton was known to be an obstinate man, in fact, an old fool. A few days after this, I was at dinner at Rideau Hall. After dinner, when the ladies retired to the drawing room, the subject of the rebellion was brought up at once and I agreed to lay down on a map the section of country where the fighting was to take place and give my opinions in writing to the Governor. I did so and pointed out on a map, for Lord Melgund, who was to be General Middleton's Chief of Staff, what ought to be done when they reached the Saskatchewan, namely that he, or someone else, should lead a part of the troops over Clarke's Crossing on the Saskatchewan where the country was open, and march down on the prairie to Batoche and take it in the rear.   I told them that the prairie on the south side of the river was mostly brush and had many ravines and was dangerous.   Instead of doing what I said, Middleton advanced on Batoche from Clarke's Crossing by the trail on the south and then had to fight and the results of that fight were that Melgund was recalled from the North Shore to assist Middleton and the army had to retreat and, eventually, take the trail from Humboldt that was to have been taken at the commencement of the campaign and, after fighting at Batoche for a length of time, the place was taken by Colonel Williams, (without the orders of General Middleton).   Lord Melgund was so disgusted with the fight at the coulee that he left the army and returned to Ottawa, and he showed me his map and pointed out how far he had got on his way when the old man recalled him.

As soon as the spring opened, I prepared to carry out my plans for an examination of the Rocky Mountains and, late in May, my son William and I started for the West.

This time, I went by the Grand Trunk by way of Chicago and St. Paul, as I was taking my son on my own account.   Willie and I were sitting in the station at St. Paul when a gentleman strolled in and, seeing us, came and sat on a bench near us and entered into conversation.   He was very affable and told us a number of things and asked me where I was going.   I said that I was on my way to Winnipeg.   "Well," he said, "I am going there myself.   I have a store at Brandon and I have just come down here to get goods."   He asked me quite a number of questions and I answered them fully and he said that he would see me in the evening on the train as he was about to return home.   I immediately turned to my son and told him that I believed that man to be a confidence man and that he would certainly come in the evening and he said he thought he would too.

In the evening, my son and I boarded the train at St. Paul and he sat facing one door in the car and I sat facing the other door.   After a while my son said: "I see the man looking in the door."   Of course, he immediately came in and sat down beside me in the seat and commenced to talk.   He talked in the usual way of a confidence man, that he was about to start for home and found he was short of funds and could I accommodate him with a little money until he got to Winnipeg, where he would have an opportunity to repay me. I immediately put my hand on his shoulder and said: "I am an old hand at this sort of thing and if you do not clear out in a moment, I will report this thing to the conductor and have you taken up." He immediately left, and, in a few moments, he came back and sat down beside me again and said that I would have been a very great fool if I had believed what he had said and that he was glad to know that I was in the same line! Further talk resulted in my ordering him out of the car. Willie and I were on our watch after that and I saw a man looking at me. Nothing happened, however. Late in the night, or early in the morning, we reached a place called Barnsville, it was on a Sunday morning. The brakesman woke my son and me. An Englishman and a Dutchman told us that we were to get off here, as this was where the road led to Winnipeg. We carried out our hand-baggage to the platform and waited to have my trunks put off the baggage car. As that had not been done, I walked over to the train and said to the baggage-man: "Why do you not put off my trunks?" He then asked where we were going, and when I told him, to Winnipeg, he said that both roads led to Winnipeg and that the train would naturally be going there now. He told us to get in the train at once, or we would be left behind. We immediately took his advice and hopped on. This was apparently another case of confidence men.

The next incident of our trip that is worth speaking of was when we all took supper at Broadview and twenty-two of the passengers were poisoned by ptomaine poisoning. We had canned braun for our supper and, as it was soft and easily eaten, I suppose I took more than my share. At this time, no one felt any ill effects and we enjoyed the evening on the train playing cards or talking with other members of the party. A number of young men were there from Ottawa and J. B. Tyrrell, of our own staff, was on the train also. While we were looking at the card game, an old man, dressed in full cow-boy costume, addressed Willie as "Sonnie" and wanted to know where he was going and my son, believing that he was another confidence man, told him that it was none of his business and made some other remarks and the cow-boy's answer was: "My boy, you have been badly brought up and I am ashamed." I fired up at once and told him that the boy was better brought up than he was himself, and there was some discussion and I asked my son why he spoke so brusquely to the man, and he said that he had thought the man another confidence man, and I explained about our encounter in St. Paul and there was quietness again.

About twelve o'clock in the night, I became very sick and went to the wash-room and relieved my stomach and, while there, must have collapsed, as I remember nothing further until early in the morning, when J. B. Tyrrell, found me lying on the platform at Moose Jaw, where we had been ordered to change trains. Tyrrell immediately had me taken to the pullman and telegraphed to Swift Current, where there was a doctor, to have him in attendance when we reached there. It was now discovered that twenty-two others were poisoned also, but only two, besides myself, were in need of the doctor's attention.

When we reached Swift Current, a gentleman from Calgary was taken in hand by the doctor and I was left alone in the wash-room of the pullman and I became deathly sick and drank whole glasses of water and vomited constantly. Every glass of water that I drank helped me on the road to recovery, because each time I drank, I vomited again and, when the doctor came to see me, I was quite well and almost ready to eat again. After a day or two at Calgary, we went on to Morley and made our first camp near the Bow River. After staying there for a few days we went on to Kananaskis and then to Canmore, where we climbed the mountains and got a great many mountain plants and my son caught a number of butterflies. Then we moved on to Banff and had our first view of the hot springs and got some of the crystals that were then being taken from the cave. Our next move was to Castle Mountain, where we botanized and climbed a number of mountains, amongst others, Castle Mountain, which is north of the Bow River, Copper Mountain, to the south, also, where there was a mine at that time. After some time there, we moved to Hector and camped there for some weeks and climbed a number of mountains, one of them being Mt. Paget, north of Kicking Horse Lake. We also went to Sherbrooke Lake which, at that time, was nameless, and climbed the mountain to the west of it and, as my son will remember, going up the ravine, he loosened a stone that passed me rather rapidly and we could see it further down the mountain tumbling more than fifty feet in the air as it sped to the bottom; this was on the 29th of July, 1885.

We moved from there to Donald, which was then the head-quarters of the Canadian Pacific Railway construction. Here, we fraternized with the officials and got many favors from them in regard to going up and down the road while we were engaged in collecting and examining the country. Golden, at this time, was a point of some importance, as it was there that the railway first touched the Columbia River and we were surprised to find wild geese breeding on the hummocks bordering the river marshes. We made many discoveries in the Columbia River Valley and lived quite close to the headquarters of the C.P.R. At that time there were three Donalds; one, where we lived; another, the commercial village, and the third may be nameless at present.

After a time, we moved from Donald and went on as far as Six Mile Creek, which was six miles above Beaver Mouth, where the railroad left the Columbia. At Six Mile Creek, we remained for possibly two weeks and made many excursions. One, in particular, when Willie and I walked up the track from where we were staying to the bridge that was being built over Stoney Creek and my son will remember that he fired a number of shots at small birds up in the trees and never killed one. We could not make out the reason he couldn't kill any and found out afterwards that it was because the trees were so tall and the branches were so high up that the charges did not carry high enough for them. All the trees were at least one hundred feet high without a branch and my son's charges were only to kill at thirty yards. The day we went up the track to Stoney Creek Bridge, we went down into the valley of the Beaver River, nearly 1,000 feet below and walked down on the tote road to Six Mile Creek, which was on a level with the water.   Another day, which may be set down as a red-letter day in our lives, dawned on us at Six Mile Creek, when the authorities were invited, and we also, to go to Stoney Creek Bridge, which was just completed and was three hundred feet high, and this, the first day that cars could cross it, Willie and I were passengers on the first train and went up and the train stopped for some hours at Rogers' Pass.   We were so absorbed in our work that we took no note of time and let the train go back to Six Mile Creek without us.   We had no alternative but to walk back. When we reached Stoney Creek Bridge and saw its condition, I confess that I was more than frightened.   There was a wide chasm that we could hardly see the bottom of and the ties were placed at uncertain distances apart and it was very difficult to stride from one to another and, there being no parapet, but just the bare ties and the iron rails, I feared to venture across. I thought more of my son than I did of myself, but he said: "We can do it very well," as I think he remembered the difficulty in climbing down the 1,000 feet on our former trip.   So I led the way across, carrying my parcel of plants, while Willie came behind, carrying the gun.   On the way across, I never spoke to him, but, when I reached the far side, and he reached it shortly after, I asked him if he had been dizzy in coming across.   He said: "Oh, no, I was not dizzy, but I often had doubts as to where I was placing my feet."   This was exactly the trouble I had had myself, and it showed how near we both had been to being dizzy.   This, I think, was the most foolhardy trip that I have ever taken and, I believe, now, that we were preserved that day for better things. I have never crossed that bridge since, but I shudder at the thought of what might have happened that day.

After this trip, we moved up to the summit of the Selkirks to the camp which was pitched between Rogers' Pass and Glacier. Here, we settled down for the remainder of our stay in the mountains, as we could not get any further west, as the Loop was still unfinished.

While at the Summit, we made frequent trips to various points, three of which I may mention, as, evidently, we were the first who climbed in the vicinity of Glacier.   Our camp was pitched

16

due north of the mountain now called Avalanche Mountain, and we decided to ascend it the day after we arrived. The lower part of the mountain was then covered with dense wood, chiefly alder, all sloping downwards, and we could only ascend by pulling ourselves up by the trunks of the small trees. When we got above this, the climbing was easy, only, when we approached the summit, it was both steep and slippery, as it was covered with short grass and the mountain heather. We had no nails in our boots and my son was unable to climb, so I advised him to take off his boots and walk in his stocking feet, which he did for the last five hundred feet. When we attained the summit, we could look down to the east and see, almost at our feet, the Great Glacier and, it being the first time we had ever seen it, we sat down and studied it for some time. The broken slope, as we saw it at that time, was very rough and apparently filled with chasms, as the water, in some places, spouted out of the openings a distance of from eight to ten feet and bore down the broad face, upon which we looked, with tremendous force. This was about the 20th of August, 1885, and quite warm weather. The descent was much easier than the ascent and, of course, we carried the same articles that we did in all our climbing while in the mountains. Our gun had two barrels and one, we kept loaded with buck shot, and the other was the one that Willie used to kill small birds. Our gun was loaded for bear and my instructions to my son were to not shoot until the bear hoisted and then for him to let him have it in the head. By good luck, we never saw a bear but smelt them very often. The day before we reached the mountains, a wounded grizzly had attacked two men when one of them was drinking at a little creek. The bear sprang upon his back and a young French boy who was with him had a gun and he put no less than eight bullets into the bear before he killed it, and the skin of the bear was hung up in the camp for everyone to see and yet, my son and myself did not seem to take any stock in it, as we went our way as usual.

A day or two after this, we made an ascent on this side of Mount Cheops. We climbed up to it from a little creek that ran down almost to our camp and we went up a large part of the as-

MOUNT SIR DONALD FROM BALD MOUNTAIN,[2] WITH MOUNT MACOUN IN THE CENTRE.

cent in the creek.   When far up on the mountain, on a ledge of rocks, we heard a loud whistle and, as we thought it was a man, my son answered and, in a few moments, we heard the whistle again, quite close to us and, on looking around, we saw our first marmot sitting on the rocks and then we knew we had seen the whistler.   We came across a mountain garden up there and I soon filled my plant press[3] and we returned the way we came.

Another day, we went up opposite Rogers' Pass and climbed to the north towards what is now called the Swiss Glacier and, after ascending almost to the glacier, I got tired of carrying my parcel and laid it down with the intention of taking it up when we came back to that point.   By good luck, I read my aneroid and wrote down the reading.   We climbed on and, shortly after, reached the glacier and, seeing a cave some distance up the face, we went into it and, as the light shone upon it, the appearance was very brilliant.   I asked my son what the ice looked like and his prompt answer was the best one I ever heard in connection with glacier ice.   He said: "Father, it just looks like rock candy."

At this stage of the proceedings, a heavy cloud settled down on the mountain and rain and cloud surrounded us so that, when we reached the point at which we left my parcel, we could not see more than a few yards.   After some thought, I told my son to stand where he was and I took the aneroid and looked at the reading and saw that we were on the line where the parcel ought to be, so I looked to the right and failed to find it, and came back to him and went to the left and, in a few moments, I had my parcel and the plants.   The rain and cloud now obscured the landscape and we could find no object to which to steer, so we bore a little to the left, where we knew there was a creek, and followed it down and came out at the base of Mount Tupper.

Our next attempt was to go up to the foot of the Great Glacier from the railway, but it was beyond our powers and we had to give it up.   On our last day at the camp, we went down with the chief bridge builder on the train carrying timbers for the Loop and, as we were approaching Glacier, the engineer lost control of the train and the bridge engineer told us that there might be serious difficulty and for us to prepare to do as he did. As the train approached the turn at Glacier, we each stood on the edge of the car ready to jump when he should give the word and, in a few moments he raised himself up and said, "the engineer has control of the train." This is the last event I shall record of our trip, as we now turned our faces homeward. Our good luck still kept with us and we obtained passage, without pay for us both, from Calgary to Port Arthur and, when we reached Port Arthur, whom did we find there but Mr. Marpole, who had charge at that time, of the western division, and Harry Beasley was his private secretary. We had intended to go from Port Arthur on a steamboat but Mr. Marpole was going down in a private car to meet the Governor-General at Biscotasing and he invited us to go with him for the company. We four were the only persons that went down, that is, Mr. Marpole, Mr. Beasley, my son and myself; and the engineer and fireman. As the road was very new, having been built that season, it was in a rough state and we stopped to put up telegraph poles and to remove obstacles that were occasionally on the track or near it.

Biscotasing, in 1885, was the end of passenger service on the eastern end of the railway and Mr. Whyte, who was vice-president of the road, was conducting the Governor-General to the west. At this time, and at this point, my son and I took the regular train home, having travelled on the Canadian Pacific Railway from the summit of the Selkirks to Ottawa. In fact, I may say, we were the first passengers over parts of the road.

On looking back now over the country, as my son and I saw it at that time, it has altogether changed. Everywhere, fine forests were around North Bay at that time and, through the Rocky Mountains and going up the Selkirks from Six Mile Creek, the trees were so tall on each side of us that birds could not be killed with an ordinary shot gun. I remember one tree that had been cut and from which thirteen ties, each eight feet and four inches long, had been made. Today, all that fine timber has disappeared and bareness has taken its place. At that time, there was a saw-mill at Palliser, in the Rockies, and another on the Columbia at the mouth of Blueberry Creek, one at Beaver Mouth on the Columbia and possibly others, all sawing up fine trees, while fires raged frequently, destroying beautiful standing timber.[4]

CHAPTER XV

1886.

THE COLONIAL EXHIBITION—SENT TO ENGLAND AS ONE OF THE CANADIAN REPRESENTATIVES—ATTENDS MANY FUNCTIONS—ENTERTAINED BY LORD BRASSEY, DUKE OF NORTHUMBERLAND, MARQUIS OF SALISBURY, EARL WARWICK, EARL OF ERNE, MARQUIS OF LORNE AND OTHERS—VISITS IRELAND AND FINDS DISTANT RELATIVES AND NAMESAKE, JOHN MACOUN, OF KILMORE—MANY PLACES OF INTEREST IN ENGLAND ARE VISITED—INTERESTING INCIDENTS.

WHEN we reached home, we found the family all well and I immediately set to work at my usual occupation. While we were absent, work on the Colonial Exhibition in London, had commenced and all were preparing for it and many were aspiring to be sent to London in charge of the various exhibits. A large collection of birds was to be sent, which had been purchased in Toronto, and also the collections we had in our Museum. Besides these was a large collection of minerals and precious stones and various kinds of timber and a complete set of plants from my herbarium. I found that Mr. Whiteaves was slated for the Natural History exhibit and Dr. Adams for the Geology, and Willmot for the Minerals. Herring expected to be sent in charge of the birds and Dr. Selwyn was to have general charge.

Early in the winter, I received a letter from Professor Boyd Dawkins, of Birmingham, England, being one of the gentlemen whose acquaintance I had made in 1884 when in the mountains. He asked me if I were going to England the coming summer and I told him candidly that others were already slated for the positions, but I thought if my friends in England asserted themselves it might be possible for me to be sent. Apparently, Dawkins had taken the hint for, in a few weeks, Mr. H. B. Small, who was secretary of the Agricultural Department, told me that Sir Charles Tupper, who was to be Commissioner, was deluged with letters from England saying that I would be very acceptable to the literary and scientific men of England at the coming exhibition. Small ventured to tell me that I was going to be appointed, as Sir Charles thought it better to please the friends in England, and, on his advice, I commenced to prepare to go.

A few days before Dr. Adams was to start, Dr. Selwyn came to me and said that he had decided that I would be the proper man to go to England instead of Mr. Whiteaves, and he would be glad if I could prepare to go at once. After simulated hesitation, I said that I thought I could and, of course, being ready, I had no trouble in leaving with Dr. Adams. I learned, before I left, that Sir Charles Tupper told Dr. Selwyn that he must send me as I would be very acceptable to friends in England. This added to my standing when I reached England, because I was placed at once on the list of distinguished Canadians and Dr. Selwyn and myself were the only two of our contingent who were on this list.

We were hardly settled down to work before invitations commenced to pour in and the first At Home that I attended was one given by the Foreign Minister to Gladstone's Government. I confess I was bewildered when ushered into the suite of rooms which he occupied in the Foreign Office in London. It was simply indescribable, as it was the first great function I had ever attended. I may state here that, while in London, one of the things that surprised me was that, on all occasions, every man that pretended to be a gentleman, wore a tall hat and I followed suit so that, on all the occasions of which I speak, the reader can think of me as going around in a frock coat and a tall hat, and, often, with a flower in my button hole. I will not attempt to go into details and give a picture of any of the gatherings I attended, but shall only mention a few of the principal ones.

A short time after we reached London, I was invited, with many others, to go to Normanhurst, the country estate of Sir Thomas Brassey. Lady Brassey had just written a book called "The Voyage of the Sunbeam" (a yacht that Sir Thomas owned) and she was with him on the voyage which lasted for nearly a year. Somehow it was mentioned while I was there that I had written a book myself and that I was now considered an author, and this gave me some standing with Lady Brassey and, while we were all taking carriages to go to Hastings, I was placed in the carriage with their daughter, Miss Brassey, and a young man, the tutor in the family.   We had a fine ride together and, in conversation, Miss Brassey asked me if I would like to see the Domesday Oak, which she pointed out, and, after a time, we passed on and saw Battle Abbey and then drove through Hastings, a great watering-place, on the coast of England.   I may mention that, on all these trips, we were at no expense as our invitation was either for a special train or our passage was paid.

Late in the summer, I had another invitation to go to Sion House on the Thames, above London, to see the rose garden and an excursion boat was hired by the Duke and we all went up the Thames together.   We were received by Lord Atherly, who represented the Duke, and I was pleased to find that his secretary had been secretary to the Marquis of Lorne and knew me because he was the man who had invited me to lecture for the Marquis at Ottawa.   He at once introduced me to Lord Atherly and it was not long before my Lord and myself were going arm in arm through the grounds, admiring the trees and, I found afterwards, *admired* by some of my friends.   Lord Atherly began to talk trees with me and took me around the grounds and showed me trees of a large size that had been planted there over one hundred years back and had been brought originally from Canada.   While with Lord Atherly, Sir Thomas Brassey came up with his Lady and they immediately remembered me.

Another very important thing took place early in November, just as I was leaving for home.   I got an invitation to attend the Temple Church in London and to bring my friends with me. We reached there in due time and stood with the general congregation and saw the commencement of the service.   The choir boys took their places and a beadle, dressed up in fantastic clothes, came and tapped me on the shoulder and asked me if I were Professor Macoun.   When I said that I was, he bowed and told me to follow him.   I followed him and he took me to the seat next to the President (of the Royal Society) and sat me down in the stall next to him and here I was placed in front of the whole congregation. After the service was over, I was asked by the President, if I would take lunch with him and I, of course, accepted and was brought into the house where all the barristers lived and we sat down to a lunch where all the chief lawyers of the Inner Temple were assembled.

After this, I was invited to what was called the Grand Dinner of the Inner Temple, and there I met the Marquis of Lorne and many other gentlemen with whom I was acquainted more or less. I chiefly remember one of the old lawyers taking me into the library and showing me the wonderful collection of old law books. There he told me that it was on account of the wonderful library that they had that law cases were referred to them from the colonies. The colonial lawyers were not deficient in knowledge, but their libraries did not contain the precedence[1] that was required to complete the cases.

In the early summer, the Marquis of Salisbury invited a large party of over two hundred to lunch at Hatfield, for which a special train was provided.

When we reached there, I found no acquaintance in the party except Dr. May, of Toronto, with whom I walked up to the House. In front of us, were two young gentlemen whom I took to be Londoners. They reached the house in front of us and an old lady received them on the steps to whom they made the most elaborate and profound bow. She was dressed like a housekeeper of standing in the olden time, and had a bright colored belt around her waist and, attached to it, a large bunch of keys, which were very prominent. Dr. May thought she was the housekeeper and, I believe, almost felt annoyed at our reception as the people who came in carriages drove round the house and were received by the Marquis himself. On account of the keys, I immediately decided that she was the Marchioness of Salisbury herself and was acting as the chatelaine of the castle. I made my bow, as well as a Canadian could do, and passed into the House. After some conversation, we were addressed by a tall young man who told us that, on account of the large party, his mother wished the company to be informed that the gentlemen, accompanied by ladies, would have lunch in the Great Hall while single gentlemen would have a separate lunch on the gallery outside. The single gentlemen went outside and, by good fortune, I was placed at the table where this young man presided. On my left, was one of the young gentlemen that I had seen making his bow to the Marchioness; on my right, sat Dr. May. Many things were talked of while we were eating lunch and, amongst others, the status of the Colonies under England. Many opinions were given and, of course, I had my say as well as the others. I took the stand that protection in Canada was the same as free trade in England, because England wanted raw materials to help their people, while we wanted to manufacture our own materials ourselves. The tall young man, who is now the Marquis of Salisbury, agreed with me and thought that the tariff was the key to the whole situation between England and the Colonies. The young gentleman, sitting on my left, asked me if I knew Ottawa. I told him that I did and that I lived there. He told me then that his brother was Governor-General there now, and asked me if I knew Lord Lansdowne. I told him that I knew him quite well and, before we left Hatfield, he invited me to breakfast with him at the Carleton,² and to bring my friend. I did so the next morning. We were through lunch before the others and the young lord asked us to walk through the rooms and see the various pictures before the others came out. We started off and the first picture he showed us was the old lady who had received us, whom he called mother, dressed in precisely the style she was in today. We went upstairs and looked at a large number of pictures and, presently, I found myself alone in front of four pictures which were very prominent. One was Charles the 12th of Sweden, the second, Peter of Russia, the third, the Duke of Wellington and the fourth, Queen Elizabeth. While I was standing alone a lady came up who turned out to be the Marchioness herself and she began to talk with me about the pictures and I, as an outspoken Canadian, gave her my opinion without hesitation. I told her that that was the first picture of Queen Elizabeth I had ever seen and I was surprised to find that she had red hair. She said: "You may not be aware that this is the house where Queen Elizabeth lived before she became Queen and our stables are the chapel in which she used to worship." She then took me to the window and showed me their stables. After that she said: "Would you like to see Queen Elizabeth's handwriting?" I told her that I would be delighted and she took me to the library and produced a book that was actually written by the Queen herself. After a little more conversation, the leaders of the party found her and I saw her no more.

Late in the summer, the Irish National Party invited Canadian and Indian Colonial visitors to take a trip to Ireland and be the guests of the Dublin City Council for a few days. Evidently the intention was to take over a large party of Colonials for the purpose of advancing the views of the Nationalists as, that summer, Gladstone had brought into the House a Home Rule Bill for Ireland. I was the only representative of the Canadians whom I knew that went to Dublin, and I accepted the invitation because I wished to visit Ireland on my own account.[3]

Early in the summer, John Macoun, of Kilmore, Ireland, had written to me in London and inquired who I was, and if I were one of the Macouns of the north of Ireland. I immediately wrote him and told him that I was a Macoun of Maralin in the County Down, and I knew that he was a distant relative. He came to see me in London and invited me to go and see him in Ireland, which I promised to do. This was why I accepted the Dublin invitation. All those, accepting the invitations, received, in London, tickets for various places in Ireland, besides one to a Grand Ball which was to be held in the Rotunda in Dublin at a certain date. In due time, we arrived in Dublin and, as usual with visitors, we were taken in hand by the leading men of the city and, as we had the freedom of the city, we were at no expense in going to the various places.

Our first excursion was around the city and each cab was numbered and the instructions were given to always take the same cab. One of our leading excursions was made to the Vice-Regal grounds and the various show places in the city. In passing through the streets of Dublin, I was struck by the absence of the Union Jack, which, to a Canadian, was at least something beyond common. In passing up one street, I saw a Union Jack floating from the window in a tall house and, immediately, I took off my hat and made a bow, a profound one, and said: "God bless the Old Flag." The others in the cab looked serious, but did not second my exclamation. A tall man, however, who sat beside me began, after that, to converse with me about various matters. This gentleman was very much interested in many of the statements that he heard from me and, when we reached my hotel, he said that, if he were allowed, he would like to sit with me and have some conversation and I told him I would be most happy to have his company, as I was alone.

After some conversation on various subjects, I said to him: "Are you going to the ball tonight?" He said: "Oh, no, they would not let me in because I am not in agreement with their ideas." He then told me that he had come over from England with us the preceding night and was on the boat that I was on. I told him that I had received a ticket to the ball while in London and, since I arrived in Dublin, I had got another. The first one had my name on it and the second was just a formal one with 'Admit the Bearer," and I said that if he wished to go to the ball, I would give him my second ticket and he agreed to come and, in the evening, a little before the ball opened, he reached my hotel and he was now dressed in the pink of fashion and carried himself like a man of position.

The Rotunda, where the ball was to take place, was only about fifty yards above my hotel, on the same street, and we walked up. When we entered the Rotunda, by the porch, there were two places where they received the tickets and each man went up to the office and gave his ticket before he was permitted to pass the usher who stood at the folding doors. My companion walked boldly up to one receptacle and I went up to the other, giving my ticket, which had my name on it. We passed into the hall and that was the last I ever saw of my friend, except on the ball-room floor.

Late in the evening, as I was wandering along, alone, after after having satisfied myself with seeing the sights, a Parsee gentleman from Bombay Indian Service, with whom I was acquainted, came up to me and said: "Did you know, there is great excitement here to-night?" I asked him how that was and he said: "Why, one of the chief men of the Secret Service of England is here and no one can tell how he got into the ball." Of course, I said that I would like very much to see him, and so he took me upstairs to the gallery, which ran around the hall, and here I saw my man dancing with one of the ladies and the Parsee pointed him out and said: "There is the man." I saw at once what the whole thing had meant all day. By my bowing to the Flag, I had shown that I was not a sympathiser and, in our later conversation, he found that, with my assistance, he could go to the ball and see what was going on.

We had a few days of sight-seeing in Dublin, but I will only mention one other expedition we had. Forty-seven jaunting cars, and gigs and conveyances of one kind and another, were started from Dublin to the Dargle in Wicklow and, on the way back from the Dargle, we stopped at Powerscourt and there was a labyrinth and a number of us went into it and some had considerable difficulty in getting out again. Others of the party were partaking of refreshments, chiefly Irish whisky, of which there was no scarcity. On our way back to Dublin, we made a great procession, forty-seven conveyances all strung out, one behind the other, on a narrow road. The cart I was in had, besides myself, a number of Australians who were flush of money and who had imbibed all they bargained for and began to bargain with our driver to get us farther ahead and they would pay him a certain amount for every carriage they passed. He immediately accepted the bargain and, with a flourish of his whip and cheers from us, made a rush and passed quite a number of carriages and fell into line quite a piece further on. As soon as the others saw what we had done, they followed suit and we had a terrible mix up, as we rushed down the narrow road, but, as far as I remember, there was no particular injury done to any of us.

Our stopping place was Bray, where we were to have supper, and I remember, distinctly, that I was placed between two Irish sympathizers, who were teachers in institutions in Dublin.

Shortly after, I left Dublin for the north and reached Kilmore in due course of time.   When I arrived there, I was very kindly received and had a grand time for two or three days, after which I left to go to Maralin, where my own friends lived.   Of course, it was thirty-six years since I had left and I knew no one and the first place I went to was the grave-yard to look up our old head-stones and found that they had been all removed but their counter-parts had all been erected and the burying plot was evidently attended to.   While there, the grave-digger came up and I asked him whether any of these people were living around Maralin now and he said: "Oh, no, they went to Canada long ago and these stones were erected by a gentleman from Belfast who said they were the remains of his relatives who were buried there.   These people went away a long time ago, but their relatives seem to look after their graves."   I then went and saw my own cousins, the Spences and the Murphys, and had a pleasant visit, returning to John Macoun's where the greater part of my time was spent. Our intercourse with his family has been kept up ever since, and my son, William, married one of his daughters.

The most important trip that I had was one in which there was a large number of the Colonials and Indians invited for a four day excursion to many parts of England with Warwick for the centre.   A whole train-load of us left London and, without a stop, went to Oxford and there we were received by the authorities of the different colleges and University, and spent a day seeing various colleges and hearing discussions from the professors in the colleges. The only thing I remember about our visit is when we were taken to where Bishops Ridley and Cranmer were burned.   We then went to the nearest college and heard a short discussion on the subject from one of the professors.   Another uncommon thing was seeing a whole ox on a spit in the kitchen of one of the colleges. This was done to show us how they cooked for large parties in the olden time.   The ox was turned on the spit by the cook by a slight touch of his hand.   Of course, the fire-place was the whole side of a room.   We had luncheon there and, at its close, they passed the loving-cup, which I had never experienced before. We were seated at a series of tables and a college Don was on the right of each visitor and talked with him on various subjects while the dinner was being served. At its end, the loving cup **was** passed, in fact, it was a bowl, and each man received it from his neighbor and drank and passed it to the next one. This was another relic of the olden time.

In the afternoon, we drove to Leamington Spa where we were to be put up for the night. It was understood that each visitor would have no expense for the trip except one pound every night that he slept in the hotel at Leamington Spa. That evening, we had a treat. The village green was illuminated and dances took place for our edification, just as they were done in the olden time. The next morning, the carriages assembled at a certain hour and the entire party was taken to Warwick Castle, which was thrown open for our benefit, and we had the privilege of seeing the relics in the castle and of walking around the fortifications that existed at that time. We passed into the castle by the gate-house that was used many centuries ago and the portcullis was still there. We were shown how it used to be used in the olden time. The objects of antiquity which we were shown were in great numbers; suits of armor and ancient weapons and, to me the most remarkable, was the helmet of Cromwell. This helmet, I tried on my own head and found that it even covered my ears so that "Old Noll," as he was called, had a larger head than mine. From the castle, we went to the city and were received by the Corporation. Our reception by them was in the old style and they were dressed for the occasion. We then went to Guy's Cliffe, which is another show place, where there were some remarkable pictures to be seen, amongst which was one locked up in a recess in the wall and only shown to special visitors. This picture was entitled "Remorse," and I remember only two figures to be seen in it. One was the dead man with a knife driven through his heart and the other was the murderer, leaving the room, and looking back at the dead man, with the most awful expression on his face I ever saw.

We now went to the ruins of Kenilworth Castle and had lunch in the gate-house. The castle is said to have covered fifteen acres but very little of it was standing except the gate-house. This was the grand entrance to the castle in the olden time. Here again, they had repaired the room over the gate for us and I remember that it was nearly a foot deep with rushes and we sat around a long table and over two hundred took lunch so it can be easily understood the number of men that could be fed in one of those castles in the olden time.   After a few more visits to places of importance, we went back to Leamington Spa for the night, where we had a grand dinner and more music and dancing on the green.

Next morning, bright and early, we were in the carriages again and taken this time to Stratford-on-Avon.   I forgot to mention, in speaking of Warwick Castle, that the Avon ran past the Castle and some of us went down and took a boat and crossed the river, and looked up at the castle from the far side.   When we went to Stratford, it was to make a pilgrimage to the home of Shakespeare and his wife, Anne Hathaway.   I remember, in going up the narrow old stairs; in her quaint little house, that I remarked that the steps were almost worn away by the multitudes who had made the pilgrimage, as we had.   After seeing the sights in Stratford-on-Avon, we were all taken to the church and a lecture recited for our edification, being the known history of Shakespeare and of Anne, his wife.   After that, we lunched with one of the local celebrities.   Later, we went where there was a village filled with tents and thousands of spectators and all the gentry in the country, and afterwards we took carriage and went to the Earl of Erne's estate.

The only thing I can remember about this is that it was near Coventry and there he told us that his ancestors were Cavaliers, while the Marquis of Warwick was in favor of Cromwell and they were constantly squabbling and sometimes fighting.   He showed us a picture of Charles First, which had only been lately discovered in the castle.   Some one had painted another picture over it so that his did not show.   Some one thought there might be a picture underneath and they got it cleaned and, behold, this picture of Charles First, one of the best extant, was unfolded.

Again, we returned to headquarters and, the next day, I think by train, we went to Birmingham, and here we were entertained by Sir Thomas Montague, the mayor, and saw the sights in the city and round it.   This ended our trip, but, in less than a month afterward, Mr. Adams and myself were invited to Francis Montague's as guests for the week, while the British Association met in Birmingham.[4] This week was filled out with everything that could possibly please a colonial. I will only mention that Mr. Montague was an alderman of the city council and a close friend of Mr. Joseph Chamberlain, and we had the run of the greenhouses, where there were a great many orchids, of which Joseph availed himself, as he was always seen with an orchid in his buttonhole. He was not at home, but his brothers were very friendly with the whole of us and we spent a good deal of our spare time there. The Marquis of Lorne was very kind to Canadians too, and, on two occasions, he had us to his home. I was not with the first party, but, at the second one I was invited to, the other guests were two of our Canadian contingent, and this was the occasion to meet the Prince of Wales and the young Princes, the late Duke of Clarence and the present King George. I watched the Princess Louise (Marchioness of Lorne) receiving her guests and the bows and curtsies they made, and compared and contrasted them, in my mind, with those she had received in Ottawa. I did not have the pleasure of speaking to the Prince of Wales, but the present King and his brother were there, two striplings with wonderfully high collars. The Palace, itself, and the grounds were in fine order and, being without companions, I enjoyed myself to the full.

One other statement and I have done with England, though I might write many pages about various places that I saw and the individuals I met while there. We were told one morning by Sir Charles Tupper that the Queen was coming to visit us that forenoon and he wished every man to be at his proper station and have the exhibit, he had in charge, put in perfect order.[5] When the party arrived, Sir Charles Tupper introduced the Queen to Dr. Selwyn, and the rest of us had the privilege of standing and looking on. I was agreeably surprised, when she came opposite where I was, to find the Marquis of Lorne, and the Prince of Wales and the Duke of Argyle, stopping beside me and having a few words of praise. The Marquis introduced me to the Prince and to his father, the Duke. The Marquis of Lorne and the Prince

17

passed on to the next exhibit, but the Duke remained and told
me that his son had been telling him that I was acquainted with
the Canadian birds and he would like to hear something in regard
to them.   I had quite a conversation with the Duke, who was a
typical Scotchman with red hair and a red face.

The Prince of Wales, to me, was the picture of Edward First
of England, as I had seen him in old prints.   The Queen was a
short, stout woman of the German type and had an imperious
look and you felt, when you looked at her, and saw the set of her
mouth, that she was never contradicted in anything that she said
or did.   With this, I may end my English adventures.

Besides the entertainments and the excursions that I have
mentioned, there were many others made, of which I will not spend
time in enumerating, except to say that Mr. Mennell of South
Croydon, was very kind and invited me to stop some time with
him at Croydon and explore the hills of Surrey, besides making
an expedition to Sandwich.   Dr. Ray,[6] of Arctic fame, also gave
a great party, so that my time was fully occupied when I was not
engaged at the Exhibition.[7]

My return to Canada was uneventful and I took up my work,
as usual, upon my return.   I now realized that my family was
grown up and that I had two marriageable daughters, besides my
eldest son, to keep in order and look out for their establishment
in life.   We were now a large, undivided family and had many
pleasant occasions together, of which the **memory still** lingers.

CHAPTER XVI

1887-1893

VISITS VANCOUVER ISLAND TO STUDY THE FAUNA AND FLORA—
ASCENT OF MOUNT ARROWSMITH—ALBERNI—CAPE BEALE—
RETURNS TO OTTAWA BY C.P.R.—APPOINTED ASSISTANT
DIRECTOR AND NATURALIST TO THE GEOLOGICAL SURVEY—
VISITS PRINCE EDWARD ISLAND, 1888—LOWER MAINLAND,
OKANAGAN DISTRICT, SHUSWAP LAKE AND GOLD RANGE,
B.C., 1889—LARGE COLLECTIONS MADE FOR MUSEUM—
ANOTHER VISIT TO BRITISH COLUMBIA, 1890—WEST KOOTE-
NAYS AND EASTWARD THROUGH THE SELKIRKS—VISITS DIS-
TRICT ABOUT BANFF, 1891—MOUNTAIN CLIMBING—PHOTO-
GRAPHING TREES NEAR LAKE ERIE AND OBTAINING SPECIMENS
OF THE WOOD, 1892—COLLECTING ON THE LOWER MAINLAND
OF BRITISH COLUMBIA AND ON VANCOUVER ISLAND, 1893—
MANY INTERESTING INCIDENTS.

BY this time, I had got a fairly comprehensive view of the Botany of Canada, as far as known and, having spent some years working in the east and one year in the Rocky Mountians, I decided to make a beginning for a more comprehensive survey of the whole flora of the Dominion. I decided, therefore, to spend the summer of 1887 on Vancouver Island. With this end in view, I took my youngest son, William T., with me and we started on our own railroad, the Canadian Pacific, from Ottawa and travelled to the terminus at Port Moody. There, we took the steamer for Victoria and landed before the middle of April. The Rev. George Taylor, whom I knew, met us in Victoria and invited us to go to Cedar Hill, where he was rector. I did so and my son and I lived part of our time in the school-master's house at that point. We made many excursions to various places, going to Gordon Head, Mt. Tolmie, Cedar Hill, Lost Lake and other localities but the places mentioned were our chief points of excursions.

At this early day, there were many species to be found which are now rare, that the Botanists of to-day scarcely ever see. Later in the month of April, Mr. Taylor and Archdeacon Scriven were going to make a visitation at Comox and we all went together on the Nanaimo Railway, which had been opened, I believe, that spring. After we passed Duncans, Mr. Taylor dared me to ride to Nanaimo on the front of the engine alongside of him, which I did, and suffered the agonies, I might say, of the damned. The road was rough, the engineer, I was told afterwards, put on extra speed, and we were so shaken that, instead of conversation, it was as much as we could do for each one to hold on to a bar that rose from the side where we sat. When we reached Nanaimo, we both decided that that was too much of an experience and we promised each other that we would never do such a foolish thing again. We remained in Nanaimo only a short time, but my son and I decided to return and climb Mt. Benson at a later date. We made many excursions round Comox and were greatly pleased with the old forests that then stood close to the village. On our way up from Nanaimo, we saw Mt. Arrowsmith on our left and both my son and I were delighted to see a snow mountain again after our experience in the Rockies two years before. I enquired, of the Captain of the boat, if there was any way by which we could reach it and he said that when we reached Qualicum, we could find out as there was an Indian there who kept what is often called in the Yukon, a "Road House," where travellers could stop. He had no doubt, he said, that "Qualicum Tom," as the Indian was called, the proprietor of the House, would guide us through the woods to the mountain. On our way down from Comox, I saw Tom again and agreed to come back in the late summer to his place and stop with him for some time. He said he could take me anywhere I wished to go.

While at Comox, there was a very low barometer and, while at breakfast one morning, Mr. Taylor, who had been a mining engineer in England, said that when the barometer was low, they were always afraid of explosions in the mines in England. The next day, when a boat came up from Nanaimo, we were told of an explosion that had taken place in the coal mine there, the day before. The remarkable coincidence has remained in my mind as a possible explanation of explosions at certain times in coal mines. When we reached Nainamo, they were then bringing the dead men out of the mine and laying them down in rows and, to a person who had never seen the like before, it was an awful shock. They laid the Chinese by themselves and the white men by themselves.

After remaining in and around Victoria for a number of weeks, we decided to leave there and go on to Nanaimo with the intention of climbing Mt. Benson. At that time, a pathless forest extended for nearly the whole way to the summit and my son and I were advised to go up from beside Wellington, where there was a farm, and the owner, who was a hunter, said he had been at the top and would guide us up. We went out and stopped there over night with him and started in the early morning and climbed through a forest of beautiful pine and fir in which the underbrush was Salal and it was with great difficulty we could force our way through it. We reached the summit, however, and had a most glorious view from the top. What I have never seen before nor since was a thunder-storm below us along the slope of the mountain. In other words, we were in bright sunshine on the summit and, over 1,000 feet below us, the thunder was rolling. After doing what we intended to do around Nanaimo, we went on up to Qualicum and took up our abode with "Qualicum Tom."

I very soon arranged with him for an expedition to Mt. Arrowsmith and his son, James, who was a boy like my son at that time, Tom, my son, and myself, started with four days' provisions. Our first day, we went down in Tom's canoe to the mouth of Little Qualicum River and went up the river until we came to rapids. We then left it and Tom led us through the woods to where the road, that had just been cut out from Nanaimo to Alberni, was. When we reached the road, we discovered we were surrounded by fire, which to me was a new experience as there was scarcely any fire on the ground, but it was burning fiercely over a hundred feet above our heads. Tom, like a good leader, said there was no special danger and to go on because we were near the bridge at Cameron Lake. Late in the afternoon, we reached there and stopped for the night—I do not say camped, because we had nothing to camp with. Tom and his son had nothing but their clothes on their backs and my son and I had a waterproof and possibly only one blanket. The mosquitoes were awful and when we lay down at dark my son and myself got under our waterproof, tucked it in at the sides, and covered our heads. Tom and his son slept either under the bridge or on it, I am not sure which, as I heard no more sounds until after daylight, when I heard a great uproar on the bridge and here Tom was hopping up and down and scourging himself with a brush to keep off the flies. When he saw us he came over and immediately lit a fire and made two or three smokes to drive away the flies. We had breakfast as soon as it could be prepared. I had no idea how to reach the base of Mt. Arrowsmith, but Tom said that he could take us to the base, so we started up from the bridge and, after some time, reached a creek that flowed along the east side of the mountain and emptied into Cameron Lake. We walked up the bed of the creek for quite a distance and reached a spur of the mountain, which came down to it. Here, I took the lead and said that we would go up the spur and that would take us up to the summit of the mountain. We travelled, for a long time, up this slope and the day was very warm and very exciting to us all. Tom and the boys got tired of the slope and thought, to get up quicker, they would attempt a steeper place. This we did and I made no objection and, shortly, they began to show signs of weariness and I took the lead again.

Some time before noon, we reached the summit of this shoulder and I called down to them that, if they could make their way to me, there was an open plateau where we could all rest. Eventually, they reached it and my son was so exhausted that he lay down in the shade and was soon asleep while I hunted around to find water, which I did, and we all rested there for some length of time and had our dinner. From that on, our way to the summit was unobstructed and we reached there late in the afternoon. We made our bivouac amongst the trees of the eastern side of the mountain and, on our right, was a snow slope which led almost to the summit. We enjoyed the view very much and, as the evening wore on, I went up to the summit and watched the change from bright sunlight to darkness. The evening was unclouded and I could look over the Pacific and, at the same time, turn around and look over the mainland and see the mountains that border the Gulf on that side. There were only a few fires at this time, but I could see almost every fire that was burning on the Island and could detect the slightest fire by its smoke. What I was most interested in was the change from light to darkness. As I stood there, each summit was bathed in sunlight, the mountains on the mainland also shone out, and the mountains to the northward of the Island stood out boldly also. Gradually darkness seemed to walk in the light and put out the light and, as the darkness increased and rose on the mountain slopes, we were in twilight and, I decided it was time for me to descend.

I found a fine fire burning and everything ready for supper. On the night of the 17th of July, 1887, we lay on Mt. Arrowsmith in British Columbia, over a mile above the sea. The next morning, my son took the gun and went up the rocks to see if there were anything to shoot and got on to a snow corridor which was very steep and he called down and I told him to throw up his feet and sit down and come down like a toboggan, and he did that, and held the gun above his head, and came down like a flash of lightning in perfect safety. After breakfast, he and Tom's son, James, each got a piece of wood and climbed up and spent the whole forenoon tobogganing down that slope. Later, I was up collecting and found that I would have to walk a long distance to get down to where I had come from, so I at once did the same and slid down as I had told my son to do in the morning. I carried a basket of plants and I seated myself and threw up my feet and, in a short time, I reached the bottom but, owing to the heat of the snow, or my putting more pressure on one part of my seat than the other, instead of going down as the boys did, as I reached the bottom, I turned around and gracefully tumbled into the great clump of heather that was underneath the snow.

After lunch, we started down from the summit in the direction I wished to climb in the morning and came to the brook without difficulty and, after a wearisome walk, we reached the bridge and remained there for the night and, in the morning, retraced our steps to the Little Qualicum River and went to Qualicum by water.

A few days after, we decided to make a trip to Mt. Mark, the southern end of the Beaufort Range. This mountain rose from Horne Lake and there was a good path from Qualicum to the Lake. We crossed the Lake in Tom's canoe and slept at the base of the mountain. During the night, a thunder-storm came up and, when we awoke we were in a thick fog. Tom's son, Jim, had been out hunting and killed a deer and brought it in on his shoulder and he looked more like a drowned rat than a human being. After breakfast, we decided to climb the mountain under Tom's guidance and climbed during the greater part of the forenoon in a fog so dense that we could only see a short distance. About noon, we reached what we believed to be a summit as, no matter which way we went, we descended. We decided to have lunch on the top and a fire was made which the boys decided to be a real bonfire. I was away gathering plants when I saw the atmosphere get lighter and the fog disappearing. I returned at once to the boys and had them pile on more wood as I was certain our fire was about to disperse the fog, or cloud, which it really did. In a few moments, through openings in the cloud, we could look down and behold, at our feet was Horne Lake, three thousand feet below us. Tom was so bewildered that he would not believe his eyes, but Jim pointed out an island in the lake upon which we had found a Loon's nest the day before. Tom exclaimed: "My God, I thought we were miles away from that." He believed that we were going north when in reality we were taking the shortest road to the summit. After making collections in the vicinity, I decided that it was wiser to return than go on and trust ourselves on the mountain summit in another fog.

Not satisfied with this trip, I now decided to go across to Alberni, as the old trail, starting from Qualicum, and crossing Horne Lake, had been made by the Government some years before. I suspected that Tom was the guide for any parties that went across, as he seemed to know all about it and the Alberni Canal, which I wanted to see. The distance across was said to be only twelve miles and, early one morning, we started for Horne

Lake and, crossing it, took the trail on the west side and proceeded to Alberni.   I found the altitude of the highest point a little over 1,300 feet, but the walk was nothing after what we had been through.   At Alberni, Tom obtained a canoe and in it we went up the river to Stamp Lake and collected many species of plants not hitherto seen.   In returning to Alberni, we went down the arm a few miles below the old saw-mill and decided to camp, as there were a number of meadows there that I thought would yield a large number of species I had not seen so far.   When it came time to retire for the night, Tom and his son repaired to the canoe and my son and I went to a little knoll in one of the meadows and spread our blankets, covered ourselves with the waterproof, and lay down to sleep.   It chanced to be the full of the moon at this time and, a spring tide flowing in the night, raised the water so high, about twelve at night, that, in stretching out my feet, I pushed them into the water, by which we had become surrounded, and was awake in a moment.   I woke up my son and we gathered up our blankets and stepped on the top of the knoll surrounded by the flood, with the full moon lighting up the whole of the vicinity.   Some distance away, I saw a piece of wooded country and I told my son to stand where he was and I would wade in that direction and, possibly, I could reach the high land.   I did so and reached where the water was quite shallow at the edge of the woods and called to him to come across, which he did, and we retreated into the woods beyond where the water was and sat down and waited to see if the flood would rise any higher.   In a short time, we saw that it began to recede and we spread our blankets in the woods and lay down and slept until morning.

During the next week, we had a most delightful time in going down the Canal to the open sea at Cape Beale.   When we reached there, the Pacific swells were so great that I would not venture from behind an island, where we were camped, while Tom and the boys went to Cape Beale.   While sitting there, I could see them rise on the top of a wave, apparently far above my head, and, in a moment or so, they would disappear and again rise a greater distance away.

After returning to Qualicum, I bade Tom farewell and

thanked him for his great kindness and care while we were with him. My son and I spent a happy and eventful summer on the Island and returned to Ottawa in the autumn and had the privilege of starting home at Vancouver as the people do at present and going the whole way to Ottawa without a change, the Canadian Pacific Railway having been completed this summer.

Some time in the fall, Dr. Ells and Hugh Fletcher asked me if I would go with them to the Minister of the Interior as they wished some one to introduce them to him. As I was acquainted with him, I cheerfully went and introduced them to him. I sat at one side, while they made their complaints and requests, and he told them to put them in writing and send them to him and he would give them careful examination. He then turned to me and said: "Mr. Macoun, what can I do for you?" I told him that I had only come to introduce the gentlemen, but I certainly had a grievance. "Well," he said, "tell me, what is wrong?" So I said: "You are aware that I stand high in England, on account of what I have done for the country, but here, I have obtained no recognition." He then said: "Put your grievances in writing and send them to me and I will see what can be done for you." Later in the month, I did so and asked that I might be appointed Assistant Naturalist, as Dr. Selwyn had led me to believe that Mr. Whiteaves was Naturalist and I, only Botanist, under him. At this time, Mr. Whiteaves wished to appoint a gentleman called Chamberlain, of St. John, New Brunswick, as Ornithologist, a position to which I aspired.¹ Time passed, and I heard nothing about the matter until Christmas Eve, when I received a communication from Mr. A. M. Burgess, Deputy Minister of Interior informing me that the Governor-in-Council had appointed me Naturalist to the Geological Survey, and Assistant Director and Botanist, with rank of Chief Clerk. Mr. Burgess, in his letter, said that Hon. Mr. White, the Minister, wished me to accept the position as a Christmas box. I immediately wrote and thanked him.

Nothing more was heard of this and, early in March, I began to think that the whole matter was a joke of Mr. Burgess' and I went up to see him and told him what I thought, and he laughed at me and turned to his secretary and said: "Henry, bring in those papers relating to Mr. Macoun's appointment." He did so and I saw that I was really appointed Naturalist. He then told me the reason that nothing had been said about it, as Dr. Selwyn was trying to have other arrangements made and, up to that time, Selwyn had not been told of my appointment. Burgess said: "The fat is now in the fire and I will send a note of notification to Dr. Selwyn today, so that you may have a chance to have a talk with him."

Dr. Selwyn was very angry and said that Mr. Whiteaves was Zoologist and that that covered all the ground necessary and that there was no necessity for a Naturalist and advised me to reject the title as it gave me no higher position than I had had before. I answered with some heat: "Dr. Selwyn, I have studied geometry and I have learned that the greater always includes the less and 'Naturalist' includes 'Zoologist,' so that, from this time forward, Dr. Whiteaves is under me and I am not his servant any longer. But this I will agree to: to leave Dr. Whiteaves just as he is and never interfere with him nor shall I take any interference from him." I kept my word and, until his death, never interfered with the Museum nor with what he did in it.[2]

An incident, which occurred about this time, was an invitation from Wolfville, in Nova Scotia, to a great Agricultural Convention which I attended along with Dr. James Fletcher and Dr. Wm. Saunders. Hon. Mr. Longley, the Minister of Agriculture for Nova Scotia, was the first one on the programme and I was the second and I pleased the audience so well that I got a wonderful reception and Longley congratulated me on my success as a lecturer.[3] The next day, he and I, with Dr. Fletcher, returned together to Halifax and, on our way, we had a political discussion as he was a noted Liberal, and I took the side of Sir John A. Macdonald. At this time, Nova Scotia was attempting to leave the Confederation and politics were very virulent. There was talk of an election, at this time, and he said that Sir John A. Macdonald would be beaten at the coming election and I said that he would win and I agreed to telegraph him, when the election took place, what Sir John's majority was and he agreed to pay for the tele-

gram.   The night of the election, I sent the telegram that Sir John
was in with a large majority, and he immediately telegraphed me
that he would pay his debt.

Spring came, and my eldest daughter was married in June,
1888, and I decided to take my other two daughters and Mrs.
Macoun to Prince Edward Island for the summer.   We proceeded
to Brackley Beach, where there was a summer hotel, and a great
number of people summering.   Amongst others, Mr. Abner
Kingman, of Montreal, and his family, and many others who were
enjoying themselves.   Our experience there was the usual round
of occurrences that take place at summer hotels.   We had fishing and botany and over forty guests and family friends to make
it enjoyable, so that my time, as well as that of the ladies, was
fully employed.   My work consisted of a thorough examination
of the Island flora, as well as other branches of natural history,
and the information I obtained and the material collected added
greatly to our knowledge of the Island for the next twenty years.

On our return home in the autumn, I took sick and was in
poor health until March, when I started for Vancouver City, where
I intended to make a commencement on a Natural History Survey of the country.   During the winter, while in poor health, I
considered the whole question and decided to make a beginning
towards gathering material for the future museum of which, at
that time, there was considerable talk.[4]   Up to this time, Mr.
Whiteaves and Herring had control of all the natural history
specimens excepting botanical ones.   I had brought a number of
bird skins to the old museum when I came and Dr. Bell had made
large collections on Hudson's Bay in 1885, and Dr. Dawson had
made large collections of birds and mammals and sea life and,
especially, a large and valuable collection in ethnology,
including many specimens from Queen Charlotte Islands.   All
these specimens were in charge of Mr. Whiteaves and, through
carelessness, the bird skins, obtained by myself, and Dr.
Bell and Dawson, were allowed to be destroyed by insects.   I
made up my mind that now I would make a change and
informed Dr. Selwyn that from this time forward all material
collected by myself would remain in my charge and be given to

Dr. Whiteaves only when it would be wanted to place in the museum.[5]

In the summer of 1888, my son, James, was commissioned to proceed with Thomas Fawcett, who was going to make a survey down the Athabasca River, and my son was to look after the natural history. On this expedition, William Spreadborough[6] was employed as cook and my son was skinning birds for the museum and he taught W. S. to do likewise. He found that he was an expert and an exceedingly valuable man as a natural history collector. On his return, my son advised me to employ William S. on my projected trip to British Columbia. This I did and, we three, started in the latter part of March, 1889,[7] but I was so poorly at the time that it was doubtful whether I could reach Vancouver or not; but I persevered and, when I arrived at Hastings, I could walk and my son and William pitched the tent (I lived at the hotel), and commenced to make collections of plants, birds, mammals and snakes. We remained at Hastings and then moved, after a few weeks, to Agassiz, then to Yale, then to Lytton and Spence's Bridge, with a long stop at Kamloops, after which we moved to Sicamous and made large collections at all these places. I made a side trip down Lake Okanagan and saw the country that has now become the "Garden of British Columbia." In my report, I showed the great value of the country and the beauties of the Lake.

After our stay at Sicamous, we moved up to the Gold Range. My son, James M., and William S. carried provisions on their backs up to the summit of the range and, after they had arranged for a camp, I went up and we lived a week just at the snow line, and made extensive collections there and shot mountain goats and buried them in the snow so that they would remain in cold storage until we were ready to take them down. We left one in the snow and I said that, possibly in coming years, it would be found and do good service to some hunter who was short of food.

After this, we returned eastward, and reached home in due time. We soon settled down in the office and I commenced to put things in shape; skins, eggs, snakes and fish, and had cases made

to put them in and, from this forward, I allowed nothing to go
into the museum without my permission.

When I went to Vancouver Island in 1887, I went to make
observations, especially on the birds, and, in the next two years,
I perfected my scheme and decided to find out the lines of bird
migration in Canada, west of Ontario. Nothing was known
at this time of the habits of birds west of Lake Superior. In the
spring of 1890, I sent William S., early in March, to Revelstoke,
B.C., and he collected there the next two months. I went in
April and made botanical collections while my son, James M.,
came in May and, shortly after, we went down the Columbia to
Deer Park and stopped there a couple of weeks making collections
on the Arrow Lakes. We then went by canoe down the Columbia to Pass Creek, close to Robson, where we camped and made
large collections there. This being the year that the Canadian
Pacific Railway was building the road from Robson to Nelson,
there was a tote-road built between the two places and I engaged
pack animals to carry our stuff across to Nelson. The boys went
with the pack horses and I walked across to collect plants. The
day was very hot, over 100° in the shade, and, when I came near
Nelson, I was very warm and, as I was plodding along the road,
a man on my left called out: "Look out there! Don't you see the
steer?" I looked up in surprise and, behold, a mad steer was
plunging on my right while the men, who had been chasing it,
were hiding behind a fence on the other side of the road. I need
not say that I was startled and, without any comments, I commenced to run and escaped and got so warm with this exertion
that, when I reached the camp, I was unable to stand. It was
soon seen that I had got sunstroke and, as I collapsed at the foot
of a tree, my son ran down to the Kootenay river, which flowed
past, and got a kettle full of water and poured it on my head as
I sat by the tree, and the second kettle of water brought me back
to consciousness and I was able to sit up during the afternoon and
sat on the barge at the edge of the Kootenay and hung my feet
over the side, where they could be in the water, and remained
there the whole of the afternoon.

In the morning, we were about to start for Kootenay Lake

on the steam boat, but I was unable to stand as I had an attack of sciatica, and all that day, when we were on the boat, I was sitting propped up on the deck unable to move. Ainsworth, where there was a hot spring, was the next place where we made a camp and, for the following three days, I had to eat on my knees, as I could neither sit nor stand while eating. I tried the hot spring for a couple of days and sat there for hours in the hot water, but it seemed to give me no ease. We had made this trip with the intention of going on the mountain, up which there was a trail, to a silver mine, and the time had nearly elapsed and I determined that I would walk on a particular day up the mountain and, that morning, I had taken my breakfast on my knees. The men said that it would be foolishness for me to attempt to go up the mountain, but I was determined to do it and so I got a staff and started off, ahead of them. They were coming along later with the pack horse and our provisions, and with a blanket or two. I found that, as I walked, my leg began to be less painful and I could use it better, so I succeeded wonderfully well and was far up the mountain when they overtook me at 2 o'clock, when we had something to eat. Shortly after, it began to rain and poured the whole afternoon. I hobbled on and reached the shanty, where the miners were located, and my son, who had been away botanizing, reached there about the same time and he looked more like a drowned rat than a human being; his clothes clung to him and he was nearly exhausted, but had obtained some very rare specimens. That night, fourteen of us lay in that little shanty on the floor and I remember that I lay behind the stove with my legs stretched out underneath it and, when I awoke in the morning, my clothes were dry and the sciatica had left me. We found that the rain of the preceding day had fallen as wet snow on the mountain and we remained throughout the forenoon and descended on the trail to the lake in the afternoon.

It was now time to go down to Nelson again and there was a gentleman with a small motor (?) boat called the "Mud Lark." We were told that it was a fast boat and found that, with very great exertion, it could not make more than two miles an hour while, later, it may have been better when we reached the Kootenay River.   After dark, the gearing got too hot and we had to stop the engine and cool it off, and, later, the canvas cover got on fire and my son put it out by throwing water on the roof; later, again, we got lost amongst the piles of a wharf and finally reached the wharf at Nelson and lay down on the beaten road and slept in our blankets.   Thus ended our trip on Kootenay Lake.

For a week after this, my son and William S. climbed the hills round Nelson and obtained many fine specimens.   We then returned to Revelstoke and camped there for a couple of weeks. While there, there were two fires at which we did good service. The first fire took place in the woods close to a saw mill in charge of a young man who was left to look after it by his father.   He came crying to our camp and said that the whole place would be destroyed and begged of us to come down and help him.   We went down and I found a lot of Chinamen who were almost crazy but seemed to be able to do nothing.   I took charge at once and, under my direction, we were able to make the fire take a direction opposite to the mill and, eventually, extinquished it.   After that, there was a serious fire in Revelstoke itself, caused by a woman who hurried home to make her husband's supper and then poured some coal oil into the stove and the whole exploded and the blaze soon had the house and others near it on fire.

Later, we left Revelstoke and moved to the Glacier Hotel, where we collected for a week and then moved to Hector and collected there for some time.   From there, we left for home and, as usual, I was busy all winter arranging our collections, which were immense, and I had much difficulty getting them all in order, and had my collections placed under my own control.

In 1891, my son, James M., went to Alaska as secretary to Dr. George Dawson, who was commissioned by the British Government to investigate the fur seal fisheries.   I sent Mr. Spreadborough to Banff early, while I came later.[8]   Very extensive collections were made there of all classes and we made an excursion to Devil's Lake and, while there, climbed Mount Aylmer and had various adventures.   We left Banff for a two weeks' trip to Devil's Lake and took a power boat to the head of the lake and a canoe for the purpose of moving around.   The evening we arrived,

William S. decided that he would try if we could not catch some lake trout, although we had been told before we left Banff, that we would have no such good luck, as the fishing season was over. Notwithstanding this he went out in a canoe and saw a large number of small grayling and, at once, concluded that, if we should have any luck, it would be by setting lines in the lake upon which a live grayling was placed. He immediately made a loop of fine brass wire and placed it on a stick and set himself to catch grayling with the loop. In a very short time, he had collected a number and immediately set to work to place them on hooks of lines that he had prepared. He paddled up the lake, a short distance, and threw a hook and line overboard and tied one end of the line to a block of wood that floated on the surface and so left it. He did this with a number of lines and, in a short time, I told him that I could see one of the floats going up the lake and he immediately got into the canoe and followed it up and found he had caught a large salmon trout. This satisfied us that we would get all we wanted, and the fact was that, by the time we left the end of the lake, we had smoked trout to last us to the end of our trip, besides eating all the fresh fish we desired. We made many trips to various points on the lake, but our chief one was to Mount Aylmer, which was the highest mountain of the district.

The day we made the ascent, it began to pour when we were about 9,000 feet up and continued the whole afternoon. I sent William S. to hurry down to the camp and save our outfit from being endangered by the rain while I walked down slowly myself. After we came to the head of the lake, we told our friends of our wonderful success in catching trout and they decided that they would outdo us and, so, a little later, they came up to our hotel with a fine fish that weighed, as they said, 32 pounds. The greatest one we had caught had weighed 28 pounds, but, in examining the fish, William S. noticed that its mouth was sewed up, but said nothing and, later, after showing us that they had done so much better than we had, they went up to the C.P.R. Hotel and I followed them up. We were there examining the fish again and a number of Englishmen there said that they had never seen such a fine fish before and I, having my doubts, and remembering

18

William's observation, said privately to an Englishman: "Ask them why the mouth is sewed up," and they made a lame excuse; then I prompted another man to have the mouth cut open and the result was that we discovered that the fish had been filled with stones, to make it heavy, and almost 10 pounds of stones were taken out of its inside—so their glory departed.

We had a great summer at Banff, and had many adventures and a pleasant time and, late in August, went up to Lake Louise where, at that time, there was only a small hut where you could sleep, but you had to take your own food and blankets, which we did.   At that time, we walked round the lake without a path and went up on the glacier at the head of the lake and looked up at the place where Mr. Abbot[9] had been killed a short time before.[10] We also climbed up to the other lakes that have since become very popular resorts and, from there, brought home many valuable species, which have since been named by specialists.   Our season at Banff satisfied me that one man, who was willing to work, and myself, could do as much as a large party with idlers attached. From this year forward, Spreadborough and myself, or my son, James M., have always constituted our party when collecting in the mountains.

That fall, in Calgary, Mr. Pearce, of the C.P.R., had built a new house and wished to have trees growing around it.   He asked me to go and see the location and there was neither tree nor shrub and I told him to do exactly as I had seen trees growing before, on the bare prairie—plant a wind break of shrubs to catch the snow and plant his trees near enough to the bushes to receive moisture from the banks formed by the wind break.   That was the commencement of tree growing in Calgary.   From Calgary, we moved on to Indian Head and I saw what I thought was a new sparrow and we collected about a dozen specimens and, later, I discovered that it was only the young of the bobolink—so much for my bird knowledge in 1891.

In 1892, my son was being sent to Behring Sea and I took William S. with me to make an examination of the country round Lake Erie, as it was noted for a great variety of plants and trees. We spent the summer there and, in the early part of the season,

I had taken Mr. Topley, our photographer, to the western peninsula of Ontario to photograph trees as I had been instructed to make a collection of wood specimens for the Chicago Exhibition, which was to take place the next year, 1893. We took photographs of each species of forest tree and the same tree when grown on a lawn, or in a fence corner, so as to show the trees in a dual state. I selected the specimens and Topley took the pictures and, as I was a specialist in my line, and he was a noted specialist in his, we made a first class collection. In fact, I may mention, that, since then, duplicates, made from his photographs, have been made into sets for people in very many foreign countries. Besides having a picture of each tree, I had each photo of each tree framed in its own wood and the result gave the collection an unique value. Late in the summer and fall, I was very busy in getting wood for the frames and, towards spring, when men were asking to be permitted to go to Chicago, I said that I preferred going to Vancouver Island this year than going there, so I got permission and, as my eldest daughter, Mrs. A. O. Wheeler,[11] was then living in New Westminster, I shut up my house and took Mrs. Macoun and my youngest daughter and started for New Westminster, B.C., early in April.

We had a delightful journey, part of the way, as Mr. Chipman, who was the Hudson's Bay Commissioner at Winnipeg, met us at the train and came across the prairie with us, so we had his company part of the way. After we left Canmore, we had a whole series of adventures before we reached New Westminster. Our first trouble came when we reached Glacier, where we got word that a snow slide had just taken place at the end of the loop and we would be detained for some time. We thought little of it but, in the evening, we were informed that very heavy snow slides had taken place east of us and the road was blocked. There were quite a number of passengers stranded at Glacier who had to be fed and we got down to oleomargarine and bread before we had an opportunity to move further west; but Mr. Marpole, whom I had known for a number of years, came to our rescue and introduced me to the chief engineer of the C.P.R. (Mr. Cambie), west of the mountains, and he invited Mrs. Macoun, my daughter and myself to take "pot luck" on his private car and so we were in luck, while the people were being starved at the hotel. While this was going on, a bigger slide than ever took place down near Revelstoke and blocked the snow in some places sixty feet deep on the track. Mr. Marpole hurried down to open up connections there and we remained with the chief engineer. Late in the evening, Mr. Marpole telephoned up for the chief engineer to come down to where the slide was and that possibly we could be put through and sent down to Revelstoke. When we reached there, we found that another slide had taken place and Mr. Marpole was blocked from coming to our aid where we were. By superhuman effort, an opening was made and we were passed over the slide in steps cut in the snow; then, on the top of flat cars, through a tunnel and another half mile or so over a rough road, we reached the train from Revelstoke and so escaped. I never learned how the rest of our passengers fared, but I was satisfied we had had our share for one trip. When we left the mountains and got fairly into British Columbia and saw growth commencing and pear trees in bloom at Yale, we felt sure we were in the land of milk and honey.

After placing Mrs. Macoun and my youngest daughter, Nellie, with Mrs. Wheeler, my eldest daughter, I went on to Vancouver Island, where William S. had been collecting from the early spring. He had made large collections of birds and mammals when I reached Victoria and, as soon as convenient, we moved from there to Comox as I desired to try and ascend the mountains west of Comox Lake, but we found that, owing to the heavy snow-fall, the winter before, the snow was still in the forest too near sea level to give us returns for our trouble. We, therefore, turned our attention to the sea and made large collections by dredging and travelling over the tide flats up in the direction of Cape Lazo. After we did what we could at Comox, we returned to Victoria and then went down to Sooke and stayed a couple of weeks there and made large collections in Sooke Bay by dredging for shells and other material. I closed up my work and invited Mrs. Wheeler to come over and I arranged for us all to live at "Cherrybank" with Mrs. Brown. We boarded there for a month and had a fine time seeing Victoria and our friends, the Tolmies, and others. Our return home was pleasant, and nothing of importance happened, and we were all benefited by our summer in the west. Of course, in all my work at this time, I had the one thing constantly before me—to gather material for the new museum.

CHAPTER XVII

1893-1897

ARRANGING MATERIAL FOR THE PROPOSED NEW MUSEUM—
VISITS THE PRAIRIES, 1894, TO COLLECT SPECIMENS—MEDI-
CINE HAT, CRANE LAKE, CYPRESS HILLS—EXAMINATION OF
SOUTHERN SASKATCHEWAN AND ALBERTA, 1895—CONCLU-
SIONS IN REGARD TO DROUGHT—COLLECTING IN MANITOBA
AND NORTHERN SASKATCHEWAN, 1896—EXAMINATION OF THE
SOUTHERN SLOPE OF THE ROCKY MOUNTAINS AND THE
CROW'S NEST PASS, 1897—ADVENTURES AND AMUSING
INCIDENTS.

DURING the winter of 1893-94, my son, James, and I were constantly mounting specimens and arranging the material we had accumulated the past year, as at this time we were becoming certain that we would have a new museum in a short time and, therefore, the more specimens we collected, the more we would have on hand for the future. My scheme of traversing the whole country and collecting specimens of natural history in each section of the country was now taking shape.[1]

I determined that William S. should go early in the spring to Medicine Hat and make a collection of the birds as they came from the south and I would join him there later and make a collection of the plants. This we did and secured many specimens in the vicinity of Medicine Hat, which I considered the warmest and driest part of the North West. While we were there we heard accounts of rattlesnakes and other large reptiles being found and I asked the teacher if it were possible for one of his boys to get me a live rattlesnake and he said he thought there was no doubt but what they could and he would see what he could do in the matter. Less than an hour after I had spoken to him, two boys came down the street to where I was and one of them had a rattle-snake and the other also had a large snake which was called a bull snake. Each boy had a string round the neck of the snake and just trailed it along behind him all along the road. (I have met, since we came to Sidney, Lieut-Col. T. Perrett, who was blinded in the Great War, and he was the teacher, of whom I have just spoken, at Medicine Hat, and through whom I obtained the snakes. He told me this himself in an interview I had with him a short time since.)

After making a large collection at Medicine Hat, we left there and moved to Crane Lake, where we camped for over a month and, through the kindness of Mr. Andrews, who had charge of the large herds at that place, we had permission to collect in all their territory. This was the dry season that people have been comparing with that of last year (1919) and Crane Lake was so low that William S. and myself, with Mr. Andrews, waded through the lake to the island, where we found a wonderful collection of water fowl and took a large quantity of eggs. It was this season that we made such an immense collection in the vicinity of Crane Lake. This was owing to the fact that Crane Lake had a greater bird life than any other part where I had been before in Canada. From there, we went with Mr. Andrews up into the Cypress Hills, where they had a large camp, and located ourselves there and collected birds, snakes, fish and plants to our satisfaction. When we returned to Crane Lake, I found a letter addressed to me by Dr. Selwyn, telling me that our appropriation had run out and that I must return east at once. So, early in July, we started for home. At that time the grass was so dry on the prairie that I noticed eight fires starting from the sparks from the engine before we reached Swift Current. When I reached Ottawa, I spent the remainder of the season, as I usually did, collecting in the vicinity of the city.

The winter of 1894-95 was spent as usual and, during the winter months, the members of parliament discussed the question whether the North West was not a failure after all, as the country was drying up, the lakes were disappearing, and many of the settlers were leaving the land. The Government decided that they would send me, with a small party, to examine the southern part of Saskatchewan and Alberta during the coming summer and see if the general belief was founded on fact.[2] So, early in the spring, I went to Moose Jaw and fitted out my small party by taking Mr. Spreadborough with me to Moose Jaw, and there we also got a young farmer, and we three had a covered wagon, like a regular old prairie schooner, to carry our outfit, with a gig for myself. With this outfit, we started on the 18th of May, 1895, for Wood Mountain. At this time, nearly all the lakes and streams on the prairie had ceased to flow, and when we reached Old Wives' Lake, we had no difficulty in crossing an isthmus between two lakes and so proceeded on to Wood Mountain. We found the country everywhere dried up and the grass crisp and brittle. About the 24th of May, we had a heavy shower and I tried the depth to which the moisture penetrated the earth and found that it entered the soil about two inches. The country near Wood Mountain was almost without water and we had difficulty in supplying ourselves. When I reached there, after consulting with the Mounted Police, I decided to go further south to the boundary and see the country in its entirety in that meridian. I then returned to Wood Mountain and started west on a line that would enable us to strike the Cypress Hills, two hundred miles away. In our progress, we met some difficulties and many adventures, but reached Frenchman's River, which flows south east from the Cypress Hills and empties into the Missouri. We rested on its banks for a few days and had the good fortune to discover the Sage Grouse, quite a large bird, which we had never seen before and, I may say, have never seen since. Keeping west, we eventually reached the Cypress Hills and joined the Mounted Police there and were directed by them how to proceed to the south, which was our next objective.

The greater part of the country south was very barren but, when we reached Milk River, we came to a very fine country and, as we found that Milk River was almost on the boundary, we turned west and, from there, went to the Milk River Ridge, which lies about thirty miles south of Lethbridge. I may mention that, in all my explorations so far, we found the country extremely dry, but I felt that we had discovered what was actually taking place—that the drouth was broken, for the next shower, which we had in June, had wet the ground down four inches, and, in

July, when south of Cypress Hills, we found that some showers had wet the land so that the water had sunk in from six to eight inches.

When camped north of the Sweet Grass Hills, we had a thunder-storm which filled a pool near our camp and William S. determined that we should have water in the morning and so dug a hole in the ground at the edge of the pool that he considered would be a well, but when we got up in the morning, we found that the "well" was the cause of the loss of all the water in the pool; it had all drained away. This taught us a lesson that I took to heart and I was able later to show the cause of the water in the lakes not being retained. It was simply this—that there was a stratum of impervious clay always in the bottom of a dried-up lake and, if this cracked in the summer heat, any rain that fell ran into the cracks and disappeared. Having made this discovery, I came to the conclusion that all that was necessary now was for a snow-fall to take place in the winter and the melting snow would wash enough of the impervious clay into the cracks to close them.

We found, shortly after leaving camp, a trail and, as we were in doubt as to where we were, we sent William S. in the cart south till he came to the Police Station, which was named "Pictured Rocks," on the Milk River. As soon as we found our position, we headed for the Milk River Ridge, which was west of us, and went up the trail and pitched our camp in a comfortable place and, for the next two days, had to remain, owing to a heavy rain-storm, which brought the fog down on the hills and blocked out the country. In my wanderings around the camp, I lost my bearings and, when it came time to move out, the fog still persisting, I maintained that we should go one way and William S. took out his compass and showed me where we should go, which was almost opposite. Of course, I maintained that I was in the right, but I conceded we would move at right angles to our observations and this we did and, late in the afternoon, it cleared up and, when we had reached the edge of the hills, to my astonishment, I found that we were heading right for Lethbridge, exactly opposite to where we hoped to be going. William S. was right and I was completely wrong.

As we descended from the hills, we saw a man and a boy in a wagon and they immediately hitched horses to the wagon and started on a gallop across the open prairie in the direction of Lethbridge and, as we wanted to know where we were and where we could find water, I started Willaim S. off in the cart to overtake them and the faster he drove, the faster they travelled and he had a long run before he caught up with them.   The owner of the wagon seemed relieved when he found that we had no connection with the police and he gave us the direction to the water and told us that we were about eight miles from it.   It was now nearly dark and we travelled until night was coming on and camped on the open prairie without water for either beast or man.   It was Saturday evening and we had never travelled on Sunday, but we decided that we would start in the morning without our breakfast and try to reach the water as early as possible.   We found Medicine River, a branch of the Kootenay, after about four miles, and camped and enjoyed ourselves very much for the remainder of the day.

We now aimed to go south and reach the Mormon Settlement.   We started on and, in due time, reached St. Mary's River and we found that it was in flood and, apparently, rapid and dangerous.   A gentleman came along who turned out to be the Collector of Customs for the Canadian Government on the boundary and he told us that he would show us the crossing, which he did. We went with him and he rode his horse across and we followed right after him and camped a few miles from the river and near the Mormon Settlement.   At first, the Mormons treated us with very little respect, but, as soon as they found that I was a Government official, they became very polite and we received all the assistance from them we desired.

Mormonism, as it is generally understood, in my opinion, is far from being what it really is.   The Mormon men are masters of all they survey and the women, apparently, have what is figuratively called a "good time" at home.   From the Mormon Settlement, we went west to the mouth of the South Kootenay Pass, near Waterton Lake.   Here we camped and called that our "furthest west."   Here we found a mountain, Sheep Mountain, about 8,000 feet high and I made immense collections for a number of days and then we turned our faces to the north and headed for Fort Macleod. At the Blood Reserve, we found the Indians working like white men, as, that year, they had taken the contract to cut 150 tons of hay for the Mounted Police and were making it and drawing it in on their wagons, just as the white settlers did at Moose Jaw.

In due course of time, we reached Fort Macleod and found the people there all of the opinion that I had had in the spring, that the country was drying up and that there was no chance of any future for farming in that part of Alberta. I still believed that the drouth was broken and that next year, 1896, would be a prosperous year, which it turned out to be.

From Fort Macleod, we went to Lethbridge and, from thence, to Moose Jaw, where I dsimissed³ the men and then I went back to Ottawa. During the winter, I wrote a report of my trip and explained to the Government that the drouth was broken and that there was every prospect of a prosperous year, if my opinions were of any account or value.⁴ At this time, all the lakes in the country were dried up and the water that fell in them all ran into the cracks and disappeared, of course; but, in conversation with Mr. Gass, the postmaster at Moose Jaw, he told me that if certain conditions were fulfilled in April, the ponds would be full again and the conditions were exactly what I had discovered when William S. dug the well at the Milk River, that, when the cracks filled, the bottom of the lake would again become impervious and would retain the water that ran into it. Mr. Gass said that, if a heavy snow-storm came in April and was blown into the ponds, when it melted it would deposit enough of mud in the cracks to stop the leaks and then the lakes would fill. This actually happened in the spring of 1896 and the railway ditches at Regina, which were entirely without water when I passed in 1895, were filled full of water when I passed going back in 1896.

In the year 1896, my son, J. M., was slated to go to Alaska as Commissioner in the Fur Seal investigation and William S. was to go with Mr. A. P. Low, down to Hudson's Bay and go across from James Bay to the coast of Labrador, starting on Hudson's

Bay and going across to the coast of Ungava. The scheme for myself was to go to Winnipeg and collect what I could in Manitoba and northern Saskatchewan. My headquarters were at Brandon for the time and, while there, I examined the country and collected and, from there, I went to Moose Jaw and took the train for Prince Albert. At that time, Saskatoon was a miserable little village and the country, generally, was in an impoverished state. I spent a month around Prince Albert and then came back to Brandon and finished up my work and reached home at the usual time. My experiences on the prairie this year were of a varied nature.[5] It was the year of the election that put Laurier in power and it also dated from the time when the crops began to get good in the North West. I gave credit to Providence for the rains and increase of production, while the politicians, of a certain class, gave the whole credit to Laurier, and the new administration. The scheme to irrigate Southern Alberta was being talked of at that time and I was asked to spend a summer on the southern slope of the Rockies and see what was the character of the country.

Having in mind my original scheme regarding the "Natural History" of Canada, I made provision for the continuation of my natural history work and started William S. early in the spring to go to Edmonton to make a collection of birds, so that we would understand bird migrations in that section of the country, this not having been studied before. He made large collections and joined me in Calgary late in June. Prior to his coming, I had gone into the mountains near the sources of Jumping Pound Creek, on the Elbow River, where Mr. A. O. Wheeler was then surveying. While in his camp, I had many adventures but chiefly in connection with the floods that took place that spring in the Bow River and large tributaries.

We were in the mountains, when the rains came and I remember that I was then at the head of Bragg's Creek with two men and we had pack horses. We slept in a shanty and the water came in through the roof and there was not a dry spot to be found in the place when morning came and we found that the water was even standing on the floor. The rains continued and, late in the afternoon, we decided to start for the main camp.   I went ahead and, during that one afternoon, I waded through Bragg's Creek thirteen times and it was a raging torrent, but there was no help for it.   I reached Jumping Pound Creek, where Mr. Wheeler had his camp, and the next day the floods came down in earnest. Where we were camped, there was a bridge across the creek and Mr. Wheeler asked us to go out and try to save it and we gathered on the bridge and used poles to relieve it of the drift wood. Shortly after, the flood rose so high that the bridge began to be covered and we retired to the bank.   In a few moments, after we left, the bridge was carried away and we rejoiced that we were on the right side.   In the evening, a farmer of the neighborhood came to see us and brought his little boy along and we went out to look at the flood and a large poplar tree, about four feet in diameter, came sailing along and, by some freak of the current, was left lying on the bank, right beside us, and I said to the little boy: "Forty years after this, my lad, you will stand on this bank and you will tell your friends that you were standing here when that tree landed where it is and they will tell you that you are a liar and that it was not at all possible for such a large tree to come down such a small stream."

After the flood, Mr. Wheeler broke camp to move further south towards High River and he decided that he would go to a certain ranch on the day that we left Jumping Pound Creek and I took my lunch and started on foot, ahead of the party, on an old trail, but, owing to the heavy rain, it was very wet and boggy, but I managed to reach the ranch late in the afternoon and found a notice on the door that the owner had started that morning for Calgary so I was shut out.   After resting for some time, I decided that I would return in the hope of finding lodging at a ranch I had seen as I was walking along in the afternoon.   The ground was almost covered with water and, as I was walking through the wild meadows, I reached a narrow brook that had a deep water course and, as the grass was covering it, I stepped right into it and, before I knew I was nearly up to my armpits in the water.   I scrambled out and immediately took charge of my watch and a few dollars I had in my pocket as they would have been destroyed by the water.   I now decided that I would have to stay all night at the ranch I was heading for and, as I approached it, I saw a man ride out of the corral on horseback but thought nothing of it and walked up to the door of the cabin and knocked, but found no one in, so I opened the door and discovered that the man had just taken his supper and ridden away.   I was soaking wet and the combination of mud, clay and hunger made me decide to stay.   I roamed around until I found some victuals and I ate my supper.   It was now getting near bed time and, as there was no appearance of the owner, I took off my wet clothes, hung them where they would dry, and crept into the man's bed, which was in the room that I would call a kitchen.   I must have fallen asleep because I was awakened by hearing the man outside and then I bethought me of myself, as it was dark, that I might get shot, so, as soon as the man opened the door, I called out to him that I had taken charge of his bed.   After some talk, I acquainted him with my position and he at once said: "Why, I have just come back from Wheeler's camp, and the men have been looking for you all afternoon, and Wheeler himself has gone to Thomas' ranch to see if you were there." He said, then, that he, also, had been riding around for the last two or three hours to try and find me.   We lay and talked until day was breaking and, as soon as it was fairly light, I got up and dressed and started for the camp, which he told me was about two miles away.   While on the way, I heard wolves howling and, as I was unused to them, I thought they were the men at the camp calling to me and I answered and, in a short time, I heard the wolves nearly upon me and then realized what it was.   Fortunately, they caused no trouble and I reached camp safely and then all the men were asleep, excepting Mr. Wheeler, who was still away.   It turned out that, when he reached Thomas' ranch, it was dark and, as the road was bad and he was tired out, he slept all night there and, in the morning, started for his own camp and reached it about an hour or so after I did.   We were all glad to be together again and I decided that I would not be advance man again for the season.

   We camped near the Elbow River and, for the remainder of

June and part of July, I wandered around collecting and, early in the month of July, returned to Calgary, where William S. met me and we started from there for the Crow's Nest Pass. This was the year that the railway through the Pass was being built and I was sent to see the character of the country in the vicinity. I bought my outfit at Fort Macleod and hired a man with a large wagon to take it up to the pass. It was about seventy-five miles away and we took the greater part of two days to make the journey. When I arrived at the Pass, I found the Northwest Mounted Police had a station there. The second day after I came to the Pass, I was out collecting when a large number of French Canadians from Ottawa arrived and they had a great quantity of supplies with them, including a lot of dynamite. This dynamite was placed within less than thirty yards of my tents and they had it covered only with tarpaulins! When coming back from my morning trip, I saw the heap of stuff and lifted the cover and looked under and saw the boxes marked "Dynamite." I immediately went to the Corporal who had command of the Police and informed him regarding the dynamite and asked him, in the name of the law, to have that removed at once to a place of safety, not merely away from my camp, but right away from the camp altogether. The Corporal acted at once and we had the dynamite removed immediately to the opposite side of the lake, which was a great relief to all parties concerned.

For the next month, William S. and I clambered round amongst the mountains and made large collections of animals and plants. In one of our excursions, when pretty well up a mountain, we looked up and could see clouds passing the other side of the mountain and, on further examination, we discovered that there was an opening through from one side to the other, but we found it inaccesible, when we tried to climb up. We noticed, further, that thunder-storms would often pass over our heads and no rain take place except on the higher mountains. The trees all showed the prevailing winds to be from the south west. After completing our work at Crow's Nest Pass, we returned to Calgary and soon after that I started for home.

CHAPTER XVIII

1897-1904

Visits Cape Breton, 1898—Sable Island, 1899—Interesting Observations on the Vegetation of the Island—Begins the Catalogue of Canadian Birds, Winter 1899-1900—Examination of Algonquin Park, Ont., 1900—Studies Flora from Niagara to Lake Erie, 1901—Visits the Klondike and Reports on the Agricultural Possibilities of the District, 1902—Interesting Observations on the Climate of the Yukon—Spends the First Summer in Thirty Years in Ottawa and Vicinity, 1903—Remarks about Politicians—Another Visit to the Rocky Mountains, 1904—Laggan, Kicking Horse Lake, Field, Emerald Lake—Collecting—Incidents.

D URING the winter of 1897-98, our work went on as usual and arrangements were made for the next season. Mr. James McEvoy, one of the Geological Survey men, was going to Tête Jaune Cache and was commissioned to examine the mountains in that vicinity during the season. I immediately arranged for William S. to go with him as Naturalist and, that year, we obtained the first collections that had been made in that vicinity since Drummond was there in 1826. While McEvoy and his men were at work, pretty high up on the mountains, they came across a grizzly bear with three cubs and, immediately, the old bear ran away and the cubs took refuge in the rocks. William S. shot one of the cubs and the men managed to get another one and yet the old bear never came near them all the time that they were killing the cubs and the poor things evidently cried for their mother as they made a great uproar. I mention this as an instance where a bear was known to desert her young, although it had been said that they never do such a thing.

I had decided to go to Cape Breton this season, 1898, and took Mrs. Macoun and my youngest daughter along with me.

We located at Baddeck for the summer and I immediately left for the northern part of the island and lived with a Mr. McLeod and made large collections and, afterwards, returned to Baddeck and made that place my headquarters, from which I made many short excursions on the island.   One excursion took me down to Louisburg, the old French city, and another of greater length took me to the North Cape.   These were the longest trips I made and, while on them, I was all the time taking notice of the capacity and possibilities of the island for agricultural purposes, as well as its natural history.   By good fortune, Graham Bell, the originator of the telephone, lived within a mile of our hotel and it was not long before we made his acquaintance and we found that he and his family were most enjoyable people.   At this time, he was working on a scheme of life-saving and had taught his daughters how to give first aid and we considered it funny for the servant man to be laid out on a bench and the young ladies rendering first aid by moving his arms and forcing him to breathe, and we enjoyed the attempts very much, but never took part in them.   Mrs. Bell was a deaf mute and very intelligent and she had been taught by her husband, as, in his youth, he was a teacher of articulation to the deaf mutes in various parts of Canada and the United States.   Mr. Bell was very anxious to get the people of the island to pay more attention to agriculture than they did and asked me if I would give a lecture at the school house and he would act as chairman.   I agreed and the lecture was arranged for.   Mrs. Bell was bound to go too, and, although she could not hear, arrangements were made in the school house by which she sat opposite Mrs. Kenyon and Mrs. Kenyon repeated my lecture to Mrs. Bell by articulation and, by this means, Mrs. Bell, the next day, could tell me a good many things that I had said.   While Mr. Bell and I were walking down the street in the dark to the school house, we came upon two men standing talking and one of them said: "Are you going to the lecture?"   And the other said: "What is the use in a man's going to hear a man who has only been here a couple of months?"   Mr. Bell immediately spoke up and said: "Come along, Jock, and you will hear more to-night than you dreamed of before."   But, whether the men came or

19

not, I cannot say. As far as attention was concerned, the lecture was a complete success, but whether it did any good or not I do not know.

On another occasion, I was making a trip to the northern end of the island and engaged a young man and a horse and buggy at Baddeck to take me along for a number of days. Our first day took us to a stopping place a few miles from Baddeck where we had lunch and, while the dinner was being made ready, I wandered around as I usually did, and collected plants in front of the hotel. About an hour after we left, a carriage drove up and in it were my wife and daughter, who were boarding at the hotel at Baddeck, and a gentleman who had brought them out, and who was an official belonging to the Fisheries Department and, of course, an important man. In conversation with the landlord, while they were having tea, he said: "If you had been here a little while ago you would have had a good chance to talk with an old tramp who was here and who was all the time hunting round amongst the rocks looking for grasses and one thing or another." My daughter, Nellie, said: "That old tramp is my father." She tells me that the poor man nearly fainted. We met a great many cultured people while at Baddeck and enjoyed ourselves very much and seemed to make a great many friends, some of whom are still friends of ours. That winter was spent, as usual, at Ottawa and Dr. Dawson, who was Director of the Survey, told me that the wish of the Government was that I should spend a season on Sable Island, off the coast of Nova Scotia, as they wished to get some knowledge of the vegetation of the island. In accordance with instructions, I left Ottawa at an early date and stopped, on my way, at Boston and Cape Cod, where my son-in-law had a summer residence. I made, while there, an acquaintance with a number of American botanists who belonged to the New England Botanical Club, and they invited me to spend a few days with their society, the members of which were then on their way to the Aroostook, a river in Maine, where they were going to botanize for a few days. I had a pleasant time with them and then went on to Halifax to learn at what time I could go down to Sable Island on a government boat. I had a few days

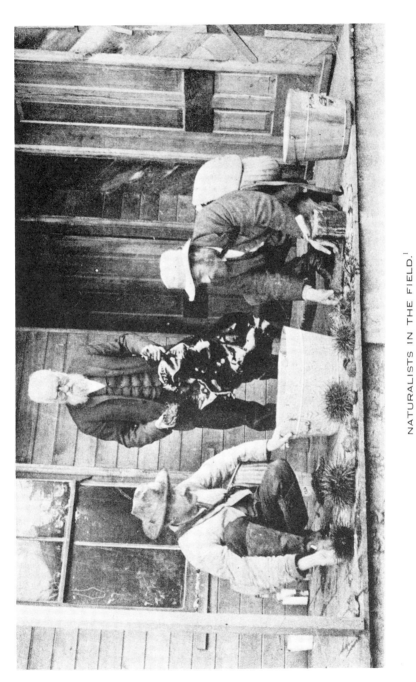

NATURALISTS IN THE FIELD.[1]

to spare in Halifax and Dr. McKay, Superintendent of Schools for Nova Scotia, took me round and we botanized together.

Early in July, I embarked for Sable Island and our trip was a pleasant one, but the wind caused a rough sea and I had to sit on the bridge all day long and watch the steersman. Early in the morning, when we started, the course was laid for the Island, and it was laid down one hundred and two miles and we were to run it in a certain number of hours. The day was beautifully clear and the wind was not very strong, but it was always from the west and, as I sat and heard the steersman, when he would leave, give the direction to the quartermaster, as he was called, I found that the direction in which they steered never altered for the whole day and I wondered why, for no account was taken of the drift that I considered was taking place on account of the wind. The result was that, although we should have reached our objective before dark, when evening came, there was no sight of the island; however, the moon, being at the full, there was no danger of running on shore, in my opinion, but, when we did not make the Island, and the "log" showed we had travelled further than we should have, the Captain suddenly woke up and discovered that something was wrong. A man was sent up the mast and, in a short time, he returned and reported that we had drifted, apparently, nearly twenty miles to the east and a swift order was given to "about ship," and we sailed to the usual anchorage and cast anchor. In a short time, a surf boat came out for us and we were taken on board and started for shore. After going over a series of shallow places, where there were considerable rollers, we reached a point where the boat could proceed no further and then each passenger got on a man's shoulders and was carried to shore and I found that, all the time I stopped on the island, this was the mode of landing. I spent nearly three months on the Island as the guest of the Superintendent and learned all that was possible in regard to the Island, both past and present.

I found that the grass, being destroyed along the south shore, caused the sand hills to be flattened out by the wind and exposed the island to the encroachments of the sea. Thus I spent a summer very pleasantly on the island and had many adventures of one kind or another, but was not in danger at any time while there. One time, I was sitting in the office writing my notes when a small land bird came in by the window and quietly sat down on my head and I found it caught flies from the window and then flew back to my head again. Arrangements were made for me to leave on the boat when she arrived from Halifax, which was shortly expected. The intention was to take up to Halifax about thirty of the wild ponies and sell them by auction as they usually did, in the autumn. The teacher on the island, a young lady, was to go up on the same boat and, when the boat arrived, it was quite stormy, and she was one of the first to go on board the small boat. The boat, she started in, was overturned in the heavy sea and she was brought on shore again half frightened to death. They had much difficulty in getting the horses on board but the next day was thought to be safe for me to leave so I was placed in the surf boat and we started for the ship, and, as I was unacquainted with the motion of the boat, I nearly had my head jerked off in crossing some of the rollers that we met on our way to the ship. When we reached the ship, lines were thrown out and we all got hold of them and boarded safely. The young lady, who was afraid of the trip, was brought off last without any mishap. We reached Halifax in due season and had a review of our ponies, which certainly were frisky and shaggy and pleased the crowd very much.

In the autumn, when I made my report, the French section still believed that trees would grow on the island and Dr. Wm. Saunders of the Experimental Farm was commissioned to go down the next year and see what he thought of the situation as my report was discounted. He reported that he saw no reason why trees would be a failure on the Island and the next spring he went down and planted 8,000 trees and, three years after, they were all gone and my report was evidently accepted, as no more attempts have been made since then to plant trees on Sable Island.

As usual, my son and I spent the winter at work on the herbarium and, as a catalogue of Canadian Birds had been spoken of, I worked part of the time preparing the first installment of that work.[2] This summer, 1900, it was decided that I should go to

Algonquin Park, Ontario, on the Canada Atlantic Railway, and make an examination of the flora and fauna of the park. As usual, I was accompanied by William S. and we made many trips amongst the islands in the lakes and throughout the whole extent of the park, and made large collections. These gave us a fairly good idea of the flora and fauna in the wilder parts of Ontario. Frequently, I made visits to Ottawa, thus breaking the tedium of the summer and, for once, I enjoyed summer in and around Ottawa. The usual work went on during the winter and there were no events of importance that I can remember excepting the usual preparation that went on constantly for future work.

The season of 1901 was devoted to an examination of the flora from Niagara along Lake Erie, and, in this, I got a good idea of the southern flora of Ontario. If I am not mistaken, that was the year of the Buffalo Exhibition and I took Mrs. Macoun, and my youngest daughter, Nellie, for an outing and they boarded at Niagara Falls and enjoyed themselves very much for nearly a month while I was travelling up and down the country making collections. After spending our time at Niagara, we moved west and had a spell of awfully hot weather while we were living in Windsor and it was so extremely warm that my daughter decided that it was better to go to Ottawa as the heat there was not so great, while Mrs. Macoun and I went up to Chatham and to Sarnia for the remainder of the season.

Many conflicting reports had been made about the Yukon and Mr. Ogilvie, who was Governor, reported that the ground was constantly frozen and Dr. Wm. Saunders issued a bulletin in which he said that potatoes only grew there when they were sheltered from the sun in the morning to allow a gradual thawing, since frosts occasionally occurred during the summer. Dr. Bell, at this time, was our Acting Director and, in conversation with him, I said that I believed most of these reports were inaccurate and that someone should be sent with authority to examine and look into the whole matter. He then asked me why I did not go myself and I said at once: "Yes, send me," and the matter was decided immediately. It was late in June, 1902, when I started for the Klondike and everything went well with me until I reached

Skagway and there I had to wait a few days for the train to take me to White Horse.   While stopping at Skagway, I collected some flowers and got some information about the interior of the country, as I believed that I was going to a frozen north, where the people bragged of seeing the "midnight sun."   I made large collections on the way to White Horse and others on the way down from White Horse to Dawson, and saw little appearance of cold.   We were thirty-six hours going from White Horse to Dawson and, in that time, we passed down a beautiful river and I, being a tenderfoot, inquired of the passengers when we would come to the Snow Mountains and an old man laughed and said: "My friend, there are no Snow Mountains!"   When we reached Dawson, I was completely upset as I saw no signs of cold or scant vegetation.   At this time, Mr. J. B. Tyrrell and his brother James W., were living in a fine house with a brother of Mr. McConnell and I was invited to lodge with them and take "pot luck."   The understanding was that I would turn in my five dollars a day and do no work, while they ran the house and attended to the cooking.

I found Dawson situated in 64° 12″.   We went to bed before it was dark for there was scarcely any night there at that time. I found that the people were out playing croquet and lawn tennis at eleven o'clock at night, the same as they would play at six o'clock in Ottawa, in fact, the sun shone into the room I slept in when I went to bed and it would be shining there when I awoke.

I reached Dawson on the 10th of July and found vegetation far advanced and James Tyrrell had dried specimens of a species of rose that grew at Aylmer, near Ottawa, and he found this rose coming in flower the very same day that I found the same species coming into flower at Aylmer the very same year.   That was the first point I fixed.   When I began to go around and climb the mountain that rose at the back of Dawson, I found that, when I was up a thousand feet, the climate seemed warmer than when I was down on the level with the river.   It was some time before I understood this.   I eventually saw that there was longer sunshine on the mountain than down in the valley.

Nothing surprised me so much as the long, sunny days and the low altitude of the sun.   It was nothing for the sun to pass behind a mountain and, apparently, end the day and, in the course of a couple of hours or so, appear again at the other side.   Apparently, night passed so easily into morning that many of the inhabitants did not seem to recognise the difference.

I remember my first trip to Honka Creek.   It was commenced after eleven o'clock at night and we reached there while it was still light and I went to bed with sufficient daylight to cause me to believe that it was evening instead of morning.

Gold washing, while I was in Honka, was still in progress and nothing pleased me better than to stand at the sluice boxes of an evening, when the weekly cleanup was taking place, and look at the faces of the various spectators as nuggets were washed out and the amount of gold became large, and the speculations that were made on the amount of the cleanup.   Every man was in a state of excitement bordering on what I might call an "Irish fight".   The claim I visited was worked in this way—a shaft was sunk in the frozen earth to a depth of about thirty feet and, every evening, steam was turned in through steel pipes to thaw the earth and, in the daytime, this was brought up and thrown in the sluice boxes and washed.   This was the constant practice on all the creeks as far as I was able to see.   Later in the season, I went fifty miles to the west of Gold Run Creek and found that they worked there in exactly the same way but the gold was found to a greater depth.

I found that Dawson had been built in a peat bog that was frozen hard and now, when the moss was taken of, the bog was settling, as the icy clay thawed, and all the houses were settling and, by this time, Dawson is likely three feet lower than the surface was in my day.   I found, wherever I went, that the moss of the soil prevented thawing just as it did in Ontario and other places where I had been and was the real cause of the frozen condition of the soil at Dawson.   All the creek beds were frozen solid, some to the depth of almost one hundred feet, but all from the same cause, hard frosts in winter and a covering of moss in summer preventing thawing to any considerable depth.

In climbing a mountain, I found that, in the valley, the spruce trees were only a few inches in size, while on the slope of the mountain at Dawson, a thousand feet above the city, I found the stumps averaged over a foot in diameter and this condition was observed in all parts of the country where I travelled, showing that the real cause of the frozen ground was the moss, and oblique rays of the sun from a low altitude. I saw immense bones in various places which were the remains of the mastodon that formerly occupied the country and, always, these bones would be found in the bed rock of a creek, showing that the animals had lived in a period long before the present one. I saw how it was that these cattle actually lived on what I found covered the most of the country, a shrubby birch tree that they seemed to have eaten as the cattle of the east, at the present day, eat the branches of the maple tree, which, in the early days, was called browsing; that is, the mastodon lived in the winter on browse. Geologists state that a continental glacier never existed there, as the snow-fall was so light that a few days of spring took off the snow and, hence, its depth was never great and the cattle could live out most of the time.

To sum up, I found that, wherever the soil was opened up and the moss taken off, the sun thawed the soil sufficiently to produce most wonderful crops. On the islands in the Klondike, I saw the largest cabbage, lettuce and various roots that I had ever seen anywhere, and the growth was so great that it was incomprehensible to me. In talking with the residents, I found that all the nonsense I had heard in the east about the Klondike was, literally, "travellers' tales," to make the people think that there were such enormous difficulties to be overcome to reach Dawson and to contend with while you were there.

On my return to Ottawa, I wrote out my report,[3] which was published, and copies sent to Dawson. The people there were so pleased and well satisfied with the information that I had given them and the favorable report I had made to the Government, that, when they held an exhibition of the products of the Klondike the next autumn, the five daily neswpapers, that then existed at Dawson, took my report and interleaved it with the photographs of the products that were exhibited, and these caused such a sensation, that a gentleman in New York, much interested in Alaska, asked me if I would not report on the Klondike for them for their exhibition in 1904. In other words, they wished to pass off our products for theirs, and I officially declined to be a party to the transaction. Since then, we have heard no more of the bareness of the country in the vicinity of Dawson and the Yukon stock has risen enormously in the writings and opinions of promoters generally. My trip to Dawson was an eye-opener to me and I felt that we, at that time, were far from realising the value of the enormous country that we had in our possession[4].

In the winter of 1902-03, we passed the time much as usual but I arranged for my son, J. M., to go and explore the Peace River[5] and I remained for the first time in thirty years in Ottawa. I spent the most of the summer at Wakefield on the Gatineau and lived with my wife and family in the village. I had a very pleasant summer and made many new friends and, amongst others, a large number of parliamentarians. There were many discussions that summer by these men at Wakefield, as it was the year that the Transcontinental was launched by the Laurier Government. As I had been a prominent figure at the time the C.P.R. was being launched, I paid particular attention to what was going on and found that the lies that were told at the time of the beginning of the C.P.R. were a mere bagatelle to the lies that were now told about the wonderful undertaking that the Liberals were going to hoist on the country. I heard Laurier say, myself, that the whole undertaking would not cost more than $13,000,000.00 to Canada as the Grand Trunk Pacific was going to take over the whole work as soon as it was finished. The people now realize what governments mean when they try to exploit any project that may be brought forward by their supporters. The statement is made and it is backed up by all the lies that can be invented and covered up properly by the powers which be. My experience is that all politicians are liars because honest statements never benefit any individuals, but only the country generally[6].

Early in the spring of 1904, I left Ottawa with Mrs. Macoun and went to Calgary, where she remained for the summer, while I went to Laggan, in the Rocky Mountains, where Mr. A. O. Wheeler, my son-in-law, had his survey camp that spring. It was understood, when I left Ottawa, that I would remain for the summer months in Mr. Wheeler's camp as he was intending to work in the mountains the whole season.   Our main camp was pitched on Pipestone Creek, close to Laggan, while branch camps were formed wherever the working parties were surveying.   After the snow was fairly well melted, towards the last of June, our camp was removed into the mountains north of Laggan and, while Mr. Wheeler's parties were surveying and climbing the mountains, I collected plants in the vicinity of the camp.   I was very success-ful and obtained a great many species and had a very enjoyable time altogether.

Our last camp, on the Pipestone, was above the timber line and just where the glaciers commenced, so that, a few yards from where our camp was pitched, I could enter the snow.   Here I made a very fine collection of Arctic plants and, as the view was unobstructed, I could see the men climbing the mountains in the distance and, at one time, I saw them, late in the afternoon, slide down a mountain and below was a great precipice, but, instead of sliding over the edge, a little to the right, they slid over to the right, passed it by and, in a short time, almost reached the place where I was waiting for them.   I asked them what they meant by sliding down and they told me that they usually did that when the slope was unbroken and they could stop when it pleased them. They called it "glisading."

After we finished the work on the Pipestone, we came down to the camp at Laggan and packed and moved to Kicking Horse Lake, where we established a camp early in August and, from there, branch camps were sent out, one of which I was at, eight miles up the creek that ran into Kicking Horse Lake at Hector. After climbing Mount Paget and a number of other mountains around Hector, I went up to the camp and from there I climbed still higher and went up to Lake MacGregor,[7] which was above the timber line and a glacier at the head of the lake was throwing off icebergs so, late in the summer, I saw the making of icebergs in the Rocky Mountains.

After we got through at Kicking Horse Lake, we broke camp and went down to Field and, from there, up to Emerald Lake, where a camp was established. The day we went to Field, the party went down on a train and I prepared to walk. When I was about half way down, a tremendous thunder-storm came on, with a great deal of rain and the lightning was so fierce and so many flashes ran along the telegraph wires that I was afraid for my life and, on two occasions, went off the railway and lay under the ledge to save myself from being killed. When I arrived at Field, I was completely soaked. I undressed and went to bed and had my clothes dried and was ready for the walk up to Emerald Lake in the morning. Mrs. Nichol and myself walked up to Emerald Lake and she remained in the Chalet while I walked up to the new camp a mile further on. I found, on the way, that the trail forked and I took the wrong road and descended into the valley and found no horse tracks and so returned and took what was called the Upper Trail. This trail was above the timber line and was very much obstructed with rock slides and, as it was both lonesome and dangerous, I felt that I had placed myself in a precarious position. I had no idea how far I had to walk and could see no hope other than reaching the camp, which I understood to be pitched somewhere near the big glaciers at the head of the valley. As I plodded on, a person dressed in corduroy came out of a tent and, while I was asking for information, I discovered that "it" was a woman, instead of a man, and three other ladies, dressed in the same way, came out of the tent and I found out later that these four women had lived up there for the last couple of months. I was informed by them that the party had passed, early in the day, and were camped somewhere further up the valley. I plodded on again and reached the camp about sundown and found that it was pitched close to Twin Falls. After supper, while talking at the campfire, we heard quite a racket in Mr. Bridgeland's tent (the assistant). On his going in and striking a light he discovered a couple of porcupines hard at work on the leather cases of his instruments. The man in charge of the horses immediately produced a pistol and the stable lamp that he had and, with the lamp in one hand and the pistol in the other, he led the pursuit of the porcupines and fired a number of shots but, of course, the animals escaped in the darkness.

After doing what work was necessary on this camp, we moved round to the head of the main valley and pitched camp in the valley just below the great Yoho Glacier.   Here we remained for a few days and, in one of my walks, I discovered a porcupine trying to climb up the face of the glacier.   He had managed to ascend about fifty feet and was sitting on a pinnacle and every time he made to come down he slipped so easily that he was afraid to move and so retired to his pinnacle again.   I watched him for about a quarter of an hour, but went on my way and left him still sitting there on his pinnacle.

On our return from the valley, we went down the main trail in the valley and camped at the foot of Takakkaw Falls, 1,200 feet high.

"We passed down and descended out of the valley in the usual way and went down by Emerald Lake to Field.   While I was stopping at Field, Lady Minto and her two daughters came in on their return from a three day's trip up the Yoho Valley, having travelled on the same road that I have spoken of.   She said that, in one place, on the upper trail, a horse made a mis-step and rolled down the hillside for quite a distance before he could regain his feet and, by good luck, he was the horse that carried the provisions. They were dressed in corduroy, just as the ladies had been whom I had seen at first."

(This is the last entry I have in the notebook this has been taken from and, as far as I can remember, was the last of the late Professor's dictation in regard to this Work—W. H. FATT.)

NOTE.—To Miss W. H. Fatt, Sidney, B.C., is due much credit for the efficient manner in which she recorded and transcribed the matter in the foregoing autobiography, the greater part of which was dictated to her by my father, who fully appreciated her assistance.—W. T. MACOUN.

BIOGRAPHY OF PROF. JOHN MACOUN, 1904-1920.

By W. T. Macoun

Although my father continued to write his autobiography to within a few weeks of his death, he was not able to bring it further than the year 1904, but, believing that readers of this book would desire to follow Prof. Macoun's activities to the close of his long and useful life, I have set down here certain facts relating to each year since that time and have closed with some reference to his personality.

W. T. Macoun.

Ottawa, Ont.
1922.

CHAPTER XIX
1904-1920

WORK ON THE ROCKY MOUNTAIN FLORA—COLLECTING ALONG THE
LOWER ST. LAWRENCE, 1905—MONTMORENCY FALLS, CAP
A L'AIGLE, MURRAY BAY, TADOUSAC—COLLECTING FUNGI
ABOUT OTTAWA—EXAMINED THE COUNTRY ON BOTH SIDES OF
THE GRAND TRUNK PACIFIC RAILWAY FROM PORTAGE LA
PRAIRIE TO EDMONTON, 1906—AMUSING INCIDENTS IN RE-
GARD TO PROF. MACOUN—RESOLUTION OF APPRECIATION OF
HIS WORK PASSED BY AGRICULTURAL COMMITTEE OF HOUSE
OF COMMONS, 1906—ARRANGING SPECIMENS FOR THE VIC-
TORIA MEMORIAL MUSEUM—OBTAINED PHOTOGRAPHS OF
TREES IN WESTERN ONTARIO, 1907—LATER IN SEASON WENT
TO GASPE BASIN AND PERCE, P.Q., TO STUDY SEA-WEEDS—
REVISED HIS CATALOGUE OF CANADIAN BIRDS, 1907-8—
VISITED VANCOUVER ISLAND, 1908—LARGE COLLECTIONS
MADE—VISITED WEST COAST OF VANCOUVER ISLAND, 1909—
GREAT VARIETY OF SPECIES AND LARGE NUMBER OF SPECI-
MENS OF MARINE LIFE COLLECTED—COLLECTED IN NOVA
SCOTIA, 1910—WROTE THE FLORA OF THE MARITIME PRO-
VINCES—MOVED TO THE VICTORIA MEMORIAL MUSEUM,
1911—WORK ON THE OTTAWA AND VANCOUVER ISLAND
FLORA WITH A VIEW TO PUBLICATION—HAS A PARALYTIC
STROKE, 1912—MOVES TO VANCOUVER ISLAND, 1912, AND
BEGINS COLLECTING THERE—MUCH TIME SPENT IN THE
COLLECTING AND STUDY OF CRYPTOGAMS—CONTINUATION
OF COLLECTING IN 1913, 1914, 1915, 1916, 1917, 1918 AND 1919
ON VANCOUVER ISLAND AND ADJACENT ISLANDS—LARGE
COLLECTIONS OF CRYPTOGAMS WERE MADE AND MANY NEW
SPECIES FOUND BY HIM—PRESENTED A LARGE COLLECTION
OF PLANTS OF VANCOUVER ISLAND, MOUNTED AND NAMED,
TO HERBARIUM OF THE PROVINCIAL MUSEUM, VICTORIA, 1917,
ALSO, LATER, A FINE COLLECTION OF CRYPTOGAMS—DEATH
OF HIS SON, JAMES M. MACOUN, JAN. 8TH, 1920, A GREAT

Shock to Him—Worked on His Autobiography—Conducted a Column in the Sidney Review under the Name of "Rambler"—Died of Heart Failure at Sidney, Vancouver Island, July 18, 1920—Personal Characteristics —Family—Species Named after John Macoun.

D URING the winter of 1904-5, Prof. Macoun continued to work on the Rocky Mountain flora, and prepared specimens of plants for exhibition at Lake Louise, Field and Glacier in the Rocky and Selkirk Mountains. He also wrote a short account of the fauna and flora of these mountains for Mr. A. O. Wheeler's book on The Selkirk Range.' As the fauna and flora of the St. Lawrence River Valley, below Quebec, had not been thoroughly worked up, it was decided that he should spend some time there and, during the summer of 1905, he made his headquarters at Montmorency Falls and Cap a l'Aigle and examined the district west of Murray Bay, and River, and eastward to Port a Persis, west of Tadousac. He had a very successful season and large collections were made. From the material obtained, he found that the coldness of the water gave arctic seaweeds, while the flora of the hill-sides indicated a summer temperature much higher than had been anticipated. After his return to Ottawa, he spent the autumn months collecting fungi in the vicinity of that city, obtaining nearly 700 species.

Prof. Macoun received instructions, in the spring of 1906, to make an examination of the country on both sides of the Grand Trunk Pacific Railway line from Portage la Prairie, Man., to Edmonton, Alta. He left Ottawa on June 1st and Portage la Prairie on June 11th. When he traversed this part of the prairies in 1872, on his first expedition with Sandford Fleming, there was only the Hudson's Bay Company's fort, where Portage la Prairie now stands, and there was no settlement beyond Rat Creek, and, from there to Edmonton, stretched an unbroken wilderness. In 1879, seven years later, when he went through, settlements were being formed at many points east of Fort Ellice and, on the publication of his report after that trip, a rush took place for land further west. Going over the country again, in 1906, when he saw great wheat fields, for mile after mile, he was, naturally, pleased that the conclusions he drew in regard to the fertility of the land and the kind of climate had been so thoroughly demonstrated by the results obtained.[2] On this trip, in 1906, his work was mainly to compare the country through which the Grand Trunk Pacific ran with that through which the Canadian Pacific Railway passed further south. He found the land was good over a large proportion of the territory through which the Grand Trunk Pacific line went, and the report which he published of each section of the country through which he passed gives an excellent idea of the topography and the character of the crops that year.

So far, the many interesting and amusing incidents of his life have been related by himself, but the following incidents of his trip in 1906 are described by Mr. W. Herriot, Galt, Ont., who accompanied him:

"While camped in the Assiniboine Valley, a very severe storm took place, which kept us in our tents over the noon lunch hour. We had a bottle of pickled white onions of which Prof. Macoun was negotiating the contents with a spoon. At this moment, a large hailstone bounced into the tent before us and he, noticing it, and thinking he had dropped one of the onions, scooped it up and put it in his mouth. The look of astonishment on his face caused much amusement and none enjoyed the joke more than he "Well, well, doesn't that beat all," his favourite phrase when anything unusual happened, was his remark.

"We were camped at Ribstone Creek on a very hot day in early August. Atkinson had provided the usual good supply of dinner but, owing to the extreme weather conditions, we were all "off our feed," and very little was eaten. As we were about to clean up, a settler sauntered up and we invited him to have dinner, which he graciously declined at first, stating that he had just finished dinner an hour ago. As we had a quantity of cooked food, we pressed him further to have some, when he started in and systematically cleaned up one dish after another until nothing was left. I remember Prof. Macoun putting this in his notes and estimating that he had eaten more than the four of us after assuring us that he wasn't hungry, having had dinner only a short time before. This was a good example of a settler's appetite and amused Prof. Macoun very much. "I wonder how much he would eat when he is hungry?" he queried.

"Long experience in the open, without the comforts of home life, made him very impatient to any fuss or complaints that ordinary mortals might make over the inconveniences of camp life. He would accept the inevitable without the slightest show of discomfort and would disdain any attempts to smooth out any ruffles that he considered trifles, and would bear them with a patience bordering on stoicism. An example of this occurred at Oak River, when he appealed to Atkinson (who was a wizard in the way of turning his hand to anything) to have a sharp tooth reduced that was cutting into his gums and making eating very difficult. Now, the files that a taxidermist carries, as you know, are of a very coarse cut, but, with one of these, Atkinson started, with Prof. Macoun reclining on a folding chair which we carried, and rasped down the sharp projection with a noise similar to a boy running a stick along a picket fence. He never batted an eyelid and pronounced the job excellent, while our own teeth were all on edge. Atkinson declared that he himself felt every rasp go through him to the quick.

"Prof. Macoun's extreme activity was a very striking part of his make-up, so much so that deliberate or systematic methods that made movement slow were very irritating to him. Used as he was, in the early days, to travel with Red River carts, when they would pick up their trappings and throw them all in and be off, perhaps, in fifteen minutes, Atkinson's methods of carefully packing all our camping outfit on the two democrat wagons and roping them on for rapid travel was too much for him in the mornings and he usually would start to walk out on the trail a half hour or more ahead of us as well as to pick up anything of interest along the way. At Fort Ellice, he started out as usual, but the old trails about here were badly cut up, and disconnected, and difficult to follow, We had travelled so far that we should have overtaken him and, seeing nothing in sight, decided to turn back and spread out in an effort to find which trail he had taken. It was an hour later before we located him sleeping peacefully under

20

a tree, waiting for us. His opinion of Atkinson's movements that morning took a very severe slump. I mention this incident to show how perfectly at home he was in the great out-doors and the idea of our losing him appeared to be very remote from his thoughts. He used to say of Indians that they never got lost. They would assert: "Indian here, wigwams lost."

"Acuteness of vision, due to close discrimination of plants, he had developed to a marvellous extent. While driving along at a rapid pace he would order a stop, when he gathered some comparatively inconspicuous plant from the grass and proceeded. While we stopped for camp, his usual custom was to look up any settlers in the vicinity and gather their views of things. Anyone passing our camp was regarded as a legitimate source of information and he always made first advances to draw them into conversation. We were away on our usual forage one morning when Atkinson, who wore a heavy drooping moustache, shaved it off and, when Prof, Macoun returned at noon, Atkinson sauntered past the camp with the expected results. "Good morning, sir, and do you live around here" was the salute. When Atkinson laughed, he saw his mistake, which he took with a mixture of chagrin and amusement. This was one time when his acuteness of vision got a set-back.

"To the inexperienced with prairie life, the mirage is a source of curious interest, as it was much so to me. In the distance, we would see a lake with innumerable islands, which, as we travelled along, would gradually simmer down to nothing on the horizon. Now it would be a line of flapping clothes, a very common delusion, always in the distance. An apparent grain elevator and a church spire of a supposed town would gradually flatten out into a settler's shack and a stack of poles. One day, I was collecting in a depression on the prairie and walking along the bank of this hollow for perhaps a mile. Prof. Macoun had been collecting at some distance, but eventually came up and discovered me in the hollow. I was wearing a white linen hat at the time, which had magnified in the distance, so that he took me for a caravan and hastened to overtake it. His supposed caravan had dwindled down to my white hat and this was great cause of amusement to him.

"We were camped north of Carberry, in mid-June, with innumerable sloughs in the neighborhood. Prof Macoun and I started to gather some aquatic plants in the shallow water where great quantities of Black Terns were nesting, as they do on muddy knolls among the vegetation. A number of them kept darting at me, being in the advance, as if to make for my eyes, then glided over my head. Feeling somewhat concerned about their actions and my eyes, I picked up a short stick and drove into the next flock that came over my head about a foot, killing one. Immediately the rest set up an alarm cry which brought a great flock over our heads where they hovered and dropped their excrement on us and we were glad to beat a hasty retreat. We were very much mussed up, and Prof. Macoun informed me at the time that this is a common means of defence among sea birds, to which the Black Tern is an allied species. When we arrived back to camp, we looked as if we had been "carrying the hod."[3]

He was called upon to appear before the Agricultural Committee of the House of Commons to give an account of this trip and, after his address,[4] the following resolution was passed:

House of Commons,
Ottawa, 23rd Jan., 1906.

"Moved by Mr. Derbyshire,
"Seconded by Mr. Wright (Renfrew)

"That the thanks of this Committee be now tendered to Mr. John Macoun, Naturalist to the Geological Survey Department of Canada, for the valuable information laid by him before the Committee, on the natural capabilities of that large section of Western Canada extending from Edmonton to Portage la Prairie, on the occasion of his appearance before us, on this subject.

"The Committee desire also to record their appreciation of the valuable services Mr. Macoun has rendered to Canada in the past thrity years of his arduous official service as a practical science officer of the

Geological Survey of the Dominion; notably, are the following explorations of territory:—

"Prof. Macoun's first trip across the prairies was with· Sir Sandford Fleming, in 1872. His glowing report of the country traversed caused him to be sent again in 1875, to explore the route that it was then intended that the Canadian Pacific would follow. When the present route was decided upon, the Government sent him in 1879, 1880 and 1881 to report upon the country that would be opened up by the railway. Optimistic as his reports and prophecies were, they have all proved true. To these are to be added Prof. Macoun's explorations in the Canadian Yukon Territory, in 1903, which revealed, for the first time, that that far northern division of Canada also possesses agricultural resources of no mean order.   Motion cordially adopted by the committee, and presented to Prof. Macoun, pro forma, by the Chair."[5]

Preparation of natural history specimens in the new museum, shortly to be built, received much of his attention from this time on and, with the help of Mr. C. H. Young, who had been employed to assist in the ornithological work, great progress was made in the winter of 1906-7 in the arrangement and cataloguing of the specimens of birds and mammals, Mr. J. M. Macoun assisting in the botanical work.

Prof. Macoun was asked, in May, 1907, to obtain photographs of all Canadian forest trees and, at the same time, to secure specimens of the wood for the new museum. With this end in view, he went to Western Ontario, where he remained until the end of July, obtaining many photographs of forest trees. Of these, some 40 species are peculiar to Western Ontario. Later in the summer, he went to Gaspé Basin and Percé, P.Q., to continue his study of sea-weeds. An extensive collection was made and a study of the species showed that the water here was comparatively warm as compared with the north shore of the St. Lawrence, where he had been in 1905.

His time, during the winter of 1907-8, was chiefly occupied in revising the manuscript and reading the proof of his Catalogue of Canadian Birds, in which he was assisted by his son, Mr. J. M. Macoun. He received orders to go to Vancouver Island for the season of 1908, and, after he had got together the information gained by his two previous visits there, in 1887 and 1893, left Ottawa for British Columbia and reached Victoria on May 29. The information already obtained of the plants, birds and small mammals was very extensive and he planned to work up the whole natural history of the Island in two more seasons. During the summer of 1908, while large collections were made on land, he spent much time in collecting sea-weeds, and made his headquarters for some time at the Biological Station at Departure Bay, near Nanaimo, Mr. C. H. Young joining him later, when much dre g-[6] ing for starfishes and other sea forms was done, and they were greatly helped by Mr. S. W. Taylor, in charge of the Biological Station. On his way home in September, he investigated the diseases causing the rotting of timber in the mines at Rossland, B.C., and suggested means for controlling them, one being creosote, and the other by soaking the timber in water raised to a temperature of from 190° to 200° Fahr., and containing enough common salt to form a thoroughly saturated solution, the latter method having been employed with good success in Great Britain.

Prof. Macoun spent the following winter in working up his collections and, on April 24th, 1909, was again on his way to Vancouver Island, this time to the West Coast, and Barclay Sound was chosen for the field of work. He was assisted by Mr. C. H. Young and Mr. Wm. Spreadborough. Much collecting of marine fauna and flora was done and a great many species and specimens were obtained. An idea of the extent of his collections this year may be gathered from the following synopsis of the collections made, which was published in his Report for 1909:[7] Starfishes 400; Crabs and Shrimps 400; Fishes 100; Isopods 500; Tunicates and Ascidians 90; Sponges 250; Hydrozoa 150; Jelly Fishes 4; Shells 37,927; Insects 850; Birds 9; Mammals 2; Toads, etc. 15; Sea-worms 150; Sea-urchins 50; Sea-slugs 75; Barnacles 35; Polyzoa 45; Actinozoa (Stony Corals) 25; Sea-spiders 10; Anemones 15. Of plants, 1,008 species were collected, numbering many thousand specimens, the various families being represented as follows: Flowering plants 361; Mosses 226; Lichens 123; Liverworts 134; Sea-weeds 164. These large collections entailed much work in mounting and identification, and much of the following winter was devoted to it. His new edition of the Catalogue of Canadian Birds was published in 1909.

The large collections made in 1909 required much study and arrangement. Many species were unfamiliar to Canadian specialists and had to be sent to the United States for identification, and not a few were unknown to science, no less than seventeen species of shells being new and many others not having been found on Vancouver Island before. A new species of fish collected that year was named *Pterygicottus*[8]*Macounii* by Bean and Weed, and a special genus had to be made for it.[9]

As the collections of the marine fauna of the Atlantic Coast were inadequate, and as there was a demand for a separate catalogue of the flora of the Maritime Provinces, Prof. Macoun was instructed to make collections during the summer of 1910 in Nova Scotia and from its coast waters, and he left Ottawa, accompanied by Mr. C. H. Young, on May 10th and commenced work at Yarmouth on May 14th. Other important collecting points were Barrington Passage, Bridgewater, Springhill and Digby. Extensive and valuable collections were made there while, in the meantime, Mr. Wm. Spreadborough was collecting sea birds and marine animals on Vancouver Island and Queen Charlotte Islands. After his return from the Maritime Provinces, Prof. Macoun was occupied for part of the remainder of that year in writing the flora of the Maritime Provinces. During 1910, Mr. James M. Macoun made an expedition to Hudson Bay to study the flora and fauna of the West Coast and, having been delayed by the injury to the boat at Wager Inlet, did not reach Ottawa until Jan. 18th, 1911,[10] having made the winter trip from Fort Churchill to Gimli by snowshoes and dog train.

Prof. Macoun and staff moved from the old museum on Sussex St. to the new Victoria Memorial Museum in January, 1911, and, before spring, he had finished his work on the flora of the

Maritime Provinces.   As soon as he had done this he commenced work on the flora of Ottawa and the district surrounding it, making also collections in this district during four months of the year, this being the first summer that he had spent in Ottawa since he moved to this city from Belleville in 1882.[11]

In 1911, Mr. P. A. Taverner was appointed to his staff, and was given charge of all the vertebrates and, during the year, did much work in the arrangement and cataloguing of the specimens. This year, Mr. J. M. Macoun worked up the very large collection of plants made by him on the West Coast of Hudson's Bay in 1910.   Because of his knowledge of the fur seal, Mr. J. M. Macoun was sent to Washington early in the summer as one of Canada's representatives at the Fur-Seal Conference.

At the close of the collecting season, Prof. Macoun wrote in the new localities into the Ottawa flora he had written the previous winter, and so completed the enumeration of the Ottawa species with their distribution in the 30-mile zone.   When this was completed, he worked over the collections of Vancouver plants in anticipation of spending the summer of 1912 there for the purpose of completing the flora of the Island.   He was taken ill on March 6th, and was not able to travel until April 24th, when he left for Vancouver Island accompanied by Mr. J. M. Macoun, and had soon begun to collect at Sidney, B.C.   By the end of the summer season he had listed and collected a large number of plants and had added many species to the Island flora.   He now decided to make Sidney his home, and he and his wife lived, until his and her death, with his son-in-law, and daughter, Mr. and Mrs. A. O. Wheeler.

He was soon sought out by the local naturalists, with whom, during the remainder of his life, he was on very friendly terms, and many collections were brought to him in 1912 for aid in identification.

During the last three months of that year, he devoted his time almost exclusively to collecting cryptogams, the autumn and winter of Vancouver Island being the best season for this purpose.   Large collections of mosses, lichens, hepaticae, fungi, and sea-weeds were made.

He attended the Convention of the Canadian Forestry Association at Victoria, in September, 1912.

His botanical investigations in 1913[12] were confined mainly to the vicinity of Victoria and Sidney, Vancouver Island, but short visits were made to adjacent islands. During the autumn and winter months, he again paid special attention to cryptogams as, previous to his residence here, little had been done in the study of them here. Many new species were added by him this year, which were determined by specialists. Twelve new species of flowering plants were added to the flora of Vancouver Island.

In 1914, he devoted most of his working hours to the study of cryptogams, no less than 196 species of fungi having been determined for him by Dr. John Dearness, London, Ont., in the autumn of that year. Other specialists who aided him in this work were Mrs. E. G. Britton and Prof. O. E. Jennings with musci, Mrs. G. K. Merrill with lichens, Miss C. C. Haynes with hepaticae, Mr. F. S. Collins with sea-weeds and Mr. C. G. Lloyd with woody fungi.

By 1915, his collection of flowering plants of Vancouver Island had reached 826 species. Of lichens, he had 195 species named and catalogued and more than a thousand species of mosses, sea-weeds, and fungi. During 1915, he spent seven weeks at Comox, B.C., and made large collections of both flowering plants and cryptogams, but the study of the latter continued to occupy most of his time.

He was not far from Sidney, B.C., in 1916. The only trip that he made beyond Victoria was to Brackendale, on the mainland, near the Coast, where he spent three weeks, and collected many species of cryptogams, which do not occur on Vancouver Island. Although he had never used a microscope to any extent in his younger days, after he went to Vancouver Island to live, he procured a very good one, and, by 1916, he was able to determine most of the mosses and lichens himself with the use of it, although he was in constant correspondence with specialists, the bulk of his collections, however, being sent to Dr. John Dearness, London, Ont., who reported on no less than 1,000 specimens during 1915 and 1916, many of them new to science.

The year 1917 found him still fairly active, though his operations were getting more confined to the immediate neighborhood of Sidney as he found walking becoming more difficult. Ever since the stroke which he had in 1911,[13] he had limped somewhat, but it was his heart which prevented greater activity. This year, he presented to the Herbarium of the Provincial Museum a large collection of plants of Vancouver Island mounted and named, also a collection of musci and lichens made by him on the Island and a poriton of the mainland of British Columbia. A list of names of the plants in this collection was published in the Report of the Provincial Museum of Natural Nistory[14] for 1917.[15] To these were added, before he died, his fine collection of cryptogams. Thus, the Provincial Museum of Natural History has now a practically complete set of the flowering and other plants collected by Prof. Macoun on Vancouver Island.

During 1918 and 1919, Prof. Macoun continued his work on the cryptogams, and got his collection in shape to present a set to the Province as above mentioned.

The death of his son, James M. Macoun, on Jan. 8th, 1920, was a great blow to Prof. Macoun. His son had been his right hand man, as it were, for nearly forty years, and his death came as a great shock to him, and, for a time, he lost ambition to do more work, but he had been too long active to remain idle while he had strength to do anything, and he devoted considerable time, in the early part of the year, to his autobiography, which he brought down to 1904. Though he was not able to move much about, himself, he conducted a column in the local paper, the Sidney Review, and, under the name of "Rambler," invited correspondents to send in specimens of plants for name.[16] This he continued to do until a few days before his death.

His vitality had been much lowered by an attack of whooping cough, which he had in the spring, and, in July, his heart gave him much trouble, and, after less than a week's confinement to the house, he died at Sidney on July 18th, 1920.[17]

Prof. Macoun had many strong and outstanding personal characteristics. His determination and perseverance are marked through all his early explorations and many accounts might be related where it was nothing but sheer determination that carried him safely through perilous and exhaustive situations. After his recovery from the paralytic stroke in 1912, which left his right hand in such condition that he could not write with it, he determined to write with his left, and, from that time on, did so in a very legible handwriting. He could never be idle and had nothing to regret in his old age over wasted days and nights, for he worked both night and day until a few years before his death, when he spent his evenings in reading. He was a very wide reader and kept himself well posted on the events of the world to the very last, and, having been a great reader for so many years, he was a veritable encyclopedia. He had a wonderfully retentive memory and could give the year and the day of the month where he had been when anything out of the ordinary occurred in his personal experience, apparently back to his childhood. He could give the scientific name on sight of thousands of flowering plants, mosses, lichens, liverworts and fungi. His quickness in this respect was remarkable, but quickness was one of his strong characteristics, both in his actions and in his speech. His repartee was so keen that he was seldom, if ever, cornered in an argument, and he delighted in discussing any matter of general or personal interest. He had an extremely logical mind and had great power of accurate deduction when given a few important facts. He was very emphatic in his statements, and his enthusiasm was so great that the combination of these two characteristics made his personality a striking one. With these two traits, however, went a very humorous disposition and many an audience and individual went into bursts of laughter over his way of putting things. His honesty was proverbial and he was very frank and outspoken in regard to wrongdoing. He was kind and generous not only to his family and near friends, but to those from whom he did not expect to receive anything in return. He believed that there was an Overruling Power, but that men had much to do in shaping their own destiny.

Perhaps the strongest trait in Prof. Macoun's character, was a sympathetic understanding of his fellow-men, one that made him hosts of friends and a much-sought adviser in questions of doubt and difficulty. The honesty of his opinion and the straight-forwardness with which his advice was given, in conjunction with his sympathetic manner of giving it, secured for him a respect and affection that lasted a lifetime. His wonderful magnetism and ready tact constituted him a leader of men, and had his great abilities turned to statesmanship, he would have been a great power for the good of his country. He was a true Imperialist and a firm believer in the strength and integrity of the British Empire.

His dearest wish was to live until the termination of the Great War, every phase of which he studied with the most intense interest, and his fervent hope was that he might be spared to see a proper readjustment of subsequent world conditions, and a ful-filment of the high ideals that were at stake.

Prof. Macoun was a Presbyterian in religion and was an elder in St. Andrew's Church, Ottawa, for many years previous to his departure for British Columbia in 1912.

He was married in 1862 to Miss Ellen Terrill, Wooler, Ont., who survived him until February 2, 1922. His children are: Mrs. A. O. Wheeler, Sidney, B.C.; Mrs. R. A. Kingman, Wallingford, Vt.; Mrs.W. M. Everall, Victoria, B.C.; and Mr. W. T. Macoun, Dominion Horticulturist, Experimental Farm, Ottawa, Ont. His eldest son, Mr. James M. Macoun, Chief of the Biological Division of the Geological Survey, predeceased him by a few months.

SPECIES NAMED AFTER JOHN MACOUN.

Perhaps no better tribute to the work of John Macoun can be paid than the list of some of the species of plants, etc., which have been named after him, most of which were discovered and collected by him but named by some other scientist. While there are 48 species in this list, it is not a complete one, but it indicates the large number of new and rare specimens collected by him. Few scientists have had as many species named in honour of them as John Macoun.

FLOWERING PLANTS

Alopecurus Macounii, Vasey　　*Calamagrostis Macouniana*, Vasey
Elymus Macounii, Vasey　　　　*Ranunculus Macounii*, Britton
Lesquerella Macounii, Greene　*Draba Macouniana*, Rydberg
Arabis Macounii, S. Wats.　　　*Potentilla Macounii*, Rydberg
Rosa Macounii, Greene　　　　*Lupinus Macounii*, Rydberg
Astragalus Macounii, Rydberg　*Gentiana Macounii*, Holm.
Oreocarya Macounii, Rydberg　*Antennaria Macounii*, Greene.
Hymenoxys Macounii, Rydberg　*Arnica Macounii*, Greene.
Bidens Macounii, Greene.　　　*Sisyrinchium Macounii*, Bickn.
Senecio Macounii, Greene　　　*Limnanthes Macounii*, Newcombe.

MOSSES

Andreaea Macounii, Kindb.　　*Distichium Macounii*, C.M. &
Encalypta Macounii, Aust.　　　　　　Kindb.
Entodon Macounii, C.M. &　　*Homalia Macounii*, C.M. &
　　　　Kindb.　　　　　　　　　　Kindb.
Hypnum Macounii, Kindb.　　*Philonotis Macounii*, Lesq. &
Pogonatum Macounii, Kindb.　　　　James.
Racomitrium Macounii, Kindb. *Cinclidium Macounii*, Kindb.
Eurhynchium Macounii, Kindb.*Heterocladium Macounii*, Best.
Neckera Macounii, C.M. &　　*Timmia Macounii*, Kindb.
　　　　Kindb.

LICHENS

Biatora Macounii, Eckfeldt   *Pannaria Macounii*, Tuckerm.

HEPATICÆ

Anthoceros Macounii, Howe.   *Cephalozia Macounii*, Aust.
Cololejeunea Macounii, Spruce.   *Fossombronia Macounii*, Aust.
Lophocolea Macounii, Aust.   *Odontoschisma Macounii*, Aust.

ECHINODERMS—STARFISH

Leptasterias Macounii, Verrill.

MOLLUSKS

Boreotrophon Macounii, Dall and Bartsch.
Turbonilla (Pyrogolampros) Macounii, Dall.and Bartsch.

INSECTS—BUTTERFLY

Oeneis Macounii, Edwards

FISH

Chauliodus Macounii, Bean   *Pterygiocottus Macounii*, Bean and
Wood.

Total, 48 species.[18]

Professor Macoun with a young friend in the Maritimes in 1895. This photograph was given to the Macoun Field Club by Mrs. Mary (Macoun) Kennedy, John Macoun's granddaughter.

Editorial Notes

by W. A. Waiser

History Department, University of Saskatchewan
Saskatoon

Abbreviations:
PAC — Public Archives of Canada
NMC — National Museums of Canada

CHAPTER ONE

1. Macoun's year of birth is often mistakenly given as 1832. The church register in Ireland confirms April 17, 1831 as the date when he was born.

2. Macoun recalled this early interest in flowers in a letter to S. Bebb "I can understand your delight in examining what may be new to you as I only feel my earlier sensations when I stand in a new field and see around me new forms and know that almost every step will add to my enjoyment. This brings up the days of yore when as a young man I tramped the woods alone yet not alone for all around me were friends that reminded me of even earlier days when I trowel in hand but without knowledge dug up the primroses and violets for *my* garden in the far off time in Ireland."

   NMC, Macoun letterbooks, v.1, Macoun to Bebb, December 5, 1887.

CHAPTER TWO

1. Frederick's family is still living on the homestead where he settled and is buried.

CHAPTER THREE

1. George Perry Graham (1859-1943) was Minister of Railways and Canals in the Wilfrid Laurier government and later held several portfolios in the Mackenzie King administration, before being named to the Senate in 1926.

2. The Linnaean classification used binomial nomenclature and was based on the simple procedure of counting the male and female parts of a flower.

3. Macoun's *Catalogue of Canadian Plants* provided the synonymy, habi-
tats and collectors of every known species of Canada flora. Published
under the auspices of the GSC., it appeared in 7 parts over a 20 year
period: Polypetalae (Montreal: Dawson Brothers, 1883): Gamopetalae
(Montreal: Dawson Brothers, 1884): Apetalae (Montreal: Dawson
Brothers, 1886); Endogens (Montreal: Dawson Brothers, 1888); Acro-
gens (Montreal: Wm. Foster Brown and Co., 1890); Musci (Montreal:
Wm. Foster Brown and Co., 1892); Lichens and Hepaticae (Ottawa:
Government Printing Bureau, 1902).

CHAPTER FOUR

1. These books explained the geographic distribution of vegetation as a
direct result of climate and exerted an immense influence on the development of biological views.

2. The Botanical Society of Canada, founded in Kingston, Ontario in 1860,
sought to encourage study and exploration in the interest of the science,
as well as the country's industry. In the newspaper advertisement calling
for the formation of the society, it was noted that botany's "relations to
industry are so important that no civilized land can allow it to fall to
neglect without suffering thereby in its material interests".

G.F.G. Starsley (ed.), *Pioneers of Canadian Science* (Toronto: Univ. of
Tor. Press, 1966), appendix B, p. 32.

3. Hastings County Directory, 1865, pp. 25-33.

4. Decorated for his service, Macoun was later awarded a section of land
near Timmins, Ontario, as part of the Boer War Veterans' land grant.

5. As his collecting efforts increased, Macoun found that he could not
name a number of his species or knew very little about them. He
consequently began to correspond with a number of botanical specialists
— a practice that greatly and permanently assisted Macoun in classifying and often lead to the exchange of specimens.

6. In the 1870's, Macoun relied heavily on Gray and his assistant Sereno
Watson for exact identification of his botanical specimens, particularly
those from the North-West.

7. Created by the Methodist Episcopal Church, Albert College or the
Belleville seminary was incorporated in 1857 and received its university
charter in 1866. Unfortunately, the early records of the school were
destroyed by fire in 1917.

8. The poem, "Lady of the Snows", was written by Rudyard Kipling for
Queen Victoria's Diamond Jubilee. Far from being uncomplementary,
it extolled the virtues of Canada's northern climate in producing a
strong, moral people.

9. David Allan Poe Watt was a Montreal merchant and, at one time, export freight manager of the Allan Line Steamship Company for North American services. He was a former editor of the Canadian Naturalist.

10. Macoun financed these extensive collecting trips by guaranteeing sale of enough specimens beforehand.

11. On July 10, 1869, he collected in two hours over 120 different species of flowering plants and ferns.

    PAC, John Macoun papers, "Notes on a Trip to Lake Superior during the Summer of 1869".

12. These initial botanical excursions revealed to Macoun those combinations of soil and climate that produced particular plant communities and resulted in his practice of determining the agricultural capabilities of a district by judging its flora and comparing it with a known area.

CHAPTER FIVE

1. In the late 1850's, while the potential of the prairies was being debated, the British and Canadian governments dispatched scientific exploring parties to the western interior to gather more reliable information. The Palliser (1857-1859) and Hind (1857-1858) expeditions clearly distinguished three steppes or prairie levels and defined those areas where agriculture could be best initiated. They extolled the merits of the wooded 'fertile belt' along the Assiniboine and North Saskatchewan Rivers, while describing the true prairie district to the south as a triangle of arid lands unfit for settlement. Macoun's failure to mention the work of the Canadian expedition is curious but understandable. Hind published a collection of letters to government officials in which he referred to the botanist's findings as "the one sided speculations of the incompetent amateur, or the grosser perversions of the unscrupulous charlatan..."

   H.Y. HIND, *Manitoba and The North-West Frauds* (Windsor, N.S.: Knowles and Company, 1883), p. 11.

2. Watts should be Watt.

3. The renowned Canadian surveyor and public servant Sandford Fleming (1827-1915) was engineer-in-chief of the Canadian Pacific Railway from 1871 to 1880.

4. JOHN MACOUN, "Botanical Report, Lake Superior to Pacific Ocean" in S. FLEMING (ed.), *Canadian Pacific Railway Report of Progress on the Explorations and Surveys up to January, 1874* (Ottawa: MacLean, Roger and Company, 1874), appendix C, pp. 56-98.

5. G.M. GRANT, *Ocean to Ocean* (Toronto: James Campbell and Son, 1873).

6. GRANT, *Ocean to Ocean,* pp. 21-23. (NOTE: Throughout the *Autobiography* Macoun often quotes from his notebooks, reports and books, as well as from the writings of his contempories. In several instances, he combined paragraphs or sentences from several pages. The source of these extracts has been indicated as precisely as possible.)

7. GRANT, *Ocean to Ocean,* pp. 35; 36.

8. GRANT, *Ocean to Ocean,* p. 44.

9. GRANT, *Ocean to Ocean,* p. 46.

10. GRANT, *Ocean to Ocean,* p. 50.

11. GRANT, *Ocean to Ocean,* pp. 59-60.

12. Mrs. Fleming should read Mr. Fleming.

13. GRANT, *Ocean to Ocean,* p. 62.

14. In the early 1800's American explorers assessed the unfamiliar trans-Mississippi plains environment as a great desert wholly unfit for settlement. This illusion of an inland desert east of the Rocky Mountains was confirmed by subsequent investigators and travellers, causing the American settlement frontier to jump almost 2,000 miles westward to Oregon. Palliser believed in the existence of the 'Great American Desert' and neatly extended it into British North American to account for his famous triangle. J.W. Watson ("The Role of Illusion in North American Geography", *The Canadian Geographer,* v. 13, n.l., 1969, p. 20) suggests that Palliser "was supported in his conclusion about a Canadian desert because of the illusion of an American one."

15. A.A. TACHE, *Esquisse sur le nord-ouest de l'Amerique* (Montreal: Typographie du Nouveau Monde, 1869).

16. GRANT, *Ocean to Ocean,* pp. 80-81.

17. GRANT, *Ocean to Ocean,* p. 130.

18. W.F. BUTLER, *The Great Lone Land* (London: Low, Marston, Low and Searle, 1872).

19. Malcolm McLeod's *Peace River* (Ottawa: J. Durie and Son, 1872) projected the railway line through the Peace River Valley.

20. GRANT, *Ocean to Ocean,* pp. 181-182.

21. CHARLES E. HORETZKY, *Canada on The Pacific* (Montreal: Dawson Brothers, 1874).

22. HORETZKY, *Canada on The Pacific,* pp. iii-iv.

23. HORETZKY, *Canada on The Pacific,* pp. 1-2.

CHAPTER SIX

1. HORETZKY, *Canada on The Pacific*, pp. 4-5.

2. HORETZKY, *Canada on The Pacific*, p. 19.

3. HORETZKY, *Canada on The Pacific*, p. 21-22.

4. HORETZKY, *Canada on The Pacific*, p. 24.

5. Photograph: Charles E. Horetzky, Fleming expedition, 1872.

6. HORETZKY, *Canada on The Pacific*, pp. 34-35.

7. In his notebook, Macoun lauded the country as being ahead of almost everything he had yet seen in beauty and fertility: "I would prefer risking wheat on any part of the prairie passed over today . . . Nothing in either soil, plants or climate would cause me to hesitate in giving this opinion."

   PAC, John Macoun Papers, 1872 field notebook.

8. HORETZKY, *Canada on The Pacific*, p. 51.

9. HORETZKY, *Canada on The Pacific*, p. 52.

10. HORETZKY, *Canada on The Pacific*, pp. 53-54.

11. HORETZKY, *Canada on The Pacific*, pp. 62-63.

12. HORETZKY, *Canada on The Pacific*, p. 74.

13. A period of intense professional rivalry, it was not uncommon for men working in remote areas to develop bitter animosities. Ten years later, Horetzky published a pamphlet questioning Macoun's methods of observation and estimates, as well as accusing him of culling his information from existing literature.

    C.E. HORETZKY, *Some Startling Facts Relating to the CPR and the North-West Lands* (Ottawa: Free Press, 1882).

14. HORETZKY, *Canada on The Pacific*, p. 78. Horetzky, meanwhile, explored the country westward to the mouth of the Skeena River.

15. In his report, Macoun related the agricultural prospects of the North-West to the various plant forms he had observed. Detecting little change in the flora from Fort Garry to Edmonton, he concluded that the vegetation's unvarying character was caused by a regional uniformity in soil conditions and climate and suggested that grazing would be profitable wherever conditions were not suitable for grain. As for his investigations in the Peace River district, the presence of plant species that were also found around Edmonton convinced him of the northward extension of summer isotherms into the region and the irrelevance of winter temperatures. He considered the Peace River country as but a continuation of the prairie with a climate sufficient for grain production.

CHAPTER SEVEN

1. A.R.C. Selwyn (1824-1902) was Director of the Geological Survey of Canada for a quarter century, from 1869-1895.

2. "When last in Ottawa I had the pleasure of reading the proof sheets of your report to Mr. Fleming and I then mentioned to him how pleased I should be if you could accompany me next year on an exploration through the Upper Peace River region from British Columbia eastward ... The Act establishing and making provision for the Geological Survey does not include botanical investigations as part of the work for which the money is appropriated and hence the fact that nothing having hitherto been done in that direction. I have however today written to the Minister of The Interior suggesting that a sizeable sum of $2500 Two thousand five hundred dollars per annum should be made to the Survey appropriation, for botanical purposes, and that you should be appointed Botanist."

   PAC, Geological Survey of Canada Director's Letterbooks, n. 3, Selwyn to Macoun, April 27, 1874.

3. JOHN MACOUN, "Report on the Botanical Features of the Country Traversed from Vancouver to Carlton on the Saskatchewan", *Geological Survey of Canada. Report of Progress for 1875-1876.* (Montreal: Dawson Brothers, 1877), pp. 110-232.

4. MACOUN, "Report on the Botanical Features . . .", pp. 116-117.

5. MACOUN, "Report on the Botanical Features . . .", pp. 120-124.

6. MACOUN, "Report on the Botanical Features . . .", pp. 134-137.

7. MACOUN, "Report on the Botanical Features . . .", pp. 139-140.

8. A.R.C. SELWYN, "Report on Exploration in British Columbia in 1875", *Geological Survey of Canada. Report of Progress* for 1873-1874, p. 40.

9. SELWYN, "Report on Exploration in British Columbia in 1875", pp. 41-42.

10. W.F. BUTLER, *The Wild North Land* (London: Low, Marston, Low and Searle, 1873).

11. MACOUN, "Report on the Botanical Features . . .", pp. 150-151.

12. MACOUN, "Report on the Botanical Features . . .", pp. 152-153.

13. MACOUN, "Report on the Botanical Features . . .", p. 154.

14. Erected on an unstable site, the massive tower that formed the entrance to the museum had to be demolished in 1916. The building now houses part of the National Museum of Natural Sciences and the National Museum of Man.

CHAPTER EIGHT

1. This was Dr. Selwyn's second attempt during the expedition to locate the elusive Pine River Pass; it ended in failure because of difficulties encountered in the ascent of the river. He had first tried following an indistinct Indian trail eastward from the junction of the Parsnip and Pack Rivers but turned back after only a few miles. The pass was finally discovered in 1877 by Joseph Hunter, a CPR location engineer who had been secretly sent to the region by acting engineer-in-chief, Marcus Smith.

2. A different version of Macoun's trip down the Peace to Fort Chipewyan is found in MARY WEEKES, *Trader King* (Regina: School Aids and Text Book Publishing Company, 1949).

3. MACOUN, "Report on the Botanical Features . . .", p. 159.

4. This decision to push on until they met the HBC boats was foolhardy. At Vermilion, the men learned that the boats, which they had expected to meet before then, were delayed for at least two weeks. This same warning was repeated at Little Red River, along with the suggestion that they should best await their arrival.

PAC, John Macoun papers, Peace River Expedition, 1875.

5. MACOUN, "Report on the Botanical Features . . .", pp. 161-162.

6. MACOUN, "Report on the Botanical Features . . .", pp. 163-164.

7. "Writing here at Chipewyan in the centre of the wild North Land, the vastness seems to overpower the mind and cause that benumbing feeling which we are prone to feel when in presence of something we cannot grasp . . . My duty becomes plainer as I consider the matter and I shall not rest until the Canadian Public knows the value of this immense country both as regarding its resources and its capability of development."

PAC, John Macoun Papers, Geological Notes on Peace River, 1875.

8. In 1876, Macoun was commissioned by the government to prepare a display of Canadian plants for the Philadelphia Centennial Exhibition, where he was awarded a bronze medal for his exhibit of Chipewyan wheat and barley. These same samples took the silver medal at the 1878 Paris Exposition.

9. At their campsite that night, Macoun wrote: "Long after the noises ceased I lay and thought of the not distant future when other sounds than these would wake up the silent forest and the whiteman with his ready instrument steam would be raising the untold wealth which lies hidden underneath the surface. It has never entered into the brain of our most enthusiastic citizen or statesman the wealth that lies hid in this land."

PAC, John Macoun papers, "Peace River Expedition, 1875", These deposits are the modern day Athabasca oil sands.

10. MACOUN, "Report on the Botanical Features . . .". p. 180.

11. "There is something soul stirring in these great solitudes — truly this is a 'Lone Land' — yet it was not always so. Here the Buffalo ranged in millions — now all are gone and the wind passes over the plain and brings no sound to the listening ear and as the eye sweeps the far horizon no sign of life meets the keenest eye. But is this solitude to last —No! 200 miles eastward a low steady tramp is heard — it is the advance guard of the teeming millions who will yet possess this land from the Great Lakes to the Rocky Mountains and when these plains will respond with the merry laugh of children and the 101 sounds of life."

PAC, John Macoun papers, Peace River Expedition, 1875.

12. "I created quite a sensation at Winnipeg when I exhibited the wheat and barley. Both were much better than are raised at that place. Consul Taylor says there is no doubt that wheat and barley do the best near their northern limit. My brother [Frederick] is going to try and raise a new variety from what I brought back with me."

PAC, Roderick MacFarland papers, Macoun to MacFarland, December 19, 1875.

CHAPTER NINE

1. In his report for the Geological Survey, Macoun declared the Peace River district better suited for agricultural settlement than the region around Edmonton and suggested a northern pass for the rail route.

2. In his classic work: *Climatology of the United States and of the temperate latitudes of the North American Continent* (Philadelphia: Lippincott and Company, 1857), Lorin Blodget combined largely American meteorological data with the recent findings of American exploratory parties to produce isothermal maps for North America. He concluded that land and water masses, as well as latitude, affected climate and that summer isotherms extended northward into the North-West to produce a favourable climate for agriculture.

3. JOHN MACOUN, "Sketch of that Portion of Canada Between Lake Superior and the Rocky Mountains with Special Reference to its Agricultural Capabilities", in S. FLEMING (ed.), *Report on Surveys and Preliminary Operations on the Canadian Pacific Railway up to January 1877* (Ottawa: MacLean, Roger and Company, 1877), appendix X, pp. 313-336.

4. Macoun did comment on the semi-arid third prairie steppe, declaring: "None of the prairie country, except that south of the Missouri Coteau,

is naturally so deficient in rainfall to prevent forest growth . . . It is to be doubted . . . that any deficiency exists."

JOHN MACOUN, "Sketch of that Portion of Canada . . .", p. 334.

5. James Melville Macoun (1862-1920) became a noted Canadian naturalist, specializing in botany. He joined the G.S.C. as his father's assistant in 1883 and quickly assumed extensive exploring duties, concentrating in northern regions. He officially succeeded his father as Chief of the Biological Division in 1917, a position he held until his sudden death in 1920. His work as secretary to the British Bering Sea Commission earned him the C.M.G. in 1912.

6. Macoun's group was the only party sent to explore the southern territory because the rail line was still being projected through the fertile belt. It is not clear, however, despite the botanist's claim (*Autobiography*, p. 151) whether they were to verify Palliser's conclusions about the aridity of the district. Fleming in the 1880 Railway Report (S. FLEMING (ed.), *Report and Documents in Reference to the Canadian Pacific Railway, 1880* (Ottawa: MacLean, Roger and Company, 1880, p. 13), simply stated that the prairie region required further exploration. In any circumstance, F.G. ROE ("Early Opinions on the 'Fertile Belt' of Western Canada", *Canadian Historical Review*, v. 27, 1946, p. 134) finds the government decision to send Macoun astounding for he was essentially being asked to pronounce upon his 'bête noire', Palliser. A reversal of Captain Palliser's findings was only natural.

7. Determined to ensure the success of his assignments, Macoun could be a tyrant, as he made plain to the House of Commons' Select Committee on the Geological Survey in 1884: "I will tell you, honestly, that I would not allow any subordinate that would be sent with me, the privilege of examining a tract of country without I had my eye on him . . . I have not the greatest of faith in subordinates carrying out their instructions."

CANADA. *House of Commons Journals*, v. 18, 1884, "Report of the Select Committee Appointed by the House of Commons to obtain information as to the Geological Surveys", Appendix 8, p. 185.

8. *PAC*, John Macoun papers, 1879 field notebook.

9. The party celebrated the 12th of July by decorating their horses with these lilies and marching from camp to the beat of the old tin pan.

10. *PAC*, John Macoun papers, 1879 field notebook.

11. At Battleford, the new capital of the North-West Territories, Macoun examined the gardens at the police farm and Governor Laird's mansion. He was amazed to find that the sandy, seemingly barren alluvium of the area produced good crops and consequently began to attach greater importance to climate in the success of Western agriculture.

12. The Cree Chief Big Bear was not the cause of the Saskatchewan Rebellion. He was, however, one of the few Indian leaders to also revolt during the largely Métis uprising.

13. Macoun attributed the apparent aridity of this region to the heavy Cretaceous clay surface and not the climate.

14. George Mercer Dawson (1849-1901) was geologist to the British North America Boundary Commission. In 1875, he joined the G.S.C., eventually becoming director in 1895.

15. Dawson reported the existence of over 15 million acres of good land. GEORGE DAWSON, "Report on a Exploration from Port Simpson on the Pacific Coast to Edmonton on the Saskatchewan", *Geological Survey of Canada. Report of Progress for 1879-1880.* (Montreal: Dawson Brothers, 1880), part B, section iii, p. 68.

16. During Macoun's short stay at Battleford, he was interviewed by P.G. Laurie, editor of the *Saskatchewan Herald*, on his summer travels.

17. The lecture, 'Our Wondrous West', was printed on the front page of the *Manitoba Free Press*, November 21, 1879.

CHAPTER TEN

1. Palliser's opinions of the capabilities of the plains region were derived almost exclusively from the vegetation. Given the climatic peculiarities of the prairies and their complete contrast with traditional agricultural experience, it was only natural for him to advise against settlement on the grasslands.

2. JOHN PALLISER, *Papers relative to the exploration by Captain Palliser of that portion of British North America which lies between the northern branch of the river Saskatchewan and the frontier of the United States, and between the Red River and the Rocky Mountains.* (London: G.E. Eyre and W. Spottiswoode, 1859), p. 16. Palliser's instructions limited his activities to the southern country, thereby preventing his exploration of the Yellowhead Pass.

3. CANADA. *House of Commons Journals,* v. 10, 1876, "Report of the Select Standing Committee on Agriculture and Colonization", appendix 8, pp. 20-43 (Macoun testimony).

4. See JAMES TROW, *Manitoba and North West Territories* (Ottawa: Department of Agriculture, 1878).

5. These acreages were contained in Macoun's own triangle of lands: "If a line be drawn from the Boundary Line where it is intersected by the 95th meridian in a north-westerly direction to where the 122nd meridian intersects the 61st parallel, we shall have the base of an isosceles triangle, which has its apex on the 115th meridian, where it intersects the 49th

parallel, one side being the Boundary Line and the other the Rocky Mountains. This triangle encloses at least 300,000 square miles, or over 200,000,000 acres of land."

MACOUN, "Sketch of that Portion of Canada . . .", p. 334.

6. A.A. TACHE, *Sketch of the North-West of America* (Montreal: John Lovell, 1870, translation). "Advantages" should read "difficulties".

7. The projected railway line was rerouted south of the Manitoba Lake region along the Assiniboine Valley to Brandon and then north-westward through the fertile belt.

8. THOMAS RIDEOUT (ed.), "The Physical Character of the Prairie Region Obtained from Authentic Sources" in FLEMING (ed.), *Report and Documents in Reference to the CPR*, Appendix 13, pp. 169-234. In this report, Western Canada was divided by longitude and latitude into squares, and information from the 1879 field parties given for each particular square.

9. CANADA. *Debates of the House of Commons,* v. 9, April 19, 1880, p. 1534.

10. Blake's exact words were "It is the map of the Hon. Minister of Railways, who has done the Hon. member for Vancouver 'Brown' ".

CANADA. *Debates of the House of Commons,* v. 9, April 15, 1880, p. 1436.

11. CANADA. *Debates of the House of Commons,* v. 9, April 15, 1880, pp. 1407-1409.

12. The Professor felt that his recent exploration and a knowledge of the work of others enabled him to classify lands with a "greater general accuracy" and he focussed his attention on the region between the Rocky Mountains and the International border and the 57th parallel. He estimated that within that 180 million acre area, there were at least 150 million acres (80 percent) of land suitable for agriculture and stock raising. Of the remaining 30 million acres, only a third could be considered sterile or irreclaimably wet; the other 20 million acres represented swamps, sand hills, banded clays and gravelly tracts.

JOHN MACOUN, "General Remarks on the Land, Wood and Water of the North-West Territories, from the 102nd to 115th meridian, and between the 51st and 53rd parallels of latitude" in FLEMING (ed.), *Report and Documents in Reference to The Canadian Pacific Railway, 1880,* Appendix 14, p. 245.

13. Dr. Charles Tupper, Minister of Railways and Canals, had good reason to support Macoun's estimates. The Conservatives wanted to attract potential railroad capitalists and investors by the offer of a twenty-five million acre land grant and the promise of wonderfully fertile lands

would greatly facilitate this task. Macoun's findings were therefore employed by the wily minister to demonstrate that the potential profit from railroad construction was very great. Their reliability was secondary to the fact that they coincided with Tupper's contentions.

14. JOHN MACOUN, *Manitoba and the Great North-West* (Guelph: World Publishing Company, 1882), pp. 656-657.

15. On August 13, Macoun visited a homestead located on the Cretaceous clay plain north west of the Cypress Hills and found to his disbelief a wonderful wheat crop. He concluded that once the seemingly arid "cactus sods" were ploughed, precipitation would prove ample for the requirements of farming, i.e. ploughing increased the effectiveness of rainfall.

16. Following the annihilation of Custer's 7th Cavalry at the Little Big Horn in 1976, the Sioux took refuge in Canada until the spring of 1881.

17. MACOUN, *Manitoba and the Great North-West,* p. 658.

18. MACOUN, *Manitoba and the Great North-West,* p. 653-654.

19. Dawson concluded that ". . . since the glacial period, the plains have never been entirely covered with forest; but that extensive prairies have continued to exist in the drier regions, from that time to the present day."

    DAWSON, *Report on the Geology and Resources of the Region in the Vicinity of the 49th Parallel, from Lake of the Woods to the Rocky Mountains.* (Montreal: Dawson Brothers, 1875), pp. 311-312.

20. MACOUN, *Manitoba and the Great North-West,* pp. 654-655.

21. FLEMING (ed.), *Report and Documents in Reference to the CPR,* p. 248.

22. FLEMING (ed.), *Report and Documents in Reference to the CPR,* p. 249.

CHAPTER ELEVEN

1. Macoun now extolled the virtues of the treeless plain as the best wheat land.

2. MACOUN, *Manitoba and the Great North-West,* pp. 612-613; 615.

3. In actuality, Macoun's revelation about the agricultural potential of the prairie region played no part in the selection of the CPR main line route. When he arrived at Jim Hill's office, the men were debating whether the rail line could proceed westward from Moose Jaw or turn northward to Battleford and proceed through the Yellowhead Pass; they had brought the rail line south without being certain of a suitable pass through the mountains. Macoun was thus summoned to St. Paul because of his

explorations in southern Alberta in 1879 and was quizzed on the suita-
bility of the Bow River Pass for a rail line. He did not convince them that
a southern line was practicable for the simple reason that the route
change had already been determined.

The decision to locate the main line through the southern grasslands was
based on the determination of the railway men to meet the threat posed
by the close proximity of the Northern Pacific Railway and thereby
secure the traffic of the Canadian West for their own line. Since the main
line could only serve or control a limited area, they consequently decided
to crowd the American boundary as closely as possible. This attempt to
exclude American inroads into the Canadian West was further necessi-
tated because the CPR was intended to be an all Canadian route running
through the wilderness north of Lake Superior. Western traffic had to be
secured to support this otherwise useless section. The CPR builders,
therefore, thought primarily in terms of national strategy and not local
settlement. They would have built across the southern grasslands even if
the area had been poorly regarded, relying on branch lines north into the
so-called fertile belt. Macoun's name was given to a town on a branch
line running south-east from Regina.

4. Macoun Point on Dawson Bay at the north-west end of Lake Winnipegosis commemorates this expedition.

5. Although he found much of the land extremely wet, Macoun still
   emphasized the region's agricultural potential.

6. The extremely popular *Manitoba and The Great North-West* was a
   testimony to Macoun's unrivalled knowledge of Western Canada.
   Drawing upon his ten years experience, it covered such aspects as
   geography, climate, agricultural prospects, history, transportation and
   wildlife, as well as provided much useful information for prospective
   settlers. When trying to pull a horse out of the mire, Macoun was the
   first one to consult.

CHAPTER TWELVE

1. MACOUN, *Manitoba and The Great North-West,* Chapter IX, pp.
   141-154. These ideas on the length and warmth of the growing season
   and the precipitation pattern in Western Canada were first argued in a
   lecture before the Canadian Institute in Toronto, 1879. (JOHN
   MACOUN, "Notes on the Physical Phenomena of Manitoba and the
   North-West Territories", *The Canadian Journal,* 3rd series v. 1, 1879,
   pp. 151-159). Unfortunately, they were misleading in that the variability
   of climate conditions from place to place or from season to season was
   rarely mentioned, let alone emphasized.

CHAPTER THIRTEEN

1. This collection consisted of 7,000 species (1745 genera) of flowering plants.

2. This letter undoubtedly influenced the direction of Macoun's work, as the eminent British botanist had advised the aspiring collector that the geographical distribution of species was as important as the discovery of new ones.

   PAC, John Macoun papers, Hooker to Macoun, August 7, 1862.

3. The following Macoun field notebooks are housed at the National Herbarium, Ottawa: 1882, 1884, 1893, 1894, 1897*, 1898*, 1899, 1901, 1902, 1903, 1904, 1905, 1906*, 1908-09*, 1910, 1911*, 1913, 1914*, 1916* (*field list only). The 'official' account of Macoun's activities are to be found in the annual reports of the G.S.C.

4. This collection of sea weeds and other marine organisms was made at the request of the Minister of Marine and Fisheries for a forthcoming fishery exhibition.

5. In May 1881, the headquarters of the G.S.C. were moved from Montreal to Ottawa, occupying a former hotel at Sussex and George Streets, a few blocks east of the Parliament buildings. One small room was set aside for the museum.

6. From 1879 to 1889, the organization was called the "Geological and Natural History Survey of Canada".

7. During the ensuing years, Macoun's collecting efforts, either through his own field work or by donation, exchange or purchase, laid the foundation of a Dominion Herbarium which by his death contained over 100,000 sheets of specimens. A large part of the actual herbarium work was performed by his son James.

8. Dr. J.F. Whiteaves (1835-1909) enjoyed a thirty-three year career with the Geological Survey of Canada as paleontologist and curator of the museum. He published over 150 titles, including *Mesozoic Fossils* 3 v. (1876-1884) and *Contributions to Canadian Paleontology* 3 v. (1885-1891).

9. William T. Macoun (1869-1933) acted as his father's botanical assistant prior to joining the staff of the Dominion Experimental farm. Here, he carried out important work in the cross fertilization of fruit and cereal, being awarded the Carter medal for Advancement of Horticulture in 1922 and the American Pomological Society medal in 1929. He was appointed Dominion Horticulturalist in 1910.

10. In his report for that season, Macoun stated that he found the remnants of a flora more closely related to that of Greenland and Europe than earlier suspected along the coast of Nova Scotia and on the islands in the Gulf.

11. In 1878, Macoun had published at his own expense a *Catalogue of the Phaenogamous and Cryptogamous Plants of the Dominion of Canada* (Belleville, Ontario).

12. The breadth of Macoun's scientific interests is evidenced by his club membership: Botanical Society of Canada; Natural History of Montreal; Ottawa Field-Naturalists' Club; Linnaean Society of Canada; Ethnological and Natural History Society of Canada; Torrey Botanical Club; American Ornithologists' Union; British Ornithologists' Union; American Society of Mammalogists.

13. Macoun has his dates confused here, for Dawson's collections of grasses were made during the 1873-1874 field seasons.

14. Macoun had confided to Fleming in May, 1874: "With what I could collect *this year* and the larger stock available from my former collections (during the coming winter) I could lay the foundation of a Dominion Herbarium that in a very short time would be a credit to the country. In conclusion I may state that whenever my services are required I will be forthcoming. I sincerely hope you will be able to put in the 'word in season' and that through your instrumentality the dream of my life may be fulfilled."

PAC, Geological Survey of Canada historical file, n. 2, Macoun to Fleming, May 15, 1874.

CHAPTER FOURTEEN

1. Dr. Chedle should be Dr. Cheadle.

2. The Sir Donald range does not include Mount Macoun, this peak being situated south of the range represented.

3. Macoun processed his specimens in the following manner: "(1) First thing in the morning *before* breakfast changed *all* my plants and placed the dry ones aside. (2) After breakfast took a common *covered* basket and collected from three to four hours, placing all my specimens in the basket *in layers*. On my return I commenced to lay them between papers and generally had this done by one o'clock . . . All the gatherings of one day I strapped by themselves and did not open them until the next morning . . . (3) After lunch I ticketed all my dry sheets and if it were a hot dry day changed my specimens that were in the press perhaps twice but always once . . . By following out the above plan I make perfect specimens and dry many species in two or three days."

NMC, John Macoun Letterbooks, v. 9, Macoun to Brodie, December 29, 1896.

4. This anxiety over the denudation of Canada's forests was vocalized in 1898 and lead to his involvement in the Canadian Forestry Association: "Apparently there is little hope of a change, for viciousness, carelessness,

cupidity and supineness of governments and people are responsible for this state of things which will continue until the trees are nearly all dead and the destruction of our noble forests all but completed . . ."

JOHN MACOUN, *The Forests of Canada and Their Distribution* (Ottawa: Government Printing Bureau, 1895), p. 5.

CHAPTER FIFTEEN

1. Precedence should be precedents

2. Carleton should be Carlton. It is a London club.

3. Macoun was a member of the Irish Protestant Benevolent Society.

4. Macoun spoke before the Geographical Section on "The Extent, Topography, Climatic Peculiarities, and Agricultural Capabilities of the Canadian North-West.

5. Macoun was responsible for the display of woods and natural products at the Exhibition. One rather amusing incident occurred on the opening day when he noticed a black ooze seeping out of the potatoes from Anticosti island. The potatoes were found to be imitations and Macoun had them removed. He had a somewhat difficult time, however, trying to explain his actions to Canadian officials back home, while keeping the fraud a secret in England.

6. Dr. Ray should be Dr. Rae

7. Macoun's impression of his summer in England formed part of his Presidential Address to the Ottawa Field-Naturalists' Club, January 13, 1887. *The Ottawa Naturalist,* v. 1, 1887-1888, pp. 17-21.

CHAPTER SIXTEEN

1. Upset by Macoun's overtures for the position, Chamberlain called into question the ornithological work of the Survey: "Mr. Chamberlain is making a dead set on us . . . I cannot understand why he makes out we have done nothing as we have over 400 species of Canadian birds in our Museum now and he knows it."

   NMC, John Macoun letterbooks, v. 1, Macoun to Vroom, March 8, 1888.

2. This rivalry among the Survey's staff was recorded by surveyor Otto Klotz, during a visit to Ottawa in 1886: "in afternoon called on Amos Bowman, Dr. Bell and Professor Macoun all of the Geological Department. What has struck me this time more than ever is the extreme jealousy that exists between the different departments and between officers of the same department. Dr. Bell called Selwyn, the director, 'a pig headed stubborn old biggar', the botanist's (Macoun's) work useless.

Prof. Macoun told me that the geologists' (topographical) surveys are unnecessary, that we (land surveyors) should do all that."

PAC, O.J. Klotz papers, diary, February 17, 1886.

3. "Regarding . . . lectures, I will say at the outset be practical and talk to *teach* not to be *heard* . . . In my lectures I give popular facts and do not burden my hearers with details which are generally very dry but I am careful to give scientific facts and not twaddle."

NMC, John Macoun letterbooks, v. 1, Macoun to Burgess, February 18, 1888.

4. The collecting efforts of the Survey staff quickly led to crowded working conditions in the new Ottawa headquarters. The provision of a larger building more suited for museum purposes became an annual request but was not realized until 1911.

5. This concern over museum conditions reflects the great importance that he attached to bringing the work of the natural scientist before the public.

6. William Spreadborough (1856-1931) became a regular member of the Macoun or other Survey parties for the next 30 years. Usually the advance man in the field, his extensive observations and collections of birds and mammals provided the first practical information on Canadian zoology.

7. In 1899, Macoun was awarded an honorary M.A. by Syracuse University, New York. As early as 1869, however, documents credit him with having the degree.

8. Macoun had been dispatched to Banff to make a collection of the region's flora and fauna for the newly created park museum. When asked by the Deputy Minister of the Interior about the selection of a curator, he advised: ". . . get a man who is willing to make himself something and who will do the country good by speaking about it. A political *bloke* should be the last one for that place."

NMC, John Macoun letterbooks, v. 5, Macoun to Deputy Minister of Interior, February 19, 1892. Some of the plants in the original collection found their way into the N.B. Sanson collection, now a part of the University of Calgary herbarium.

9. Phillip Stanley S. Abbot was a member of the Boston Appalachian Mountain Club. He was killed in 1896 when he fell from the summit of Mount Lefroy in British Columbia. The pass below Mount Lefroy was subsequently named after him.

10. Mr. Abbot was not killed until 1896.

11. Arthur O. Wheeler (1860-1945) was a surveyor and topographer in Western Canada. Known as the "grand old man of the mountains", he

was founder and first president of the Alpine Club of Canada. His grandson, John Wheeler, is Deputy Director-General, G.S.C.

CHAPTER SEVENTEEN

1. Inspired by the success of his plant catalogues, Macoun proposed to publish the data from his collecting efforts in a Catalogue of Canadian Birds, Canadian Freshwater Fish, and Canadian Mammals.

2. F.G. Roe ("Early Opinions of The 'Fertile Belt' . . .", p. 146) ridicules Macoun's mission from the outset: ". . . the government would seem to have felt that the original prophet of the wealth of Canada might be trusted to vindicate his persistent policy. He did not disappoint them."

3. Dsimissed should be dismissed.

4. In his report, Macoun failed to emphasize the variability or inadequacy of precipitation, simply noting that the dry period was but a periodic change. He did, however, describe southern Assiniboia as a difficult country to settle and occupy that was best suited for grazing. This opinion is not the contradiction it seems of his earlier statements about the fertility of the arid country (see ROE, "Early Opinions on the 'Fertile Belt' . . .", p. 146). The same conclusion about this particular district had been reached by him in 1880 but had been overshadowed by his emphasis on the wheat growing capabilities of the southern prairie.

5. Ironically, Macoun's examination of the North Saskatchewan region confirmed the Palliser/Hind conclusions: ". . . I . . . am satisfied that 300 miles north of the boundary the climate is as good if not better (especially to the west) . . . the brush and aspen district . . . is best suited for immediate settlement".

   JOHN MACOUN, "Summary of Botanical Work" in CANADA. *Sessional Papers,* 1897, n. 13A, Annual Report of the Geological Survey for 1896, part A, p. 136.

CHAPTER EIGHTEEN

1. C.H. Young (left), John Macoun, William Spreadborough, 1909, Departure Bay near Nanaimo, B.C.

2. Planned as early as 1888 but delayed because of gaps in Western Canadian bird knowledge, Macoun collaborated with his son James to publish a *Catalogue of Canadian Birds* (Ottawa: Government Printing Bureau) in two parts (1900; 1904). Drawing upon existing published material on the topic, as well as information from correspondents and his own extensive field experience, the work gave the name, range and breeding habits of all the known birds of Canada. A new revised and enlarged one volume edition appeared in English and French in 1909 and 1916 respectively.

3. Continually adding acreage to his estimate of the land available for agriculture, Macoun reported: "... we are quite safe in predicting a great future for the Yukon district . . . all of the land having a suitable soil within this immense area will in the future produce enormous crops of all the cereals, wheat included."

JOHN MACOUN, "The Climate and Flora of the Yukon District: in CANADA, Sessional Papers, 1903, n. 26, Annual Report for the Geological Survey for 1902, part A, pp. 50-51.

4. Macoun set out to correct this situation when he appeared before the House of Commons Select Committee on Agriculture and Colonization on April 17, 1903. Intimating that the Committee members were there to listen and learn, he repeated the laudatory remarks of his report and then staunchly defended their truthfulness.

5. James advised against settlement of the region, labelling it a "poor man's country". When asked about his son's pessimistic report, the Professor evidently replied, "James was always the cautious sort!"

G.E. BOWES (ed.), Peace River Chronicles (Vancouver: Prescott Publishing Company, 1964), p. 211.

6. This general disillusionment with politicians probably originated with the questioning of his findings in the 1870's, particularly during the railway debates.

7. Lake MacGregor should be Lake McArthur.

CHAPTER NINTEEN

1. JOHN MACOUN, "Notes on the Natural History of the Selkirks and adjacent mountains" in A.O. WHEELER, The Selkirk Range v. 1 (Ottawa: Government Printing Bureau, 1905) Appendix B, pp. 391-404.

2. The Professor evidently felt that Palliser and Hind deserved no credit for their part in first drawing attention to the North Saskatchewan country. He reported: "The conclusions regarding the fertility of the soil which I published in 1872, 1879 and 1880 have been practically illustrated by the results obtained by actual experience . . . the growth of grain throughout the whole of what was formally called the "Fertile Belt" is no longer an experiment but an actual fact and can be relied on for all time."

JOHN MACOUN, "On the explorations along the Grand Trunk Pacific Railway Between Portage la Prairie and Edmonton" in CANADA. Sessional papers, 1906-1907, n. 26, Annual Report of the Geological Survey of Canada for 1906, part A, p. 81.

3. The source of this extract is unknown.

4. Besides reporting on the land along the Grand Trunk Pacific, Macoun claimed that Canadians as nothern people were destined to be a domi-

nant society: "After I am dead and gone . . . this northern country will be a glorious country filled with happy people growing enormous quantities of wheat and other products . . . there is not the slightest doubt about it. It is our wrong impression that is causing all our trouble."

CANADA. *House of Commons Journals*, v. 42, 1906-1907, "Report of the Select Standing Committee on Agriculture and Colonization, Appendix 4, pp. 8-9.

5. "Report of the Select Standing Committee on Agriculture and Colonization", 1906-1907, p. 24.

6. Dre -ging should be dredging.

7. JOHN MACOUN, "Natural History Branch" in CANADA. *Sessional Papers*, 1910, n. 26, Summary Report of the Geological Survey Branch of the Department of Mines for 1909, pp. 277-279.

8. *Pterygicottus* should be *Pterygiocottus*.

9. Erroneously given a special genus, this fish (scalyhead sculpin) was actually the male of an already named species, *Artedius harringtoni* (Starks 1896).

J.L. HART, *Pacific Fishes of Canada*, Bulletin 180, Fisheries Board of Canada.

10. The Victoria Memorial Museum, erected at the corner of McLeod and Metcalfe Streets, has since become an Ottawa landmark. In 1916, it was temporarily taken over when the Parliament Buildings were burned, effectively bringing museum work to a stand still.

11. Macoun spent the 1903 field season in Ottawa and vicinity. See p. 285.

12. In June 1913, a special order-in-Council retained Macoun on the active list of the Department for life, paying his living expenses while engaged on official field work.

13. The date of his stroke is 1912.

14. Nistory should be History.

15. "List of Vancouver Island Plants Collected and Presented to the Provincial Museum".

BRITISH COLUMBIA. *Sessional Papers*, 1918, v. 11, Provincial Museum Report for 1917, pp. 017-028.

16. There are 20 short "Rambler" columns, chiefly botanical in context, in the 1920 *Sidney Riview*. The last instalment read as follows: " 'Rambler' is dead. The beautiful flowers of the forests, which he loved so well, will never again receive the gentle touch of 'Rambler'. The flowers among which he spent the greater part of his life will miss him no less than those of our readers who took much interest and pleasure from this Depart-

ment of the Review. Professor John Macoun, 'Rambler', died last Sunday morning."

17. A fitting memorial has been the creation of the Macoun Field Club. Co-sponsored by the Ottawa Field-Naturalists' Club and the National Museum of Natural Sciences, it encourages a love for wildlife and concern for conservation among young naturalists.

18. All of the species appear to be named after John Macoun. Verification of the botanical names is made difficult because Macoun's son, James Melville, is not clear as to whether the collector was father or son. The problem is further complicated by the fact that the species name is not always based on the collector. Several species collected by others were named after Macoun, who was the corresponder and friend of the author of the type. Exact verification would entail checking the original specimen and unfortunately Macoun usually gave the holotype to the author of that type. Hence, one would have to contact each herbarium in question.

The following list of additional species were all named after John Macoun in as far as he was the collector or corresponder for these types. There probably are others.

FLOWERING PLANTS.

Amsinckia macounii Brand
Aster macounii Rydb.
Chrysothamnus macounii Greene
Eucephalus macounii Greene
Erigeron macounii Greene
Draba macounii Schulz

Carex macounii Dewey
Bromus macounii Vasey
Danthonia macounii Hitche
Poa macounii Macoun
Astragallus macounii Greene
Salix macounii Rydb.

MOSSES

Alsia macounii Kindb. *in* Mac.
Dicranum macounii Aust.

Didymodon macounii Kindb.
Orthotrichum macounii Aust.
Bryum macounii Aust.

Messia macounii Aust.
Polytrichum macounii Kindb. *in* Mac.
Macounia Kindb.
Macouniella Kindb.
Neomacounia Irel.

LICHENS

Arthonia macounii Merr.
Cetraria lacunosa Ach. var. *macounii* Du Rietz
Lecanora athroocarpa Duby var. *macounii* Tuck.
Melanaria macounii Lamb
Pyrenula macounii R. Harris

It should be emphasized that most of the Macoun names have gone into synonymy. The fact that they were originally named after him, nonetheless, is significant. (Bernard Boivin, Irwin Brodo, Robert Ireland, John Lawrence and Mike Shchepanek verified and updated the Macoun species list.)

Bibliographical Essay

by W. A. Waiser

History Department, University of Saskatchewan,
Saskatoon.

The *Autobiography of John Macoun, M.A.* is a valuable memoir by one of the great scientific explorers and public servants of nineteenth century Canada. Not simply a chronicle of his long and exceedingly active life, it also provides a unique insight into the man's character and aspirations. Its reliability, however, is limited. Dictated largely from memory to a secretary during the final two years of his life*, it is an unavoidably biased, at times questionable, personal record. It is also incomplete. Macoun died before the work was completed and the last sixteen years of his life are sketchily traced by his son William. In light of these shortcomings, this essay is intended to provide some idea of the additional sources that are available for study of the man and/or one of the many facets of his varied career.

Primary Sources
Unpublished

The personal papers of John Macoun, except for newspaper clippings, photographs and other memorabilia, have been lost over the years. Descendants consequently remain the only source of information on the Professor's personal and family life.

Official papers exist in a number of Ottawa institutions. The Public Archives of Canada have a small collection of John Macoun papers, consisting of journals for the years 1869, 1872, 1875, 1879 and 1880, and a letter from the eminent British botanist, Sir William Hooker, dated August 7, 1862. There are a few letters to/from Macoun in the Sandford Fleming papers, the Geological Survey of Canada Director's letterbooks and G.S.C. Historical File, and it is possible that there may also be references to him in the papers of some of his contemporaries. The National Museums of Canada

---

Personal communication Mary (Macoun) Kennedy, December 1974.

Library has nine volumes of Macoun letterbooks, dating from November, 1884 to April, 1902. For correspondence prior to these dates, it is necessary to check with the various depositories that hold the papers of Macoun's correspondents. For example, the library of the Gray Herbarium, Harvard University, has a file of Macoun letters written during the 1870's. Most of the botanist's field notebooks while he was attached to the G.S.C. are housed at the National Herbarium. It also holds 10 boxes of correspondence, and an office book (1901-1910), as well as most of his plant collections. Macoun's zoology field notebooks are currently held at the Vertebrate Zoology Division of the National Museum of Natural Sciences.

Published

The official reports of Macoun's five major Western explorations from 1872 to 1881 are contained in government publications. His first transcontinental journal, his first exploration of the true prairie district and his 1877 assessment of western lands, in which he wrote as much truth as he dared, were published in the railway reports: "Botanical Report, Lake Superior to Pacific Ocean", *Canadian Pacific Railway Report of Progress up to January, 1874,* appendix C, pp. 56-98; "General Remarks on the Land, Wood and Water of the North-West Territories, from the 102nd to 115th meridian, and between the 51st and 53rd parallels of latitude, *Report and Documents in Reference to the Canadian Pacific Railway 1880,* appendix 14, pp. 235-245; "Sketch of that Portion of Canada Between Lake Superior and the Rocky Mountains, with Special Reference to its Agricultural Capabilities", *Report on Surveys and Preliminary Operations on the Canadian Pacific Railway up to January, 1877,* appendix X, pp. 313-336. Macoun's return to the Peace River district in 1875 as botanist to the Selwyn expedition is documented in the Annual Report of the G.S.C. for that year: "Report on the Botanical Features of the Country Traversed from Vancouver to Carlton on the Saskatchewan", G.S.C., *Report of Progress for 1875-1876,* pp. 110-232. Finally, his 1880 and 1881 journeys as explorer for the Canadian government in the North-West Territories are contained in the *Sessional Papers:* "Extract from a Report of Exploration in the North-West Territories", Report of the Department of the Interior for 1880, pp. 8-40; "Report of Exploration", Report of the Department of the Interior for 1881, pp. 67-88. In each of these reports, Macoun outlined what he observed and how he arrived at his subsequent conclusion; they are fundamental to understanding the scientific basis of his enthusiastic assessment.

In the late 1870's, the Professor helped in classifying botanical specimens collected by the G.S.C. staff and the plant lists appear in the *Reports of Progress* for 1878-1879, 1879-1880 and 1880-1882. He joined the Survey in 1882 and for the next 25 years his annual activities in the field and office were chronicled in the *Report of Progress* (1882-1884), *Annual Report* (1885-1904) and *Summary Report* (1905-1907). A reading of the Director's and other specialists' reports in these G.S.C. publications will provide a perspective for Macoun's work.

Macoun appeared before the House of Commons Standing Committee on Agriculture and Colonization three times (1876, 1902, 1906) and was also called before the 1884 Select Committee appointed to obtain information as to the Geological Surveys. His testimony, to be found in the *House of Commons Journals,* enlivened the otherwise dull committee meetings and usually concluded with him in full charge of the proceedings. This situation was reversed in the House of Commons in the late 1870's and 1880's when his findings were debated and he had to watch 'quietly' from the visitor's gallery (see CANADA. *Debates of The House of Commons*).

Macoun's extensive lecturing activities were recorded in newspapers. He was also a member of numerous scientific societies of the period and his varied contributions are documented in their published proceedings. Apart from his charter membership in the Royal Society of Canada, Macoun had a long and valued association with the Ottawa Field-Naturalists' Club, which included the presidency in 1886-1887. Essentially an educational institution initiated to study the natural history of the Ottawa region, the club sponsored summer excursions, classes on nature study and a special evening lecture program. Macoun was a central figure in all of these activities, as evidenced in the club's monthly transactions, and because of his and other scientists' involvement, the OFNC had an important influence on the development of Canadian natural history.

In addition to the *Autobiography,* Macoun authored several books during his career. His ideas of the North-West's unsurpassed fertility and Canada's future as a great agricultural nation were brought together in *Manitoba and the Great North-West* (Guelph: World Publishing Company, 1882). Remarkable for its wealth of information, it substantiated on scientific grounds the general Canadian feeling of optimism for the region and was hence very timely. Several books from this period should be read in conjunction with *Manitoba and the Great North-West*. Geographical knowledge of the western interior at mid-nineteenth century is available in the reports of the Palliser and Hind expeditions: I.M. Spry (ed.), *The Papers of the Palliser Expedition, 1857-1860.* Toronto: The Champlain Society, 1906; H.Y. Hind, *Narrative of the Canadian Red River Exploring Expedition of 1857 and of the Saskatchewan Exploring Expedition of 1858,* reprint, Edmonton: M.G. Hurtig Ltd., 1971. Of the numerous books on the North-West that appeared at the time of Macoun's first western exploration, W.F. Butler's *The Great Lone Land* (London: Low, Marston, Low and Searle, 1872) and A.A. Taché's *Sketch of the North-West of America* (trans., Montreal: John Lovell, 1870) offer two different views of the region's future. This 1872 expedition is recorded by fellow travellers, George Munro Grant (*Ocean to Ocean* Toronto: James Campbell and Son, 1873) and Charles Horetzky (*Canada on the Pacific.* Montreal: Dawson Brother, 1874). The work of Dr. John Richardson (in Sir John Franklin, *Journey to the Polar Sea.* London: J. Murray, 1823) and G.M. Dawson (*Report on the Geology and Resources of the Region in the Vicinity of the 49th Parallel, from Lake of the Woods to the Rocky Mountains.* Montreal: Dawson Brothers, 1875) offer comparisons for the botanist's northern and southern surveys, respectively. Macoun's conclusions about the North-West were questioned by Hind (*Manitoba and the North-West Frauds.* Windsor, N.S. Knowles and Company, 1883) and Horetzky (*Some Startling Facts Relating to the CPR and the North-West Lands.* Ottawa: Free Press, 1882). Finally, the American counterpart to *Manitoba and the Great North-West* appeared in the same year (L. Brockett, *Our Western Empire* 2V. Philadelphia: Bradley, Garretson, 1882) and the parallels are fascinating.

    Macoun published the results of his natural history endeavours in the *Catalogue of Canadian Plants,* the *Catalogue of Canadian Birds* which he co-authored with his son James, and in *The Forests of*

Canada and Their Distribution, a Royal Society of Canada lecture. A Catalogue of Canadian Freshwater Fish and Catalogue of Canadian Mammals were in an advanced stage of preparation at the time of his retirement to Vancouver Island. These annotated works presented the synonymy, range and collectors of every known Canadian species and are a testimony to Macoun the systematist; by presenting information on Canadian species as accurately as possible, he tried to lay the groundwork for theoretically oriented scientists. They also reflect his great concern to get the work of the naturalist before the public and promote natural history in the public school curriculum. To further this end, the Professor collaborated with H.B. Spotton in 1882 to produce *The Elements of Structural Botany.*

Secondary Sources

Almost two-thirds of the *Autobiography* is devoted by Macoun to his travels in the North-West and his reversal of the Palliser/Hind conclusions about the region's potential. It is not surprising then that most studies of the man focus on this aspect of his career. W.A. Mackintosh (*Prairie Settlement. The Geographical Setting.* Toronto: The Macmillan Company of Canada, 1934) and A.S. Morton (*A History of Prairie Settlement.* Toronto: The Macmillan Company of Canada, 1937) in the Canadian Frontiers of Settlement series assess the botanist's work in terms of its contribution to the geographical knowledge of the Canadian West. This work has been continued by John Warkentin in *The Western Interior of Canada* (Toronto: McClelland and Stewart Limited, 1969), and more particularly in "Steppe, Desert and Empire" in A.W. Rasporich: H.C. Klassen (eds.), *Prairie Perspectives 2.* (Toronto: Holt, Rinehart and Winston of Canada Limited, 1973, pp. 102-136). An unkind critic is F.G. Roe ("Early Opinions on the 'Fertile Belt' of Western Canada", *Canadian Historical Review,* V. 27, 1946, pp. 131-149) who claims Macoun "offended in the light of knowledge, history and experience". The most recent study of the Professor's enthusiastic endorsement of Western Canada's capabilities for agricultural settlement is W.A. Waiser's unpublished M.A. thesis, "Macoun and the Great North-West" (University of Saskatchewan, 1976). The thesis argues that Macoun's assessment was the product of his great dreams for the region, as well as his extensive field work and related discoveries. Of comparable interest is W.H. Goetzmann's *Exploration and Empire. The Explorer and the Scientist in the Winning of the American West.* (New Haven: Yale University Press, 1966), and the little recognized but valuable *The Grassland of North America.* (Ann Arbor, Michigan, Edward Brothers Incorporated, 1947) by J.C. Malin.

There still exists no serious study of Macoun's years with the Geological Survey of Canada. Morris Zaslow has, however, provided a good understanding of the problems and concerns of the survey during Macoun's tenure in *Reading the Rocks: The Story of the Geological Survey of Canada, 1842-1872.* (Toronto: Macmillan Company of Canada Limited, 1975). The history of the 'national museum' is traced by W.H. Collins in *The National Museum of Canada.* (Ottawa: King's Printer, 1928). There are numerous biographical studies of early survey figures.

A recent study of Macoun's botanical work is Judith Dean Godfrey's "Notes on Hepaticae collected by John Macoun in south western British Columbia", *Canadian Journal of Botany,* v. 55, n. 20, 1977, pp. 2600-2604. Godfrey criticises Macoun for attempting to collect, identify and catalogue too many kinds of specimens from too extensive a geographical area. The history of Canadian botany has been largely treated by survey articles: D.L. Baily "Botany" in W.S. Wallace (ed.), *Centennial Volume, 1849-1949.* (Toronto: The Royal Canadian Institute, 1949, pp. 25-35); Frère Marie-Victorin, "Canada's Contribution to the Science of Botany" in H.M. Tory (ed.), *A History of Science in Canada.* (Toronto: Ryerson Press, 1939, pp. 35-40); D.P. Penhallow, "A review of Canadian Botany from 1800-1895", *Transactions Royal Society of Canada,* series ii, v. 3, 1897, section iv, pp. 3-56; R.B. Thomson, "A Sketch of the Past Fifty Years of Canadian Botany" in *Fifty Years Retrospect, 1882-1932.* (Toronto: Royal Society of Canada, 1932, pp. 173-179). The American literature in this area is extensive and instructive. A.H. Dupree's *Asa Gray, 1810-1888.* (New York: Atheneum, 1968), and A.D. Rodger's *American Botany 1873-1892. Decades of Transition.* (Princeton: Princeton University Press, 1944) are particularly relevant to Macoun's activities.

It has only been in recent years that Canadian naturalists and conservationists of the 19th and early 20th centuries have received the scholarly attention that they deserve. The results have been rewarding, as evidenced by Janet Foster's *Working for Wildlife. The Beginning of Preservation in Canada.* (Toronto: University of Toronto Press, 1978) and John Wadland's soon to be published doctoral thesis on Ernest Thompson Seton (York University, 1977). Again, American study is prolific. Keir B. Sterling's biography of C. Hart Merriam, *Last of the Naturalists.* (New York: Arno Press, 1977) is noteworthy. Merriam was roughly Macoun's counterpart in the U.S. governmental service.

John Macoun and the ornithologist Percy A. Taverner on a collecting trip, possibly at Point Pelee, Ontario. National Museums of Canada No. J5535.

Index

Compiled by W.A. Waiser

For an index to John Macoun and his exploratory surveys and related activities, the reader is directed to the chapter breakdown in the table of contents, pp iii-vi.

Flora and fauna have been indexed* according to the name used in the text. Wherever possible, the corresponding scientific or common name has been provided in brackets.

---

*J. R. Lawrence, Biology Department, University of Saskatchewan.

Professor John Macoun, Mrs. Macoun, Mrs. A. Wheeler (Miss Macoun), and Professor Skotsberg, a Swedish Botanist, at Sidney, Vancouver Island, B.C. in 1913. Photo from H.M. Ami collection.

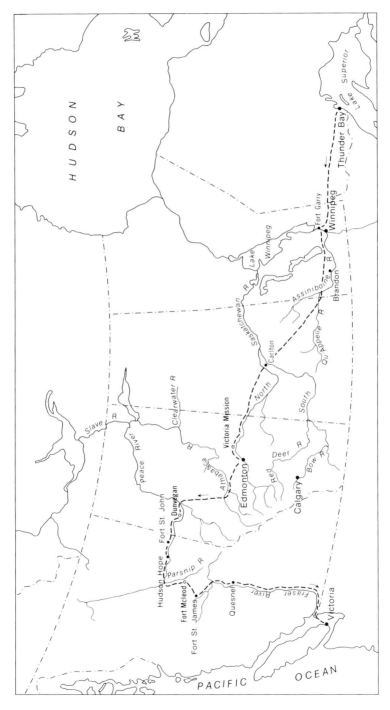

John Macoun's Expedition, 1872

Drafted by HARRY A. THOMSON

358

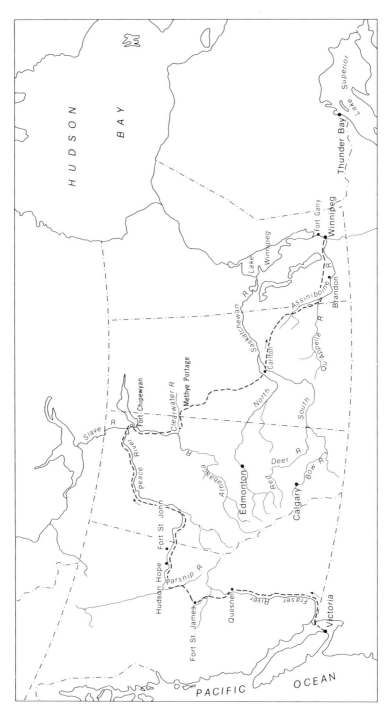

John Macoun's Expedition, 1875

Drafted by HARRY A. THOMSON

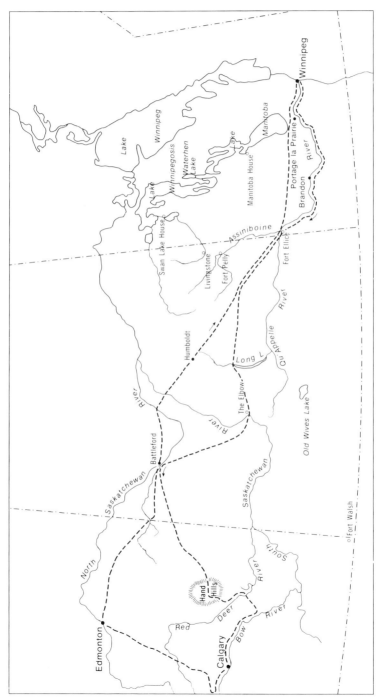

John Macoun's Expedition, 1879

Drafted by HARRY A. THOMSON

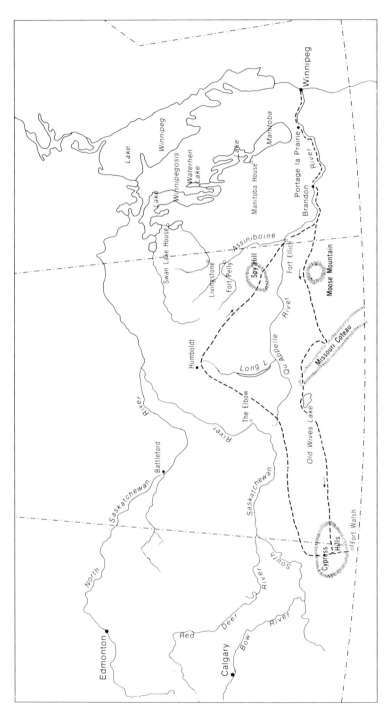

John Macoun's Expedition, 1880

Drafted by HARRY A. THOMSON

John Macoun's Expedition, 1881

Drafted by HARRY A. THOMSON

35,799